Programmable Logic Controllers

The Complete Guide to the Technology

FIRST EDITION

Clarence T. Jones

PATRICK-TURNER PUBLISHING COMPANY

Atlanta • Philadelphia

This publication includes general information related to the subject of programmable logic controllers, their design, principles of operation and application as a control system. It was designed with the express intent of assisting those wishing to learn about this topic. It is not intended to be, nor should it be used as, authority for design, implementation and installation of such control systems. The design, implementation and installation of such systems should only be undertaken by competent professionals in light of currently accepted design and engineering practices, and the guidance of the pertinent user manuals.

While great care has been employed to ensure that the examples, tables and illustrations contained herein are free of errors, absolutely no warranties, whether expressed or implied, are made as to the accuracy or completeness of any such examples, tables and illustrations contained herein.

Those preparing and/or contributing to this publication specifically disclaim any warranty of any kind, whether expressed or implied. The warranties of merchantability and fitness for a particular purpose are hereby disclaimed by Patrick-Turner Publishing Company and all other parties involved in the creation, production, or delivery of the publication. Because some states do not allow the exclusion or limitation of liability for consequential or incidental damages, the above limitations may not apply to you.

Neither Patrick-Turner Publishing, Inc., or anyone else who has been involved in the creation, production, or delivery of this publication shall be liable for any direct, indirect, consequential, or incidental damages arising out of the use, the results of use, or inability to use such publication even if Patrick-Turner Publishing has been advised of the possibility of such damages or claim. This publication may not, in whole or in part, be reproduced, translated or converted in any form without written permission from Patrick-Turner Publishing Company, Inc.

Copy Editor: Pat Grindel
Text and Layout Design: Garon Hart Graphic Design
Technical Illustrations: Ian Greathead, Greathead Studio Inc.
Cover Design: Garon Hart

To Janis, Bryan and Isaac
for their patience and support

Acknowledgments

The production of "Programmable Logic Controllers: The Complete Guide to the Technology," is the result of the tireless effort and dedication of some very special professionals. Patrick-Turner Publishing is set on providing automation readers with the very best books on various topics relating industrial automation technologies. That commitment begins with a team of individuals, each of which bring unique talents to the book production process, and the highest level of professional standards in their respective fields.

To Garon Hart, I am enormously grateful, for his many hours of labor and direction on the total project — especially the cover design and, as always, for providing unequaled graphic design.

Words fail me in conveying the importance of our technical illustrator to this project. Ian Greathead, was indeed an answer to prayer — coming on the scene, not a moment too soon, bringing the greatest of skills and the best of attitudes. He has truly illustrated the age old adage that a picture is worth a thousand words and that there's no substitute for quality.

And last, but certainly not least, a most hearty appreciation is extended to my friends and colleagues, Felipe Aponte, Stephen Jackson, and John Popiak, all of which contributed generously from their years of PLC and automation experience.

About the Author

Mr. Jones, who holds a Bachelor of Science in Electrical Engineering from Howard University, Washington, D.C., has made his career in the Industrial Automation Industry for over twenty years. During this time he has been an Electrical Control Systems Engineer, and an outstanding achiever for leading automation vendors in roles including applications engineer, technical instructor, and marketing consultant. Mr. Jones' premier book on the subject of programmable controllers, published in 1983, sold over 100,000 copies in over 90 countries. As an automation consultant and PLC instructor, Mr. Jones has conducted hundreds of classes for manufacturing companies around the country.

Preface

If you are a student, seeking to learn about programmable controllers, or a seasoned veteran looking for a single reference on PLCs and important related topics, this book has been designed specifically with you in mind. In writing this book, my goal was twofold — first, to provide the most comprehensive book available on the subject of PLCs, written in *clear and concise language*, to be used by individuals with varying backgrounds. The second goal was to provide students and veterans alike, a valuable reference tool to be used on any project, from conceptual design and programming, through installation, startup, and maintenance.

What I have tried to do, in this my second book on PLCs, is to extend to students and practitioners more than just a body of material to aid in their understanding of the hardware and software components of PLCs. By incorporating and examining the entire process by which PLC systems are implemented and maintained, I have attempted to give the reader the benefit of my years of experience in the field. These processes, which I hope to convey, are certainly not as visible as I/O racks and CPUs; most are not tangible at all. Rather, they are procedural, attitudinal, and amalgams of the tasks performed by the users of PLCs. Yet, they are every bit as important as the tangible components, and to the ultimate success of your experience in applying this technology. To achieve these goals I have included some important presentation design features that, throughout my years of PLC instruction, I have found to vastly improve learning.

First, a *generic presentation* lays an excellent foundation upon which students are able to learn quickly and fearlessly to work with any PLC. Having taught many individuals of different backgrounds and skills, I have found that most individuals that encounter difficulties in learning about and applying PLCs have usually lacked this foundation. A foundation based only on product-specific knowledge, usually results in learning to mimic instructions for programming and operating a particular system. With a generic understanding, individuals are unencumbered by the limitations of their product-specific knowledge. This basic understanding, will allow you to employ logical and systematic methods to your approach to designing and configuring the system, developing programs, diagnosing problems, and installing and maintaining any control system.

A *modular presentation*, allows important topics to be covered thoroughly in one place, and easily presented, and assimilated. Modular topics, combined with a *detailed table of contents* and extensive subject index, allow readers to quickly find and use topics of interest. Since the PLC embodies symmetry, using a *symmetric presentation* enhances understanding, as well as the ability to anticipate how things should come together and, ultimately, how they should work. Symmetry is immediately apparent in the I/O system, for example, when we look at discrete inputs and discrete outputs, analog inputs and analog outputs. In short, wherever this type of presentation could be used, it was — both with the text and with the use of numerous *detailed illustrations*. When carefully studied, each illustration can present deeper insights into the topic being discussed.

I have done my utmost to convey my knowledge and years of enthusiasm for programmable controllers. However, the more actively you are involved in your own learning, the more successful your experience with PLCs will be, and the more enjoyable too.

Organization

Chapters 1 and 2 are introductory and, therefore, should be prerequisites for beginning students. Chapter 1 covers every major topic of programmable controllers. Every topic covered here, is covered later in a chapter of its own. Upon completing these two chapters, readers should have a basic understanding of the operation and scope of PLC technology, and the benefits that can be derived from its application.

Chapter 3, "The Central Processing Unit and Power Supply," introduces the responsibilities and operations of the PLC's central processing unit and system power supply. New users, will gain an in-depth understanding of the CPU and power supply.

Chapter 4, "The PLC's Application Memory," examines the organization of the PLC memory, various memory types and best uses of each, and finally, memory addressing and its mapping to the I/O system.

Chapters 5, 6, 7, and 8, provide detailed coverage of the Input/Output system. Chapter 5 presents and overview of the major components of the I/O system, presenting the principles of operation of each. It is followed by three chapters devoted entirely to Discrete I/O Modules, Analog I/O Modules and Intelligent I/O modules respectively. Each of the three chapters cover the operation, application, specifications and connections of standard and special purpose modules of that category.

Chapter 9, "Programming and Documentation Systems," presents alternative systems available for programming, documenting and maintaining the PLC system, as well as features required in each to produce an effective environment that facilitates efficient development, documentation, installation, and maintenance.

Chapter 10, "Introduction to Local Area Networks," presents a thorough overview of LANs. A tour of the OSI protocol model, lays the foundation for understanding standard network protocols.

Chapters 11 and 12 presents PLC programming languages. Chapter 11 presents the operation of a generic set of commonly used Ladder instructions. Chapter 12, introduces languages alternative to Ladders, and examines the areas in which each is best suited.

Chapter 13, "Control System Configuration and Hardware Selection," presents an expanded analysis of the PLC product ranges first introduced in chapter 1, as well as an analysis of control system requirements that impact product selection.

Chapter 14, "Programming and Documenting the Control System," presents a broad overview and methodology of the process for program development, from conception and design to documentation.

Chapter 15, "Installation, Start-Up, and Maintenance," provides a detailed approach to the tasks associated with installation, startup and maintenance of a PLC system.

TABLE OF CONTENTS

2 Number Systems, Data Formats, and Binary Codes 23

3 The Central Processing Unit and Power Supply 49

4 The PLC's Application Memory 75

5

Input/Output System Overview 95

8   Intelligent Input/Output Modules 173

9 Programming and Documentation Systems 201

11 The Ladder Programming Language 253

13 Control System Configuration and Hardware Selection 321

14 Programming and Documenting The Control System 343

15 Installation, Startup, and Maintenance 379

1 INTRODUCTION TO PROGRAMMABLE CONTROLLERS

Definition and Principles of Operation

Typical Areas of PLC Application

Benefits of PLC Application

PLCs vs. Alternative Control Systems

The PLC Product Spectrum

A Tour of PLC Evolution

During its first twenty years, the programmable logic controller (PLC) experienced an evolution resulting in the most prominent industrial control device of the twentieth century. Like other computers, the PLC continually evolved; yet after twenty years of many innovations, it still reflected original design intentions of ease of understanding and application.

This chapter presents a brief overview of the programmable controller. In a step-by-step manner, the basic operation of each of the major elements that make up a programmable controller is presented. The benefits of applying PLCs are explored, along with a sample of the typical areas of application. A brief introduction to the functional categories of PLC products is presented and, finally, a tour of evolutionary milestones of PLC development provides an historical perspective of technology advancements. Upon completing this chapter, readers should have a basic understanding of the scope of PLC technology and the benefits that can be derived from its application.

1-1 Definition and Principles of Operation

A programmable logic controller (PLC) is an industrial control device, designed specifically for controlling machines and processes by means of a stored program and feedback from field sensing and actuating devices. As defined by the National Electrical Manufacturers Association (NEMA), a programmable controller is "a digital electronic apparatus with a programmable memory for storing instructions to implement specific functions, such as logic, sequencing, timing, counting and arithmetic, to control machines and processes."

The block diagram in Figure 1-1 shows the three major components that form a programmable controller. These components include the *input/output system*, which provides the interface to field sensor and actuator devices; the *central processing unit*, which processes the program for making control decisions; and the *system power supply*, which supplies power to the central processing unit and input/output system. The programming device, although not considered part of the controller, provides the user interface to the PLC for creating, storing, and troubleshooting the control program.

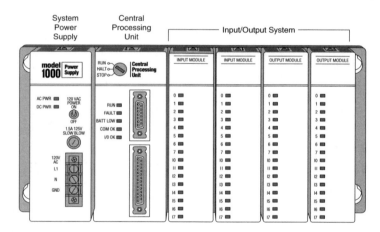

Figure 1-1. Major programmable controller components

Central Processing Unit

The central processing unit (CPU) is the "brain" of the programmable controller. It makes all decisions relative to controlling a machine or process. As illustrated in Figure 1-2, the CPU comprises a *processor* and its *memory*. During operation, the CPU receives input from various sensing devices, performs logical decisions based upon the program stored in memory, and controls output devices according to the results of programmed logic. This process of reading the inputs, executing the program and controlling the outputs is known as *the cyclic scan*.

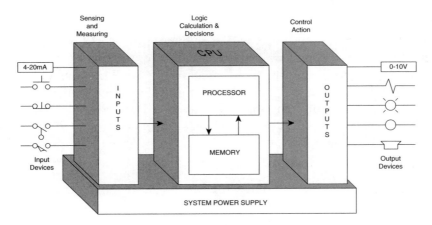

Figure 1-2. Interaction of the major components

Input/Output System

The input/output (I/O) system is that section of the PLC to which sensor and actuator devices are connected and through which the CPU monitors and controls a machine or process. A major strength of the PLC system is its I/O system. Its purpose is to condition various field signals input to the controller and output from the controller, as well as to provide isolation between the PLC and the often "noisy" field environment.

Each PLC's I/O system is comprised of a variety of input and output circuit cards that provide interfacing to a wide range of standard current and voltage signals. *Input modules* accept and condition signals from devices such as limit switches, selector switches, pushbuttons, relay contacts, and analog sensors. *Output modules* accept commands from the CPU then condition and control the signals that drive devices such as motor starters, solenoids, indicator lights, and position valves.

The System Power Supply

The third major component of the PLC system, the *system power supply,* provides low-level DC voltages required to drive the electronic circuitry of the other components of the programmable controller. It converts the high-level line voltages (e.g., 115V or 230V AC) to low levels (e.g., 5V, 15V, 24V DC) required by the CPU and the input/output modules. An important point to note is that the PLC power supply is designed only to supply power for the internal operations of the I/O modules and CPU. Power required to operate field devices is normally derived from external user-supplied sources.

Programming Devices

The programming device, typically a CRT-based unit, a handheld device, or a personal computer-based system, is a peripheral component of the PLC required to enter the application program into memory. Once a program has been entered, the programming equipment may be disconnected from the controller. However, it may also be used to later modify the program and to monitor the controlled system while in operation. The programming device also serves as a troubleshooting aid and, as a means for documenting the control program.

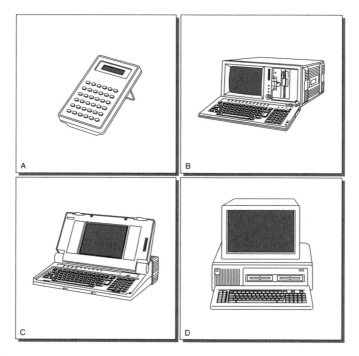

Figure 1-3. PLC programming devices. a) handheld type; b) protable industrial PC; c) laptop PC; d) desktop PC system

The Programming Language

Ladder Diagrams, the primary language for programming PLCs, is a graphic element language, consisting of electrical schematic-type symbols similar to those of hardwired relay logic diagrams. The ladder language was designed to be similar to relay logic since PLCs were generally maintained and kept operational by plant electricians and technicians who were already familiar with relay logic representation. The simplicity of the ladder language helped lead to the rapid application of the PLC in practically all manufacturing industries.

The basic function of the ladder language is much like the relay logic that it replaces. The objective of both is to control the state of a device based on certain logic conditions. Figure 1-4 illustrates a simple relay diagram. The way in which the switches are physically connected determines the operation of the devices. To change the operation would involve changing the wired logic. Figure 1-5 illustrates that the same logic implemented in a PLC requires no physical connection between the switches (input devices) and the solenoids (output devices). In essence, the wiring is replaced by programmed logic, that is easily changed if required.

Although the ladder language was originally designed to solve logic sequences involving discrete signals, it has evolved to perform analog and positioning control, arithmetic operations, data processing, and communications. A complete discussion of the instructions and operations of the ladder language is presented in chapter 11. Alternative programming languages for PLCs are discussed in chapter 12.

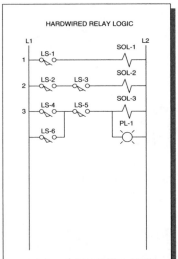

Figure 1-4. Hard wired relay logic

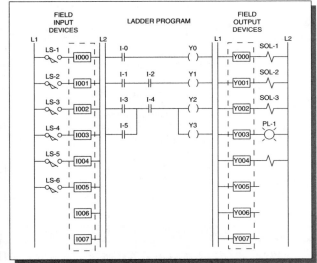

Figure 1-5. PLC logic implementation

1-2 Typical Areas of PLC Application

Since the PLC's inception, applications to industrial control functions have gone far beyond simple relay replacement and the automotive industry. The PLC has been successfully applied to discrete parts-, continuous process-, and batch-process manufacturing operations in virtually all industries.

PLCs perform a great variety of control tasks, including discrete logic, analog measurement and control, and positioning. In addition to its control capabilities, the PLC is capable of gathering production and diagnostic information from the controlled machine or process, generating messages to the operator, or outputting complete maintenance and production reports. The communications capabilities of the PLC allow it to pass information between it and other controllers or to any intelligent device. Table 1-1 lists a small sample of PLC applications and the industries in which they are used.

Table 1-1. Typical Programmable Controller Applications

MANUFACTURING	FOOD & BEVERAGE	PULP & PAPER/FOREST
- Assembly Machines - Blow Molding - Boring - Conveyor Systems - Drilling - Extrusion - Grinders - Injection Molding - Metal Forming - Milling - Painting - Test Machines - Transfer Machines	- Baking - Blending - Brewing - Bulk Material Handling - Capping - Container Handling - Conveyor Systems - Distilling - Filling - Finished Product Handling - Load Forming - Palletizing & Wrapping - Warehouse Storage/Retrieval	- Bark Burning - Batch Digestors - Calendaring - Chip Handling - Coating - Cutting - Cutting-to-length - Debarker - Demineralizer - Log Bin Sorter - Pulp Batch Blending - Slitter - Wrapping & Stamping

GLASS & FILM	TRANSPORTATION/MACHINE TOOL	PETROLEUM/CHEMICAL
- Cullet Weighing - Lehr Control - Finishing - Forming - Glass Batching - Material Handling - Packaging - Palletizing	- Engine Test Stands - Flight Surface Contouring - Machine Sequencing - Positioning - Railroad Switching/Signaling - Robot Welder - Spray Painting - Tracer Lathe	- Batch Processing - Blending - Drilling - Fan Control - Finished Product Handling - Gas Trans./Distribution - Materials Handling - Pipeline Pump Control

POWER	METALS	MINING
- Burner Control - Coal Handling - Flue Control - Fossil Plants - Generators - Load Shedding - Nuclear Plants	- Blast Furnace Control - Continuous Casting - Cranes - Forging - Loading & Unloading - Rolling Mills - Soaking Pit	- Bulk Material Conveyors - Cracking - Crushing - Loading & Unloading - Elevators - Ore Processing & Handling

1-3 Benefits of PLC Application

The very nature of PLC design, as well as its application, offers numerous benefits to industrial users. Its architecture is modular and flexible in nature, allowing hardware and software components to be easily added or removed. Moreover, PLC architecture allows for easy alteration and expansion as system requirements change, and for unique tailoring of each application. Its solid-state makeup allows compact designs that reduce space and electrical power requirements and that are highly reliable since there is no mechanical wear. Table 1-2 lists some general characteristics and benefits of programmable controllers. The most prominent of these are briefly described in the topics following the table.

Flexible Control System

Flexibility was undoubtedly the primary concern of the original PLC design criteria and, consequently, this feature is derived from more than one aspect of its hardware and software design. It is the "programmable" feature, however, that provides the greatest advantage over hardwired control systems. The elimination of hardwired control, in favor of programmable control, is the first step toward achieving flexibility in a control system.

Once installed, the control sequences of a PLC can be manually or automatically altered to meet day-to-day control requirements. Since no physical connections exist between field input and output devices, no rewiring is necessary. Instead, most changes are possible through programming. A typical example might involve a device controlled by two switches connected in series. Changing the operation of the device by including another signal in parallel with the two switches or adding a time delay could take as few as two minutes. The change could even be made without stopping operation. The same change in a hardwired system could take as long as 30 to 60 minutes—a costly loss to production.

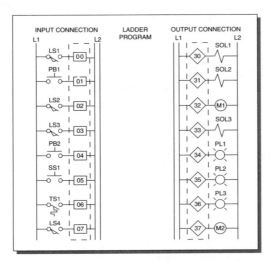

Figure 1-6. In PLC systems, no connection exists between input devices and output devices

Table 1-2. Typical PLC Features and Benefits

PLC CHARACTERISTICS	USER BENEFITS
Solid-state Components	- Low component failure - Low space and power consumption - No mechanical wear
Microprocessor-based	- An intelligent decision-making device - Communication with other smart devices - Multifunctional capabilities
Programmable	- Simplifies logic changes - Allows flexible control system design - Allows better accuracy and repeatability
Modular Components	- Easily installed and replaced - Minimizes hardware purchases - Flexible installation configurations - Neat appearance inside control panel - Easily wired and maintained
Diagnostic Indicators	- Reduces troubleshooting/downtime - Helps isolate field wiring problems - Signal correct operation and faults
Variety of Standard I/O Interfaces Modules	- Controls variety of standard devices - Eliminates customized interfaces - Reduces engineering design time/costs - Allows standardized wiring diagrams
Quick I/O Disconnects	- Serviceable without disturbing field wiring
Local and Remote Input/Output Subsystems	- I/O interfaces can be conveniently placed - Elimination of long wire/conduit runs
Software Timers & Counters	- Eliminates hardware cost and problems - Achieves better timing accuracy - Easily changed presets
Software Control Relays	- Eliminates hardware cost and problems - Reduces space requirements - Unlimited number of relay contacts
All Process Data Stored in Memory	- Production management and maintenance information can be used to generate reports

The PLC hardware also provide flexibility and cost savings. The CPU is capable of communicating with other intelligent devices, allowing the controlled system to be integrated into local or plant-wide information and control schemes. In such a configuration, the PLC can send useful messages regarding the control system to an operator printer, display device, or plant computer. On the other hand, it can receive supervisory information, such as production changes or scheduling directions, from the host computer. Standard input/output interfaces include a variety of digital, analog, positioning, and other special interface modules that allow sophisticated control without using expensive customized electronics.

Reduced Design and Installation Cost

Many attributes of the PLC simplify system design and installation. The use of standard input and output interfaces, combined with the fact that no physical connections exist between sensing and actuating devices, means that device wiring diagrams are simple and uncomplicated. The modular nature of PLCs allow the required hardware components to be purchased and installed once installation drawings are developed. While the hardware installation is in progress, the programming effort can proceed. If properly scheduled, completion of both efforts can coincide.

On small-scale changeovers from electromechanical controls, the PLC enclosure can be mounted and prewired to terminal strips. Later, a quick changeover can be made by simply connecting the input/output devices to the prewired terminals. In larger installations, remote input/output subsystems can be optimally placed near the field devices, thereby reducing the labor and cost normally associated with hundreds of long wire runs. With remote I/O subsystems, segments of a total system can also be prewired and tested by the machine builders or by a panel builder prior to reaching the installation site.

In most plants, many systems are similar or even duplicated, which means many of the control circuits are also similar or duplicated. Once these circuits have been programmed for one design, they can be saved on disk and reused later. After a number of applications, users also find that they can duplicate drawings or slightly alter many drawings for input/output signal and power wiring. If a particular controller is selected as standard equipment, then enclosure design and layout can also be standardized. Many aspects of the PLC implementation, if properly planned and well organized, will result in a reduction of engineering design and programming effort with each job.

Improved Maintenance and Troubleshooting

Like flexible control, ease of maintenance and troubleshooting have always been primary concerns in PLC design. With virtually all system components being solid state, problems such as mechanical wear, short-circuiting and contact welding associated with electromechanical components are practically eliminated. Since the system consists mainly of modular components, maintenance is practically reduced to replacing plug-in type components when failures occur.

Each PLC component also incorporates fault detection circuits and LED indicators that signal whether the component is working properly or is malfunctioning. This feature allows quick identification of any component failure. With the aid of the programming device, each programmed logic circuit can be viewed to see the actual status of each driving element. Since the PLC can communicate with external devices such as message displays or printers, logic sequences can be written to generate English messages announcing exact failures, as well as the time and location of each failure.

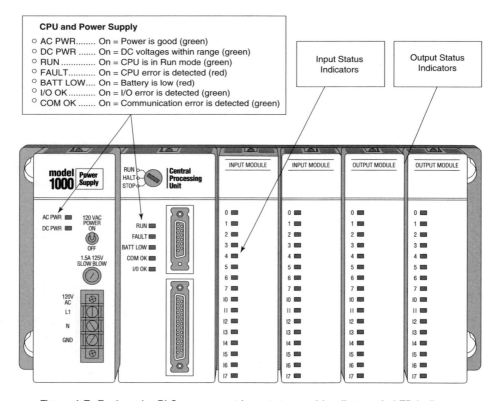

Figure 1-7. Each major PLC component has status and/or diagnostic LED indicators

1-4 PLCs vs. Alternative Control Systems

In early years of the PLC, deciding what type of control system should be used for discrete logic usually involved a choice between the PLC and electromechanical relays. However, innovations in control systems, including programmable controllers, have led control system designers to consider PLC control in favor of or in conjunction with other control systems, including minicomputers, process controllers, and analog loop controllers.

PLCs vs. Relays

For many years, applications requiring discrete logic control used electromechanical devices such as relays, timers, counters and drum sequencers. Replacing such controls is how PLCs were originally applied. During the period that programmable controllers were primarily relay replacers, their cost was naturally higher than relays. The choice to use a PLC instead of relays had to be based on the merits and benefits offered by PLC application. With present technology and the availability of a wide range of products, the question of relays versus PLCs as a control system is not the concern it once was. There are, however, a number of plants in which relay control systems still exist and where PLC application should be considered.

Undoubtedly, relays will always have a place in control systems. However, as the primary means of control, relays are not only inflexible, but they are also limited in function. Relays offer no way of extracting useful information from the system under control, or of integrating the system into a plant-wide control system. In our modern world of automation and stringent performance requirements, inflexible, unintelligent, and outdated control systems should no longer be tolerated.

From a cost standpoint, low-end PLCs are more cost competitive than the electromechanical devices (e.g., relays, drum sequencers, timers, counters) that they are designed to replace. Low-end PLCs are available for as little as $300, which is roughly the equivalent cost of seven industrial 6-pole relays, 3-timers, and a counter. The difference, however, is that PLCs in this cost range may offer an equivalent of 96 relays, 48 latching relays, 64 timers and counters, as many normally open and normally closed contacts as the memory will allow, and much more in terms of the benefits already described.

In addition to cost savings, using programmable controllers over relays provides the industrial user the following advantages:

Table 1-3. Merits of using PLCs instead of Relays

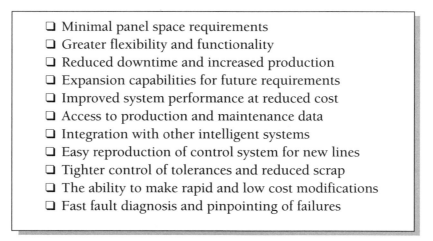

- ❑ Minimal panel space requirements
- ❑ Greater flexibility and functionality
- ❑ Reduced downtime and increased production
- ❑ Expansion capabilities for future requirements
- ❑ Improved system performance at reduced cost
- ❑ Access to production and maintenance data
- ❑ Integration with other intelligent systems
- ❑ Easy reproduction of control system for new lines
- ❑ Tighter control of tolerances and reduced scrap
- ❑ The ability to make rapid and low cost modifications
- ❑ Fast fault diagnosis and pinpointing of failures

PLCs vs. Computers

The PLC is in fact a computer itself, but it is designed specifically for industrial control applications. Although the PLC has the same basic architecture of its relative, the general purpose computer, it has several important distinguishing traits. First, the PLC, unlike general computers, has been designed for placement directly onto the factory floor, where the environment is harsh and often unstable. The circuitry of the various components is built to survive in areas of substantial temperatures, humidity, electrical noise, mechanical vibration, and electromagnetic and radio frequency interference.

Another advantage of the PLC is that its hardware and software are designed to provide standard interfacing to field sensing and control devices, as well as easy installation and maintenance by plant electricians and technicians. Modular and self-diagnosing hardware components pinpoint their own faults and are easily removed and replaced. PLC software programming uses conventional relay ladder symbols and fill-in-the-blank type instructions or other languages that require little training.

PLCs and Personal Computers

The personal computer (PC) has made great strides in industrial manufacturing. Initial acceptance of these computers has resulted mostly from widespread software development, including the areas of engineering and statistical analysis, design systems, and database management systems.

Since the mid-1980s, PCs have been established in two major areas in industrial control applications. First, personal computers have become the standard programming device for most programmable controller systems. In many applications, they have also become a means of linking the programmable controller to the rest of the world (i.e., other computers and software facilities). A typical application has been to connect the PC to the PLC over a serial link to allow the PC access to the PLC's production data. Once in a file stored in the PC, the data can be exported to other software packages such as spreadsheets or database programs.

While PC manufacturers have also made industrial "hardened" versions of these products, in many cases they are still found only in workstation situations on the shop floor and not in direct competition with PLCs. PCs are used quite extensively in data collection, process monitoring, and test applications. A disadvantage of MS-DOS based PCs is that the operating system is neither a multitasking nor a real-time processing system. With the exception of data acquisition and statistical analysis, the PLC is still best suited for the complete control system task, including measurement and control, fault monitoring, and annunciation of alarms and messages.

PLCs vs. Process Control Systems

Process control systems, for the purpose of this discussion, are those large distributed control systems (DCS) developed for and found primarily in continuous processes. These systems, which are primarily involved with large numbers of analog loop control and small amounts of digital control, are generally based on minicomputers and PC-based systems. Typically, these systems use multiple CRTs for dynamic representation of the process, including analog loops, alarming, trending and loop tuning. Interactive, menu-driven or fill-in-the-blank configurations allow the user to adapt the control system to individual processes.

In relation to the process controller, the PLC was originally oriented toward discrete logic and sequential operations, with no analog capability. In continuous processes, it was therefore originally used in conjunction with process control systems to handle the discrete logic within the overall system. To facilitate the necessary interlocking of these two different types of systems, process control and PLC vendors developed communications devices and protocols that allowed these systems to share data.

In the mid-1980s, PLCs became much more versatile, fully capable of performing closed-loop analog control. This functionality allowed the PLC to expand into batch manufacturing processes. With features such as high-speed analog I/O modules, PID algorithms and enhanced communications capability, the PLC was eventually able to offer competitively priced systems for low-end continuous processes with up to 64 control loops. Original disadvantages of using the PLCs was that the bulk of programming would be placed on the user and there was a lack of good operator interface software. These disadvantages, were later offset by the introduction of intelligent PID modules, and third-party operator interface and process configuration and display packages.

PLCs vs. Single- and Multiloop Controllers

Process loop controllers are a class of stand-alone type device designed to provide closed-loop control for either single or multiple analog loops. These devices range from units that provide only basic set point control for a single loop to microprocessor-based devices that handle single or multiple loops. The more intelligent loop controller has communications capabilities and offers a range of control functions such as alarm annunciation, self-tuning, cascading of loops, feed-forward, and multivariable control.

When compared to loop controllers, the cost per loop using a PLC is higher, especially if local operator display panels are used. However, if several loops or other functions are required, the drawbacks of loop controllers become more apparent — as do the benefits of using PLCs. Start-up of several loop controllers can be difficult and time consuming, especially if several loops are related and require precise setups. As the number of loops increase, so does the labor for adjusting and maintaining each. The inability to communicate is also a drawback of some loop controllers. Although some can be interconnected to a CPU using a communications network that allows them to accept new parameters, in general they cannot communicate with one another to coordinate their individual control actions or to warn the CPU of fault conditions.

The PLC as a loop controller offers many features and flexibility not possible with stand-alone controllers. A sample of features found in PLCs that support closed-loop control include absolute deviation and rate of change alarms; reverse acting control; bad transmitter detection; set point clamp; and ramping and loop cascading. Since the hardware is modular, additional loops can be added as required. Although loop programming is required in some PLCs, others are preprogrammed and only require that loop parameters be entered using fill-in-the-blank program templates.

In addition to handling process loop control, the PLC is also used in configurations with loop controllers in which both devices operate independently, with the PLC supplying a remote set point to each loop controller and monitoring alarm outputs from the loop controllers.

14

1-5 The PLC Product Spectrum

Traditional Product Ranges

Typically, PLCs were categorized into three major segments: *low-end, mid-range*, and *high-end controllers*, as shown in Figure 1-8. These categories were based on the maximum number of input/output devices the controllers could accommodate. The capabilities of each category were fairly standard among the products offered by different PLC manufacturers. Low-end PLCs typically handled up to 128 I/O and were considered relay replacers, having only discrete I/O and little or no arithmetic capability. Mid-range controllers handled up to 512 discrete and analog I/O devices, and performed basic arithmetic and data processing operations. The typical high-end controller accommodated up to 4,096 digital and analog I/O, allowed remote I/O connections, and offered extended arithmetic and data processing functions.

With product offerings as they were, users often had to purchase a PLC that exceeded the application requirements in order to get certain capabilities. In other cases, a user purchasing a low-end PLC may have quickly outgrown the capabilities of the product if application requirements changed. This incompatibility with system requirements arose because functional features and capabilities of each product class were based on what was thought of as "standard requirements" for a system that would control a certain number of devices. The gaps in this product offering led to a new product offering based on the concept of a *family of PLCs*

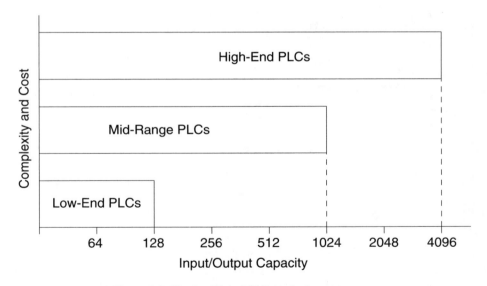

Figure 1-8. The traditional PLC product spectrum

PLC Family of Products

A *family* of controllers can be graphically illustrated as shown in Figure 1-9. This design concept provided a group of controllers that covered a span of application requirements from simple to complex. It also allowed users to select a product that closely matched the application requirements without having to purchase more capability than required.

The PLC family of products is also segmented into low-end, mid-range, and high-end controllers. The low-end also encompasses a class of products with fewer than 64 I/O, referred to as *microcontrollers*. These controllers, typically relay replacers, generally have little flexibility and expansion. Shaded areas A,B, and C which overlap the major categories, represent controllers with enhanced versions of each standard product segment. For instance, area A represents controllers having feature enhancements to the standard low-end PLC. The major distinctions between the standard and enhanced product categories are discussed in chapter 13, *Control System Configuration and Hardware Selection.*

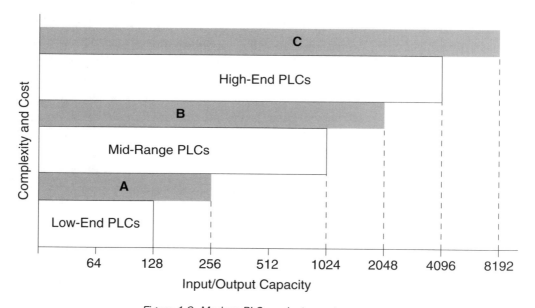

Figure 1-9. Modern PLC product spectrum

1-6 A Tour of PLC Evolution

In the following discussion, we will tour the evolution of programmable controllers from their inception. This review offers a detailed account of the chronological developments of PLC technology. While it does not cover every detail, it does include brief explanations of the major milestones. This historical review of how the most significant features of PLCs have evolved will provide a basic foundation for the remaining topics of this book. Our tour begins by taking a look at the initial design philosophy of programmable controllers.

The Initial Design Concept

The design basis for the first programmable controller was set forth in 1968 by the Hydramatic Division of the General Motors Corporation. At that time, various automotive production lines were primarily controlled by hardwired, electromechanical devices (i.e., relays, timers, counters, etc.). Whenever control requirements changed, control circuits had to be physically rewired. This process was costly and time consuming, especially for a complete model changeover. Electromechanical components, which used large amounts of space and energy, were also subject to wear and were expensive to install and maintain.

The basic design criteria for the first PLC are listed in Table 1-4. Objectives of the original specifications were to define the basis for a device that would eliminate the high cost of installation and changes to wiring, as well as the cost of downtime resulting from mechanical failures. The intentions were also to improve the manufacturing process by reducing scrap levels and by improving product consistency and quality through better control and information from the control system.

Table 1-4. Initial Design Requirements for PLCs

> ❑   Solid-state components
> ❑   Flexible computer-based architecture
> ❑   Built to sustain industrial environments
> ❑   Programmable stored program
> ❑   Perform relay-equivalent functions
> ❑   Modular interfaces to standard field voltages
> ❑   Easily installed and maintained by plant personnel
> ❑   Reusable system

1969-1972

The first programmable controller was introduced by Modicon, Inc. in 1969. Although the first PLC was primarily a relay replacer, it provided many more benefits than originally anticipated. The programming language, ladder diagrams, was an elegantly implemented symbolic language that expressed instructions using conventional relay diagram symbols widely used by plant technicians.

The first PLCs met with immediate acceptance. They were easily understood and installed, used considerably less space and energy, and incorporated self-diagnosing LED indicators that aided in troubleshooting failures. By 1972, the application of programmable controllers had spread rapidly beyond the automotive and machine tool industries to other areas, including pulp and paper, food and beverage, mining and metals.

1973-1977

Major milestones between these years included Cathode Ray Tube (CRT) programming devices, expanded memory capacity, remote I/O capability, analog I/O modules, and peripheral communications. Overall, these enhancements added greater flexibility to PLC application, improved the operator interface, and contributed greatly to reducing wiring and installation costs.

CRT Programming Device. The CRT programmer with its large screen display, offered a tremendous advantage over original programming devices, which were manual entry devices, with small single-line displays that were tedious to use. Instructions were entered and viewed one at a time. With the CRT programmer, several rungs of relay-like sequences could be entered and displayed simultaneously. Program monitoring and troubleshooting were simplified since energized elements in each programmed circuit were highlighted to show actual logic continuity.

Expanded Memory Capacity. Memory expansion in PLCs naturally allowed storage of larger programs and amounts of data, and in turn, this allowed greater control flexibility. Now, prestored control data or "recipe data" could eliminate the need to stop a process for manual data input by the operator. Parameters such as new timer presets or the amounts of different ingredients could be changed automatically by the program as needed.

Remote I/O. In 1976, wiring and labor cost were significantly reduced with the new ability to locate the input/output racks up to 5000 feet away from the CPU and nearby the sensing and control elements of the machine or process. Now, instead of bringing hundreds of wires and long conduit runs back to the central location of the CPU, two twisted pairs of conductors would link each I/O rack to the CPU.

Analog I/O Interfaces. With the introduction of analog input and output modules in 1976, a new world of applications opened for the PLC. Before this milestone, the PLC had been limited to on/off control or relay replacement, using its discrete I/O. Analog I/O made it possible to measure and control process variables such as temperature, flow, pressure, and speed, which are common elements in continuous and batch processing.

Peripheral Communications. The first point-to-point serial communications modules were available for PLCs in late 1977, allowing communication with host computers, printers, color graphic CRT displays, and other intelligent devices. PLC communications with peripherals opened a new window that gave operators an inside view of the controlled machine or process. Operator messages or process faults could be output on color screens, and management and production reports could be output daily. Communications was one of the first steps toward exploiting the computer capabilities of the programmable controller.

1978-1983

Significant changes took place during this period of development— innovations that were largely the result of the introduction of the microprocessor as the central processing unit for PLCs in 1978. User demands and high-spirited competition among vendors also stimulated many advancements. These developments included but were not limited to mini-PLCs, local area networks, redundant (hot-backup) controllers, intelligent I/O modules, enhanced instructions sets, intelligent CRT programming devices, and the PLC family.

Mini-PLCs. In 1978 and 1979, the first microprocessor-based PLCs were introduced as what were referred to as *mini-PLCs*. This class of controllers began a decrease in the physical size of PLCs and the eventual low-end PLC category. Mini-PLCs generally could handle up to 128 discrete input/output devices and were considered relay replacers for small-scale applications. Eventually, mini-PLCs handled both digital and analog I/O. The developments in this area led to even smaller PLCs (in approximately 1983), referred to as *micro-controllers*, that were the size of a shoe box, sold for as little as $400, and cost effectively replaced as few as ten relays.

Local Area Networks. In 1979, the first *local area networks (LANs)* were introduced for PLCs. Before this development, communication between PLCs required point-to-point connections. Many machines and processes under the control of individual PLCs existed as "islands of automation," with no ability to talk to each other or to plant information systems. LANs allowed controllers to share information over a single communications bus that also allowed communication with other systems. With LANs also came the move away from centralized control systems toward distributed control. The control task could be divided among several controllers that would communicate necessary interlocking over the network.

A major drawback of the original networks was that PLC vendors had different networks, and only their specific products could be attached. Later, in 1982, General Motors released the original specifications for *Manufacturing Automation Protocol (MAP)*, a network communications protocol that became the basis for open systems communications between different types and brands of products in industrial applications. MAP was based on the International Standards Organization's (ISO) Seven-layer *Open Systems Interconnection (OSI)* protocol model.

Intelligent I/O Modules. *Intelligent I/O modules*, like other input/output modules, provide the interface between the CPU and various types of field devices. The difference, however, is that intelligent I/O interfaces contain their own microprocessor and memory and can be programmed to perform specific functions independent (stand-alone) of the CPU. Like the local area network, intelligent I/O allowed control tasks to be distributed, thereby reducing the overall burden on the CPU. Typical intelligent modules included closed-loop PID control and axis positioning modules. While the first intelligent I/O appeared in 1980, not until later in the eighties, did it become a major area of development for PLCs.

Redundant Controllers. Redundant PLC systems first appeared around 1982. This development involved a primary and a back-up controller controlling the input/output devices of a single machine or process. The primary controller controlled all operations until a failure caused an immediate and automatic switchover to the back-up unit. Redundant PLC systems were the result of user requirements in applications that were unable to tolerate interruptions to the process.

Enhanced Ladder Instructions. Between 1981 and 1983, PLC instruction sets expanded to include computer-like functions to support the many hardware enhancements. The ladder language, which had already expanded to include basic arithmetic and data manipulation operations, now included file manipulation, machine diagnostic, and program flow instructions. These new enhancements were implemented using *function block instructions*. Function blocks were simple block-formatted instructions in which arithmetic, data processing, and data transfer operations were implemented using a black-box, fill-in-the-blank approach.

Intelligent Programming Devices. The "intelligent" CRT programming device emerged on the scene around 1981. It was considered intelligent because it had its own microprocessor and memory, and the supporting software and hardware to allow users to develop, modify and store programs "off-line" or without being connected to the controller's CPU. Intelligent programming devices also brought about menu-driven operations, which provided a new user-friendly programming environment.

The PLC Family. The PLC family concept was brought major benefits to users. With product families, PLC vendors moved away from developing incompatible products that had different memory organization and used different programming systems, instruction sets, I/O modules, and other system resources. Major vendors now offered PLCs ranging from microcontrollers having as few as 20 I/O, to high-end PLCs supporting up to 8,000 I/O devices. Family members utilized the same I/O modules, programming devices, and programming instructions. Compatible systems allowed reduction in spares inventory, training requirements, and engineering design time.

1984-1989

During this period, advancements were primarily further improvements and development of trends already started. Areas of focus included programming languages and instructions, faster and more flexible program processing, local area networks, and intelligent I/O modules.

New Programming Languages. In the early 1980s, ladder diagrams the primary PLC language for nearly twelve years, came under scrutiny from users who felt that more versatile languages were needed. Arguments claimed that ladder diagrams were cumbersome for performing complex calculations, intensive data processing, communications, and, in general, for solving complex control algorithms. The scanning method in which the ladder program was processed was also cited of shortcomings in certain sequential applications. An initial solution by some vendors was to enhance the ladder language using function blocks (See *Enhanced Ladder Instructions*). New languages for PLCs began with commonly used BASIC and other high-level control languages.

Standard Communication Protocols. Version 1.0 of the MAP specification was released in 1984; Version 2.0 in 1985; Version 3.0 in 1987. With the manufacturing communications protocol, automation and communications products vendors could now develop systems directly connected to networks conforming to the new standard. Products manufactured by a number of different vendors could understand one another using the *manufacturing message system (MMS)," the uniform message format of MAP.

Universal Programming Devices. By 1986, most PLC vendors offered a personal computer-based programming system, in addition to their proprietary CRT programming devices. The move away dedicated programming devices to MS-DOS-based systems offered many benefits, including lower cost, greater use of the equipment, and a wide selection of both hardware and software additions. Universal programming devices also opened the door for increased third-party development of integrated manufacturing software packages that would take advantage of the vast amounts of plant-floor data available to the PLC.

Developments of the 1990s

As previously noted, the developments during the mid- to late eighties were more or less enhancements to developments of the early part of that decade. The fact that PLC vendors were becoming more focused in their developments, only reflected the level of maturity that PLCs had already reached. During the 1990s, vendors and users will seek to exploit more of the computer capabilities of the PLC while at the same time driving more and more toward open systems architectures. A major challenge will be to increase the capabilities of the PLC while still allowing it to be operated and maintained by people with different skill levels.

Specialized Intelligent I/O. Highly specialized intelligent I/O modules that perform specific application functions will continue to be a main area of focus in PLC development. In contrast to the generic nature of first generation intelligent I/O, these products will be aimed at solving problems within specific industries (e.g., injection molding, parison control, extrusion), as well as serving horizontal markets (e.g., temperature control, message communications, operator interfaces). These products will relieve the user from the burden of complex programming, thereby allowing them to concentrate on the desired application results. Programming these specialized I/O modules will be reduced to supplying the appropriate application parameters using a fill-in-the-blank approach.

Alternative Languages. The objective in this area will be to create a programming environment that uses different languages to create a single program. Three needs must be met by this objective. First, a combination of alternative languages will be needed to allow a choice of the best-suited language for a a specific function. Second, the environment must allow for simultaneous development by several individuals. Third, the combination of languages must allow programs to be written and maintained by people having varying programming skills.

Architecture. To achieve the functional expectations held for future PLCs, including computer-like flexibility in program processing, multitasking operations, high-speed data channels, and support of multiple languages, PLC hardware and operating systems must undergo some significant changes. The challenge will be to marry the stringent, real-time processing characteristics of fast and predictable response already inherent to the PLC to the sophisticated operating systems of computers that provide portability of software, canned programs, open architecture, and a host of object-oriented programming tools.

2

NUMBER SYSTEMS, DATA FORMATS, AND BINARY CODES

Number Systems

Number Conversions

PLC Data Formats

Binary Codes

The internal operations of programmable controllers and other digital computing devices are based largely on numbers. Numbers, emulated by electronic circuitry, are used to encode and store information that in turn allows these devices to process stored instructions and data required to perform each and every operation.

In this chapter, we will examine the various number systems and data formats used in PLCs and how and why each is used. If you are already familiar with digital systems, you may want to skip the first sections on number systems and conversions. Perhaps you will find the review section on PLC data formats more useful.

2-1 Number Systems

In your work with PLCs, an understanding of number systems and how they are used is essential. Like other digital machines, the PLC relies on numbers to perform even the most basic of its operations and to store various types of information. While most of the ways in which number systems are used will be transparent to the user, there will be many cases in which a knowledge of different number systems will be required. Numbers are used to signify device status, to represent analog signals as quantitative values, to recognize and communicate with each externally connected device, and to represent various process quantities such as the number of gallons of an ingredient in a recipe.

Basic Number System Concepts

A *numbering system* is an ordered scheme whereby a fixed set of symbols is used to represent numeric values. In application, these numeric values are used as codes or for counting various quantities. Each system is based on a number, referred to as the *base number*, or *radix*. This base number determines how many unique symbols the system uses for representing numbers. For instance base 10, or the decimal numbering system, has the number 10 as its base and therefore has ten symbols, the numerals 0 through 9.

Table 2-1 lists the number systems commonly used in PLC operations, along with their associated symbol set. Base 10, base 2, base 8, and base 16 are also called decimal, binary, octal, and hexadecimal, respectively. Examination of these number sets reveals that the number of symbols is equivalent to the base and that the largest symbol is always one less than the base. Theoretically, a number system may be based on any number — base 4 for instance, would use as symbols the numerals 0,1,2 and 3. Our review of numbers also reveals however, that a number system is selected and applied based on the particular convenience it provides.

Table 2-1. Commonly Used Number Systems

BASE	NAME	COUNTING SYMBOLS
2	Binary	[0,1]
8	Octal	[0,1,2,3,4,5,6,7]
10	Decimal	[0,1,2,3,4,5,6,7,8,9]
16	Hexadecimal	[0,1,2,3,4,5,6,7,8,9,A,B,C,D,E,F]

Finally, an important basis of number systems is the concept of place value, sometimes referred to as *position weight*. This concept involves assigning a fixed value to each position of a number, thereby allowing a number of any size to be expressed using the fixed set of symbols of the number system. For instance, in base 10, all numbers, no matter how large, are expressed using the symbols 0-9. In base 2, all numbers are expressed using the numerals 0 and 1. Our discussion of the decimal number system will shed more light on the subject of place values.

Decimal Number System

The *decimal number system*, or base 10, consists of a set of ten counting symbols — 0,1,2,3,4,5,6,7,8, and 9. It is often said that base 10 was chosen as our numbering system, because we have ten fingers. Since decimal is the most familiar number system, it is the system used most often in PLC applications for timer and counter presets, math operations, and general numerical quantities.

Being so familiar with the decimal system, we rarely consider that decimal numbers, no matter how large, are formed using the basic decimal symbols 0-9 (e.g. 9346). This ability however is possible because of the concept of place values, which applies to any number system. By assigning a weighted value to each position of a number, we keep track of how many times that value (place value) is reached during the process of counting.

The place values in base 10, starting from the right column, are 1, 10, 100, 1,000, 10,000, and so on, as shown in Figure 2-1. The decimal value is obtained by multiplying each digit by its corresponding place value and adding the results. Based on this process, the number 9,346 represents 9(1,000s) + 3 (100s) + 4 (10s) + 6 (1s). This method, illustrated in Figure 2-1, is referred to as the *sum of the weights method*.

Position	n	5	4	3	2	1	0
Place Value as Power of 10	10^n	10^5	10^4	10^3	10^2	10^1	10^0
Place Value		100000	10000	1000	100	10	1
Decimal Number				9	3	4	6

$6 \times 10^0 = 6$

$4 \times 10^1 = 40$

$3 \times 10^2 = 300$

$9 \times 10^3 = 9000$

$9{,}346_{10}$

Figure 2-1. Computing a decimal number, using the sim of the weights method

From our examination of decimal place values we can make a general statement about place values in any number system. The place value of the first column of a number is equal to the base of the number system raised to the zero power. The place value of the second column is equal to the base raised to the first power, the third place value is equal to the base raised to the second power, and so on. Consequently, the place value is always equal to the base raised to a power equal to the column minus one. Remember that any number raised to a power of zero always equals 1.

Binary Number System

The *binary number system*, or *base 2*, has only two symbols, the digits 0 and 1. Binary is the primary number system used by digital devices. Such devices operate on the basis of digital circuits whose input and output signals are either ON or OFF, represented by two distinct voltage levels. Since digital circuits only involve two voltage levels (e.g., +5V, 0V), digital electronics conveniently applies the binary system by allowing the binary 0 to represent the lower voltage and the binary 1 to represent the higher voltage. By grouping the right digital circuits, these devices perform control, arithmetic and logic operations, and represent, manipulate, and store numerical quantities.

All binary numbers are expressed using only ones and zeros. Table 2-2 shows that since there are only two counting digits, each binary position can go through only two changes before starting over and carrying a one to the next column.

Table 2-2. Binary and Decimal Counting

DECIMAL	BINARY
0	0
1	1
2	10
3	11
4	100
5	101
6	110
7	111
8	1000
9	1001
10	1010

Like a number in any system, a binary number may be as large as required by simply using more positions and applying the principle of the weighted position. Each digit in a binary number is called a *bit*. The term bit, is formed by contracting the words Binary digIT. In binary, 4-bits are called a nibble, 8-bits are called a *byte* and 16-bits are called a *word*. Bytes and words are the most common units for storing digital information in a computer's memory. They are used to represent a letters, numbers, punctuation marks, machine instructions, and virtually any information type. The binary number in Figure 2-2, for instance, is comprised of 8-bits and is equivalent to the decimal number 255.

Position	11	10	9	8	7	6	5	4	3	2	1	0
Place Value as Power of 2	2^{11}	2^{10}	2^9	2^8	2^7	2^6	2^5	2^4	2^3	2^2	2^1	2^0
Place Value	2048	1024	512	256	128	64	32	16	8	4	2	1
Binary Number					1	1	1	1	1	1	1	1

$$1 \times 2^0 = 1$$
$$1 \times 2^1 = 2$$
$$1 \times 2^2 = 4$$
$$1 \times 2^3 = 8$$
$$1 \times 2^4 = 16$$
$$1 \times 2^5 = 32$$
$$1 \times 2^6 = 64$$
$$1 \times 2^7 = 128$$
$$255_{10}$$

Figure 2-2. Computing the decimal equivalent of a binary number

In base 2, each place value is a power of two as shown in Figure 2-2. Starting from the right column (*least significant digit*) the place values are 1,2,4,8,16,32,64,128,256, and so on. The decimal equivalent of a binary number is obtained by multiplying each binary digit by its corresponding place value and adding the results of each position. Later in this chapter our discussion of binary codes will show how various patterns of bits are used to represent ASCII (*American Standard Code for Information Interchange*) characters and other coded information.

Octal Number System

The *octal number system*, or *base 8*, has eight counting symbols — the numerals 0,1,2,3,4,5,6, and 7. Table 2-3 illustrates how counting in octal progresses. Octal numbering is much like decimal, except that their are no 8s or 9s. The next entries under the octal column in Table 2-3 would be 20 to 27, then 30 to 37, 40 to 47, and so on.

Table 2-3. Octal Numbering with Decimal/Binary Equivalents

OCTAL	DECIMAL	BINARY
0	0	0
1	1	1
2	2	10
3	3	11
4	4	100
5	5	101
6	6	110
7	7	111
10	8	1000
11	9	1001
12	10	1010
13	11	1011
14	12	1100
15	13	1101
16	14	1110
17	15	1111

Each octal position has a place value that is a power of eight ($8^0, 8^1, 8^2, 8^3, 8^4$, etc.). Computing the decimal equivalent of an octal number is illustrated in Figure 2-3.

In many PLC systems, base 8 is used for *addressing* memory and input/output terminal locations. Using octal for numbering is convenient in these cases since memory is comprised of groupings of eight binary digits (bytes) and I/O modules are normally in one or more groups of eight points per module. As you become more familiar with PLCs, it will become obvious that eight is a fundamental unit of groupings.

Addressing I/O in octal is illustrated in Figure 2-4 for a system having a total of eight I/O racks. Each rack has eight slots and modules with sixteen terminals (1,024 I/O terminals). The racks are numbered rack-0 through rack-7, slot numbers are 0- 7, and terminal points on each module are numbered 0-17. Based on this numbering scheme, the address of a specific termination point is easily defined by its rack number, slot number, and terminal number. For example, terminal 0117 is located in rack-0, slot-1, terminal-17.

Position	n	4	3	2	1	0
Place Value as Power of 8	8^n	8^4	8^3	8^2	8^1	8^0
Place Value		4096	512	64	8	1
Decimal Number			0	1	7	7

$$7 \times 8^0 = 7$$

$$7 \times 8^1 = 56$$

$$1 \times 8^2 = 64$$

$$0 \times 8^3 = 0$$

$$127_{10}$$

Figure 2-3. Computing the decimal equivalent of an octal number

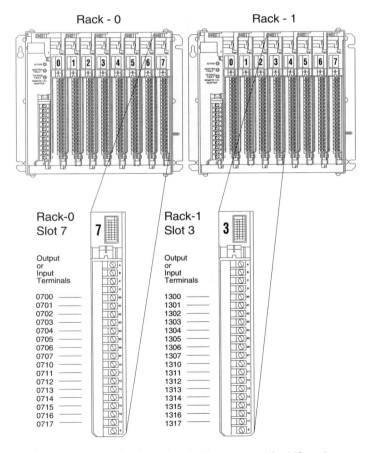

Rack - 0   Rack - 1

Rack-0 Slot 7   **7**

Output or Input Terminals

0700
0701
0702
0703
0704
0705
0706
0707
0710
0711
0712
0713
0714
0715
0716
0717

Rack-1 Slot 3   **3**

Output or Input Terminals

1300
1301
1302
1303
1304
1305
1306
1307
1310
1311
1312
1313
1314
1315
1316
1317

Figure 2-4. Illustration of octal numbering. Many PLCs use octal for I/O and memory addressing

Hexadecimal Number System

The *hexadecimal (hex) number system* is based on the number 16 and therefore contains sixteen counting symbols — the numerals 0-9, borrowed from base 10, and the letters A,B,C,D,E,F. The letters A-F are equivalent to the decimal numbers 10-15, respectively.

Table 2-4. Hexadecimal Numbering Table

HEXADECIMAL	DECIMAL	BINARY
0	0	0
1	1	1
2	2	10
3	3	011
4	4	0100
5	5	0101
6	6	0110
7	7	0111
8	8	1000
9	9	1001
A	10	1010
B	11	1011
C	12	1100
D	13	1101
E	14	1110
F	15	1111

Computing the decimal equivalent of a hex number, as with other systems, involves multiplying each digit by its corresponding place value and adding the results as shown in Figure 2-5. Each place value of a hexadecimal number is a power of sixteen. Note that whenever a hex number includes one of the letter symbols, its decimal equivalent is substituted in the computation. For instance, decimal 10 is substituted for the "A" digit, and decimal 11 is substituted for "B."

Thus far, you have learned that in digital systems, binary numbers are used to store numeric data or coded information. You learned also, that this information is commonly held within groups of eight bits, called bytes. There will be many instances in which you will need to interpret a particular binary pattern. The problem, however, is the difficulty in distinguishing or remembering different binary patterns. A number system that can

Position	n	4	3	2	1	0
Place Value as Power of 16	16^n	16^4	16^3	16^2	16^1	16^0
Place Value		65,536	4,096	256	16	1
Decimal Number			7	A	3	B

$$11 \times 16^0 = \qquad 11$$

$$3 \times 16^1 = \qquad 48$$

$$10 \times 16^2 = \ 2,560$$

$$7 \times 16^3 = 28,672$$

$$31,291_{10}$$

Figure 2-5. Computing the decimal equivalent of a hexadecimal number

be used as a shorthand method to represent information stored in a byte is needed. This system, however, must be closely related to binary to allow simple conversion between itself and binary. The hexadecimal system most conveniently suits this purpose.

Hex numbers easily express coded digital data that is otherwise expressed in binary. Such codes are typically used when two devices communicate. While the binary data may be easily interpreted by a receiving device, hex-coded characters are really used for the convenience of human operators. For example, it is much easier for us to use or to recall a command code of FA (hex) instead of 11111010 (binary).

Conversion between binary and hexadecimal is quite simple. From Table 2-4, we see that each hex digit is expressed in exactly four binary digits. Conversion from binary to hex numbers or from hex to binary is a matter of substituting the equivalent number from the table, as you will see later in this chapter.

Counting in Any Number System

Thus far, the discussion of number systems has been concerned with representing numeric quantities in different number systems. Another purpose of number systems in PLC applications is that of numbering — more commonly referred to as addressing. Memory locations, input/output devices, and devices connected to a local area network are all identified by a unique number. This form of numbering is essentially a counting process in which numbers are generally assigned in a consecutive manner. For instance, if there were a total of 256 input/output devices or memory locations, each could be identified by a number from 0 through 255_{10} or 0 through 277_8.

Since the octal (base 8) number system is commonly used for addressing memory locations and I/O terminals, it will be used to illustrate the basic rules of counting in any number system.

> *Rule 1:* Start with 0 in the least-significant position (right column) and count by 1, cycling through each counting symbol, until reaching the largest counting value — 7 in the case of octal (i.e., 0, 1, 2, 3, 4, 5, 6, 7).

> *Rule 2:* After the largest counting value is reached in any one or more position (s), set those positions back to 0, add a 1 to the next highest position and again increment the lower-place position by 1 until reaching the maximum counting value (e.g., 0, 1, ..., 7, 10, 11, 12, 13, 14, 15, 16, 17, 20, 21, 22, 23, 24, 25, 26, 27, 30).

> *Rule 3:* When two or more consecutive positions cycle through to the maximum counting value (e.g., 77 in octal , 11 in binary, or 99 in decimal), according to Rule 2, each position is set to zero, one is added to the next highest place, and the counting process resumes by incrementing the lower place positions (e.g., 70, 71, 72, 73, 74, 75, 76, 77, 100, 101, 102, 103, ...177, 200, ...277, 300, ...377, 400, ...477, 500, ...577, 600, ...677, 700, ...776, 777, 1000).

These guidelines for counting in any number system become clearer with a little practice or by examining the counting progression in the familiar decimal system. Just as we give little thought to these rules when counting in decimal, the rules will soon become second nature with regular use of binary, octal, and hexadecimal. Table 2-5 illustrates counting progression in the four commonly used number systems.

Table 2-5. Counting in Different Number Systems

DECIMAL	OCTAL	HEXADECIMAL	BINARY
0	0	0	000000
1	1	1	000001
2	2	2	000010
3	3	3	000011
4	4	4	000100
5	5	5	000101
6	6	6	000110
7	7	7	000111
8	10	8	001000
9	11	9	001001
10	12	A	001010
11	13	B	001011
12	14	C	001100
13	15	D	001101
14	16	E	001110
15	17	F	001111
16	20	10	010000
17	21	11	010001
18	22	12	010010
19	23	13	010011
20	24	14	010100
21	25	15	010101
22	26	16	010110
23	27	17	010111
24	30	18	011000
25	31	19	011001
26	32	1A	011010
27	33	1B	011011
28	34	1C	011100
29	35	1D	011101
30	36	1E	011110
31	37	1F	011111
32	40	20	100000
33	41	21	100001
34	42	22	100010
35	43	23	100011
36	44	24	100100
37	45	25	100101
38	46	26	100110
39	47	27	100111
40	50	28	101000
41	51	29	101001
42	52	2A	101010
43	53	2B	101011
44	54	2C	101100
45	55	2D	101101
46	56	2E	101110
47	57	2F	101111

2-2 Number Conversions

Numbers representing the same quantity, but written in different numbering systems are equivalent to each other. The numbers expressed below, in base 10, base 16, and base 2, all have equal value even though the symbols or characters making up the numbers are different. As already stated, the system chosen to represent a value will depend on the convenience it offers. Each of the numbers below represents a quantity of ten.

$$10_{10} = A_{16} = 1010_2$$

It is possible therefore to change or convert from one number system to another and still retain the value of the original number. In dealing with numbers in PLC applications, conversion from one system to another is often useful and in some cases necessary. Already, we have seen how a number represented in any system can be converted to a decimal equivalent. Here, we will examine the techniques used for converting from decimal to other number systems and converting among binary, octal, and hexadecimal numbers.

Decimal Number Conversions

In the previous discussions of individual number systems, we saw that converting from any number system to decimal involved the same basic method — a common method is also used to convert from decimal to other systems. Converting a decimal number to its equivalent in another system involves a process of dividing the decimal number by the base number of the system to which the conversion is being made. For example, a conversion to binary involves division by 2, conversion to octal involves division by 8, and to hexadecimal, division by 16.

Decimal to Binary. Example 2-1 illustrates conversion of a decimal number to binary. The binary equivalent of 35 (base 10) is determined by dividing by 2 until a result of 0 is reached. Each remainder obtained is a digit of the equivalent binary number, starting with the least significant position.

Example 2-1. Convert decimal 35 to its binary equivalent

Division	Result	Remainder
$35 \div 2 =$	17	1 (LSD)
$17 \div 2 =$	8	1
$8 \div 2 =$	4	0
$4 \div 2 =$	2	0
$2 \div 2 =$	1	0
$1 \div 2 =$	0	1 (MSD)

Solution: $35_{10} = 100011_2$

Decimal to Hexadecimal. A decimal number is converted to its hexadecimal equivalent in the same manner, as illustrated in Example 2-2. The process starts by successively dividing by 16, while keeping track of the remainder. Each remainder contributes a digit to the resulting hexadecimal number. Conversion from decimal to octal would involve the same process, except that the division would be by 8.

Example 2-2. Convert decimal 16,024 to its hexadecimal equivalent

Division	Result	Remainder
$16{,}024 \div 16 =$	1001	8 (LSD)
$1{,}001 \div 16 =$	62	9
$62 \div 16 =$	3	14 (E_{16})
$3 \div 16 =$	0	3 (MSD)

Solution: $16{,}024_{10} = 3E98_{16}$

Octal and Hexadecimal Conversions

A grouping method of conversion is a simple and fast procedure for finding the binary equivalent of both octal and hexadecimal numbers and, conversely, finding the octal or hex equivalents of a binary number. The grouping method of conversion for octal and hex, as illustrated in the following examples, is possible since both 8 and 16 are powers of two.

Binary to Octal. When converting from binary to octal, the first step is to separate the binary number into groups of three digits, starting from the right column, as illustrated in Example 2-3. Three digits are used since the largest octal digit (7) is expressed in exactly three binary digits. If the last grouping has fewer than three digits, then 0s are used to pad the leading digits. Each three-digit group is then assigned its octal equivalent. Use Table 2-3 to find the octal equivalent of each binary grouping if necessary.

Example 2-3. Find the octal equivalent of binary 1011010011100

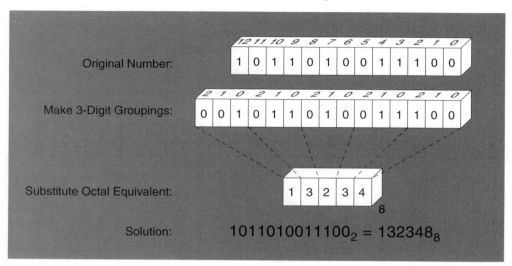

Octal to Binary. Converting from octal to binary is the reverse of converting from binary to octal. Each octal digit is assigned its three-digit binary equivalent. Again, refer back to Table 2-3 to find the binary equivalent of each octal digit. Remember that octal 0-7 have the same binary patterns as decimal 0-7. With a little practice, the octal/binary equivalents are easily memorized. Conversion from octal to binary is illustrated in Example 2-4.

Example 2-4. Find the binary equivalent of octal 256

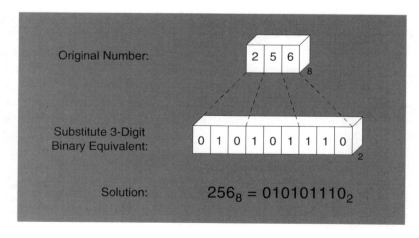

Binary to Hexadecimal. Conversion from binary to hexadecimal involves the grouping method used with binary to octal conversion, except hex conversions involve four-digit binary groupings, referred to as nibbles. Four-bit groupings are used since each of the hex digits can be expressed in exactly four binary digits. Once the groupings are made, the conversion is accomplished by replacing each nibble of the binary number with its hexadecimal equivalent, shown in Table 2-4.

Example 2-5. Find the hexadecimal equivalent of binary 1110010111111010

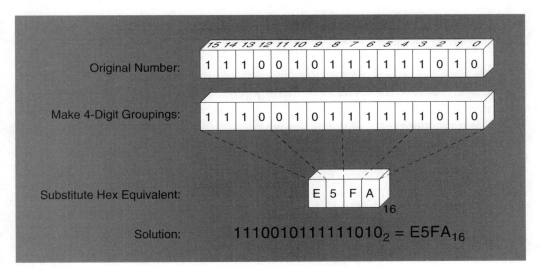

Example 2-5 figure

Original Number: 1110010111111010

Make 4-Digit Groupings: 1110 0101 1111 1010

Substitute Hex Equivalent: E5FA$_{16}$

Solution: $1110010111111010_2 = E5FA_{16}$

Hexadecimal to Binary. Converting from hexadecimal to binary is the reverse of converting binary to hexadecimal. Given a hexadecimal number, each hex digit is assigned its four-digit binary equivalent. As with octal/binary conversions, this process becomes straightforward upon committing to memory the binary/hexadecimal equivalents from Table 2-4. Conversion from hexadecimal to binary is illustrated in Example 2-6.

Example 2-6. Find the binary equivalent of hexadecimal F177

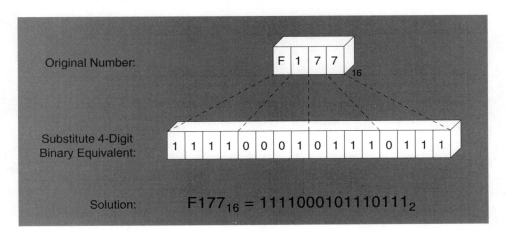

Original Number: F177$_{16}$

Substitute 4-Digit Binary Equivalent: 1111 0001 0111 0111

Solution: $F177_{16} = 1111000101110111_2$

2-3 PLC Data Formats

Numeric and other types of data stored in the PLC are always represented in binary. The *format* in which data is represented, however, dictates how the binary pattern should be interpreted. For instance, numeric data is normally interpreted as decimal instead of octal or hex — data input to the PLC from thumbwheel switches is in binary-coded-decimal. In this section we'll examine various numeric data formats used to represent numeric values in PLCs. First, let's look at the basic memory storage units for holding all data types.

The Basic Word Format

In PLCs, as well as in other computers, numeric data is stored in groupings of binary digits. The actual size requirement of the grouping will depend on the type of data or the format in which the data is represented. We learned earlier, that a byte or eight bits is a basic unit of storage for digital information. If all 1s are placed in each position of a byte, as illustrated in Figure 2-6, a maximum value of 255 decimal can be expressed.

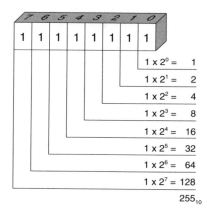

Figure 2-6. One byte is eight bits wide and can represent a maximum decimal value of 255

To handle numbers larger than 255, computers and PLCs generally operate on a unit of bits consisting of two or more bytes. This grouping is referred to as a *word*. Although a grouping of two or more bytes is considered a word, PLCs generally store data in a word composed of two bytes, as illustrated in Figure 2-7. In our discussion of memory in chapter 4, you will see how thousands of sixteen-bit words are organized to provide the storage requirements of the PLC.

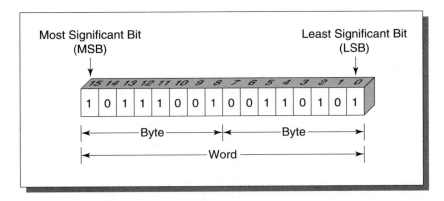

Figure 2-7. A PLC word is typically composed of two bytes, or sixteen bits

Of the two bytes shown in Figure 2-7, the right-most eight bits are called the *least significant byte*, while the left-most eight bits are called the *most-significant byte*. Bit positions are typically numbered in decimal from 0 to 15, with 0 being the least-significant bit and 15 being the most-significant bit.

Decimal Numbers

The decimal number format is the most common form in which numbers are represented in the PLC. This format uses the basic sixteen-bit word to represent whole decimal numbers. The decimal format is also referred to as *fixed-point format* because it represents whole decimal numbers, or as binary format since the binary 1s and 0s represent a decimal number and are not coded in any fashion. In other words, the decimal equivalent is directly determined using the sum of the weights method.

Decimal numbers may be stored as *unsigned numbers* or *signed numbers*. Unsigned numbers have no positive or negative sign and therefore simply represent an absolute number or count. Given a sixteen-bit word, a maximum unsigned decimal value of 65,535 can be represented as shown in Figure 2-8, when all sixteen bits are occupied by a binary 1. If decimal numbers are represented as signed numbers, the most-significant bit is used as the *sign bit*, leaving the remaining fifteen bits to store the numeric value.

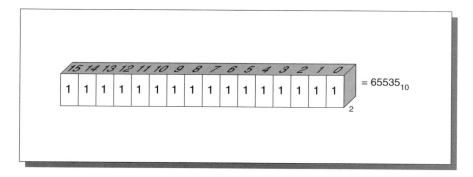

Figure 2-8. An unsigned 16-bit word holds a maximum decimal value 65,535

Using sign notation, a maximum value of +32,767 can be represented in sixteen-bit decimal format; -32,768 is the minimum value. As shown in Figure 2-9, +32,767 is represented when all positions except the sign position are occupied by 1. The value of -32,768 is obtained using the *twos complement* method of representing negative numbers, as described later in this section.

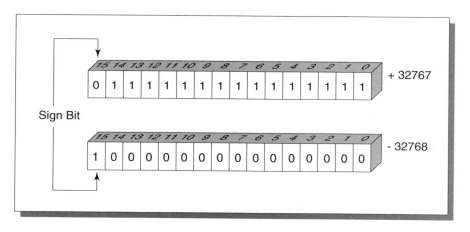

Figure 2-9. Maximum and minimum decimal values of signed 16-bit numbers

Double-Precision Decimal

Decimal numbers larger than +32,767 are stored by using two PLC words together to form a thirty-two-bit decimal format, or what is known as *double precision*. Double-precision numbers are also whole numbers and are typically signed numbers. Using 32-bit signed notation, the maximum decimal value is +2,147,483,647 and the smallest value is -2,147,483,648. Numbers this large may be required for tracking part counts on high- volume production lines or when the expected results of a math operation will exceed +32,767.

When double-precision numbers are used, only the first PLC word location needs to be explicitly specified — the second location is assigned implicitly by the program to be the next consecutive location. For example, if word location 1000 is referenced in the program as double precision then 1001 would be assigned by the program. As illustrated in Figure 2-10, the lower of the two locations is typically treated as the *least-significant word*. If numbers larger than those represented in double-precision decimal are required, then floating-point numbers may be required.

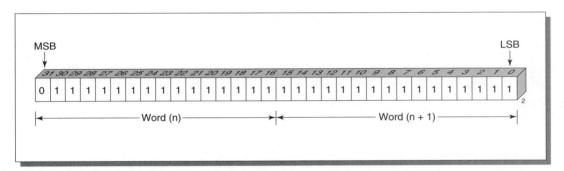

Figure 2-10. Double-precision decimal format, with two PLC words

Representing Negative Numbers

Two methods for representing negative numbers are used by PLCs — the *ones complement*, and *twos complement*. When either method is used, an extra bit called the sign bit, is appended to the most-significant position of the number. A 1 in the sign position indicates a negative number; a 0 indicates a positive number. Figure 2-9 shows that using the most-significant position of the sixteen-bit word as a sign bit leaves the remaining fifteen bits for holding a number. Determining the value of the negative number depends on which complement method is used.

Ones Complement. In the ones complement method, a negative number is expressed by simply complementing or inverting each bit of the positive binary number. To complement means to change each 1 to 0, and each 0 to 1. Let us assume that we want to represent +25 as a signed sixteen-bit binary number. Using a sign bit, +25 would be represented as shown here:

0 000000000011001 = +25

The negative binary representation of the number 25 using the ones complement method is simply obtained by inverting each bit, or changing 1s to 0s, and 0s to 1s. The ones complement of binary 25 then is shown here.

1 111111111100110 = -25

If a negative number were expressed in binary using the ones complement method, its complement or positive value would be obtained in the same fashion. Examining the first number below, a 1 in the sign position indicates a negative value. Complementing or inverting each bit and then using the sum of the weights method to compute the decimal value reveals a +14. Therefore, the number had been -14.

1 111111111110001 = -14

0 000000000001110 = +14

Twos Complement. When numbers are expressed using the twos complement method, an extra digit is also used to represent the sign. It differs slightly, however, from the ones complement. Using ones complement, all bits were inverted to find the complement — in twos complement, each bit from right-to-left is inverted, but only after the first 1 is detected. Let's use the number +28 as an example:

0 000000000011100 = +28

Its twos complement would be:

1 111111111100100 = -28

Note that in the positive representation of the number 28, starting from the right, the first digit is a 0 so it is not inverted; the second digit is a 0; the third digit is the first 1 — all digits after this 1 are inverted.

If a negative number is given in twos complement, its complement (a positive number) is found in the same fashion.

1 111111111110010 = -14

0 000000000001110 = +14

All bits from right to left are inverted after the first 1 is detected. Other examples of twos complement are shown here:

$$0\ 000000000010011 = +19 \qquad 0\ 000000000000111 = +7$$

$$1\ 111111111101101 = -19 \qquad 1\ 111111111111001 = -7$$

$$0\ 000000000000001 = +1$$

$$1\ 111111111111111 = -1$$

Binary-Coded Decimal Numbers

When numeric data is represented in binary-coded decimal (BCD), each of the decimal digits, 0 through 9, is represented by its binary equivalent. Many devices, such as bar code readers, encoders, and thumbwheel switches, output BCD numbers for input to the PLC. This particular coding is also a method by which decimal numbers are input to or output from the PLC to conveniently suit human operators. A more thorough discussion of binary-coded decimal is found in the following section on binary codes.

Since each decimal digit is represented using four-binary digits, it is possible to represent a four-digit BCD number using our standard sixteen-bit PLC word, as illustrated in Figure 2-11. A single PLC word then would allow a BCD range of 0000 through 9999. Some PLCs may use three BCD digits (000-999). Three BCD digits require only twelve bits of the standard 16-bit word. In either arrangement, each group of four binary digits represents a decimal number that cycles from 0 through 9. Inputting and outputting BCD numbers to and from the PLC is discussed in chapter 6.

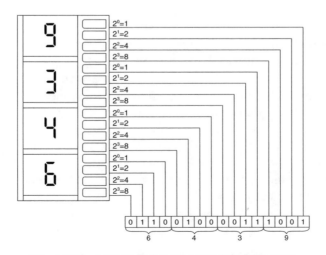

Figure 2-11. A 16-bit PLC word holds four BCD digits

Floating-Point Decimal Numbers

Whereas fixed-point numbers include only whole numbers or integers, the number 25 for example, floating-point numbers are comprised of a whole number and some fraction, such as 25.375.

Floating-point numbers are used primarily when it is necessary to work with fractional numbers or with numbers larger or smaller than what is possible with single- or double-precision decimal. Because floating-point numbers allow decimal fractions, they also allow calculation results or measured quantities of greater accuracy than with fixed-point numbers.

Floating-point numbers are represented in the PLC using decimal scientific notation. Scientific notation is a form of expressing very large or very small numbers in a shorthand notation that expresses numbers as a fractional part and a power of ten. The elements of scientific notation and the floating-point format are both illustrated in Figure 2-12.

SCIENTIFIC NOTATION	DECIMAL	FLOATING POINT
1.234567×10^4	12345.67	1.234567 +04
1.234567×10^{-1}	.1234567	1.234567 -01
$-1.234567 \times 10^{+1}$	-12.34567	-1.234567 +01
-2.300000×10^{-6}	-.0000023	-2.300000 -06

Figure 2-12. Floating-point number format

In the floating-point format, a fixed number of digits, called the mantissa, express the significant digits of the number. Two digits are used to express the exponent of the number. The exponent is a signed power of ten that determines the direction and the number of places the decimal point must be moved with respect to the most-significant digit to determine the actual decimal number being represented.

The floating format represented in binary requires two PLC words, as illustrated in Figure 2-13. Typically, twenty to twenty-four bits are used to represent the mantissa and eight to twelve bits are used to represent the exponent. The format shown here is based on the ANSI/IEEE Standard 754-1985 format. Both the mantissa and the exponent are signed numbers. If the sign of the exponent is positive, the decimal point is moved to the right. If the exponent has a negative sign, then the decimal point is moved to the left.

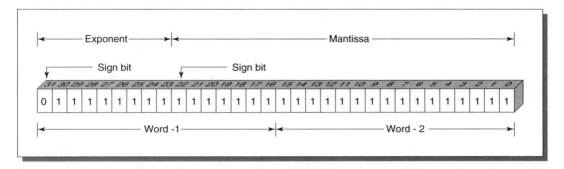

Figure 2-13. PLC representation of floating-point numbers

2-4 Binary Codes

In performing its operations, the PLC must store and manipulate information of a variety of forms. This information may include raw numbers, character strings, or even text messages. Handling different types of information is done by assigning certain meaning to different binary patterns, otherwise known as binary encoding. Several binary codes have been developed. For us to interpret the meaning of various patterns of 1s and 0s, it is important to know the data type and how it is coded. In this section, three binary codes are introduced.

Binary-Coded Decimal

In PLC applications, the need often arises for numeric data in the form of decimal numbers to be input to the controller and, conversely, for the controller to output numeric data in the form of decimal numbers. Inputting numbers in binary or interpreting numbers output in binary would be impractical for a human operator. A solution calls for a means of taking a decimal number (e.g., 3,950 gal.) and converting it to binary for direct input to the PLC and taking a binary number to be output from the PLC and converting it to decimal to be easily read by an operator. The result is binary-coded decimal (BCD).

To code decimal numbers in binary, the decimal digits 0 through 9 must each be assigned a binary representation for direct PLC input as binary signals. A simple solution was to assign each of the ten symbols with its natural binary equivalent. From Table 2-6, we see that the binary equivalents of the numbers 8 and 9 have four binary digits. Establishing a uniform code therefore required a minimum of four binary digits to represent each of the decimal digits. The binary representations for the numbers 0 through 7 were simply padded with preceding zeroes, as illustrated in Table 2-6.

Table 2-6. Binary and Binary Coded Decimal Equivalents

DECIMAL	BINARY	BCD
0	0	0000
1	01	0001
2	10	0010
3	11	0011
4	100	0100
5	101	0101
6	110	0110
7	111	0111
8	1000	1000
9	1001	1001

The BCD equivalent of a decimal number is easily obtained by replacing each decimal digit by its BCD equivalent from the table. An example of deriving the BCD equivalent of a decimal number is shown for the number 3,950 in Figure 2-14. It should be noted that the four digits in the number 3,950 are simply substituted with their four-bit BCD equivalent that is restricted to the cyclic pattern of 0000 through 1001.

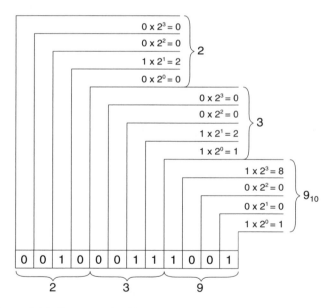

Figure 2-14. Representing binary coded decimal (BCD) numbers

The cyclic nature of binary-coded decimal is emphasized here to point out that BCD is a fixed code and that binary patterns other than these are invalid. For instance, 1010 (decimal 10) is invalid in BCD. This fact is also evident with BCD devices such as thumbwheel switches or seven-segment LED displays. Each digit of these devices continually cycles from 0 to 9. To handle numbers larger than 9 or single digit numbers involves additional BCD digits. In chapter 6, you will learn how BCD devices are wired to the PLC for data input and output.

The ASCII Code

ASCII, pronounced "askey," stands for American Standard Code for Information Interchange. This code, developed by the American National Standards Institute (ANSI), provides a standard set of coded characters to be used for information interchange among digital computing systems, communications systems, and peripheral equipment manufactured by different companies. While other standard character sets exist, ASCII has nearly attained universal acceptance. It is used in virtually all small computers and their peripherals and in many large computers as well.

When two devices communicate — for example a computer to a printer — messages may consist of alphabets, numbers, punctuation and special symbols. What is actually transmitted, however, are sequences of electrical highs and lows (binary 1s and 0s). Individual letters, numbers, or punctuation marks each have a unique ASCII code that is interpreted by the receiving device. A device receiving a binary 01000010, for example, interprets it as the uppercase letter B. Whole words or multidigit numbers are composed by stringing ASCII characters together, separated by encoded delimiters.

ASCII is a seven-bit binary code and hence offers 2^7 or 128 unique bit patterns allowing 128 character codes. Appendix A lists the ASCII characters and their associated codes. Included in the ASCII set are upper and lower case alphabets, the numerals 0 through 9, punctuation marks, standard symbols, and nonprintable codes such as start of text (STX) and end of text (ETX) used for control codes during ASCII transmissions. Extended ASCII character sets are possible using eight bits, which allow 2^8 or 256 different characters. Since each character is represented in seven or eight bits, a single PLC word can store two ASCII characters.

Gray Code

The Gray code is a binary code similar to BCD in that it is used for representing decimal numbers. It differs from BCD and other number systems in that it is strictly a code and is nonanalytic. We saw that in binary, for instance, counting produced a methodical and natural pattern of 1s and 0s and the number itself was based on the assigned place values of each position. Gray code, however, is a binary-coded counting system in which decimal values are represented by unique binary patterns, based not on place values, but on the basis that the sequential numbers must not have more than one bit change as the count increments by 1.

In examining Table 2-7, we see that with a transition of only one count, the binary equivalent could have as many as four bit changes. This is seen with the transition from decimal 7 to 8. With larger numbers and more binary digits, the number of bit changes could be even greater — for example, when going from 1111111 to 10000000. Such a drastic change increases the chances for bit errors to occur. For this reason, certain digital devices using binary encoding, such as absolute encoders, would not find straight binary representation suitable.

Table 2-7. The Gray Code with Binary and Decimal Equivalents

GRAY CODE (4-BIT)	BINARY	DECIMAL
0000	0000	0
0001	0001	1
0011	0010	2
0010	0011	3
0110	0100	4
0111	0101	5
0101	0110	6
0100	0111	7
1100	1000	8
1101	1001	9
1111	1010	10
1110	1011	11
1010	1100	12
1011	1101	13
1001	1110	14
1000	1111	15

Gray code was developed for applications that require counting accuracy. It is used by positioning encoder devices for tracking linear or angular displacement. In an optical encoder measuring angular displacement, 360 degrees must be counted. Each decimal count from 0 degrees to 360 degrees would output a unique Gray code pattern. If we look closer at the Gray code, we see that while the numbers are unique, they are also identical except in one position. Thus, in counting from one decimal value to the next, only one binary position changes its value.

Gray code output signals from encoder devices are typically input to the PLC using a Gray code input module or an absolute encoder input module. Typically, these modules which are referred to as high-speed encoder counter modules, convert the Gray code input to a decimal number between some minimum and maximum value. This conversion allows easier data manipulation of the Gray coded information.

3

The Central Processor and Power Supply

This chapter introduces the responsibilities and operations of the PLC's central processing unit and system power supply. New users, students, or those anticipating the first PLC application will find this chapter of most importance. It will provide an understanding of the principles of PLC operation, as well as the characteristics and features that make one controller more suitable than another in a given application.

3-1 Introduction

In chapter 1, we saw that a programmable controller system was comprised of three primary sections, the central processing unit (CPU), the input/output system and the system power supply. The CPU, however, is the PLC's foundational component, upon which all of the system's capabilities are based. The CPU is responsible for coordinating and controlling all system activities. A block diagram of the PLC's central processing unit section is illustrated in Figure 3-1. It consists of three main elements — the *memory and processor sections* and an *I/O interface section*.

Together, the elements of the CPU provide the intelligence of the controller, but it is really the processor component and all of its supporting circuitry that is the "brain" and chief commander of the PLC. For this reason, the terms Processor and CPU are often used interchangeably. In performing its duties, however, the processor relies on both the memory and power supply systems. The CPU's interface to the I/O system is discussed in chapter 5.

The memory section of the CPU, as illustrated in Figure 3-1, can be divided into two major sections — *application memory* and *system memory*. As a PLC user, you will be primarily concerned with the application memory since it stores programs and data that you will generate for controlling a machine or process. Because application memory is an important part of the CPU, it is covered in greater detail in Chapter 4. The system memory contains the *operating system,* a collection of permanently stored programs that is an integral part of the PLC system. These programs tell the CPU what to do and how to do it. Hence, we will examine the basic elements of the system memory here with our discussion of the PLC processor.

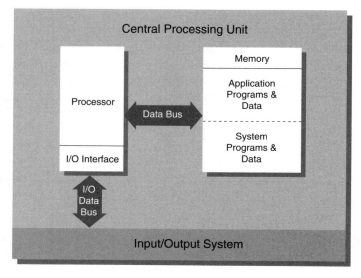

Figure 3-1. Block diagram of the central processing unit

3-2 The PLC Processor

Mechanical packaging of the CPU components vary. However, the most common configuration is a processor module that incorporates memory and a separate power supply module, each of which is placed into a rack housing referred to as the *CPU rack*. In high-end controllers, memory may also be available on a separate card to accommodate larger memory capacities.

LED indicators on the front casing of the CPU signal normal operational modes (e.g., STOP, RUN, PROGRAM) and error conditions (e.g., MEMORY ERROR, CPU FAULT). The communications port to which a programming device is connected is also normally contained in the processor module. Some processor modules might also have I/O communications ports for connection to expansion input/output racks, as well as an integral serial communications port for direct communication links to other intelligent devices. A typical CPU module is illustrated in Fig. 3-2.

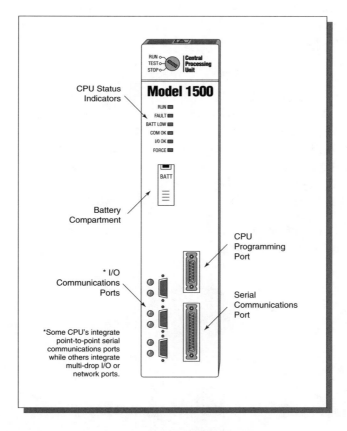

3-2. Front plate elements of a typical CPU module

Basic Processor Architecture

The PLC's central processor, like many of today's computers, is microprocessor based. While low-end controllers generally use a single microprocessor as its CPU, mid-range and high-end controllers often incorporate several microprocessors to form the central processing unit. Instead of a single microprocessor performing all mathematical, logic, I/O control and communications operations, each may be performed by separate processors working simultaneously. By sharing the control and processing responsibilities, a technique known as *parallel processing,* the total system processing speed is significantly increased.

Another processor arrangement, referred to as *distributed processing*, involves placing processing intelligence in so-called *intelligent I/O modules.* In this arrangement, the processing that would normally be performed by the CPU is performed by I/O modules placed in the field. These microprocessor-based modules have their own memory and can be programmed to perform control, communications or other specific tasks independent of the main processor. A typical intelligent I/O module is the *proportional-integral-derivative (PID) module,* which performs closed-loop control independent of the central processor. (*See chapter 8.*)

The System Memory

The central processor determines the overall functionality of the PLC. As the central point of intelligence, it is responsible for computing, decision making, and coordinating the supporting PLC components. It must also monitor the integrity of the major system components, including itself. It does this by performing diagnostic tasks, reporting the errors, and taking the appropriate action. As previously mentioned, the Processor performs its duties by executing stored programs from the system memory.

System memory consists of two basic sections as illustrated in Figure 3-3, the operating system and the system data area.

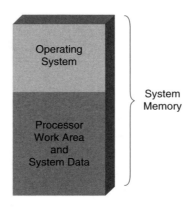

Figure 3-3. The PLC system memory

The Operating System

Operating system software, also referred to as *system firmware*, is a set of programs that typically resides on EPROM chips located on the CPU module. These permanently stored programs, which are considered a part of the machine itself, give a particular controller its unique capabilities. The system firmware determines what the CPU is capable of doing, as well as how and when each of its operations is performed. This is true whether the operation is an ADD instruction or reading the status of connected devices.

A simplified summary of the major operating system functions is listed below. These basic functions include monitoring and controlling the I/O, processing the control program, communicating with programming and other external devices, performing system diagnostics, and a variety of other routine functions. By executing the operating system programs, the Processor is able to perform all of its operations, including that of processing the application program.

> **Supervisory System Software**
>   Process stored application program
>   Process I/O hardware interrupts
>   Process time-driven interrupts
> **Perform System Diagnostics**
>   Perform power-up test on system components
>   Perform self-testing routines
>   Perform run-time test routines
> **Coordinate Communications Control**
>   Interact with programming port communications
>   Coordinate communications with network modules
>   Process input/output updates

Although all PLCs perform most of these basic functions, how they are implemented can differ dramatically. The operating system is what makes one PLC different from another. It determines what functions are available to the application program, how the program is processed, how and when the I/O is serviced, what happens with each starting and stopping of the CPU, as well as the actions taken when internal faults occur. For example, some PLCs perform diagnostic routines at power up only while others perform continuous on-line testing during program execution. In some, so-called major faults cause the CPU to halt while in others the user can determine what happens.

The System Data Area

The *"system data area,"* sometimes referred to as the *processor work area,* is a relatively small amount of memory utilized by the processor to store data vital to ongoing operations. Items stored in this area include configuration parameters of the PLC system, operational status of the CPU, and other components and temporary data or status information about the user program currently residing in application memory.

Generally, the system data area, or some portions at least, can be viewed by the user. Typically, the user is restricted from making any modifications to the processor work area. However, there are exceptions to this rule in some controllers. The items listed below are examples of typical parameters that might be stored in the processor work area.

- ❑ CPU Model
- ❑ Application Memory Available
- ❑ Application Memory Used
- ❑ Watchdog Timer Preset
- ❑ Installed I/O Modules
- ❑ I/O Address Allocations
- ❑ CPU Operational Mode
- ❑ Average Scan Time/Last Scan Time
- ❑ System Faults/Errors
- ❑ System Clock Pulses

Processor Resources and Features

PLC processor specifications define hardware and software characteristics of a particular controller — its functional capacity, as well as its limitations. That is, the usable resources of a particular model are outlined by the processor specifications. By reviewing the processor specifications of a particular PLC, it is possible to make a fair judgment as to whether it can satisfy the hardware and software needs of an application. This is true since the hardware requirements of the CPU will be largely related to the physical requirements of the system to be controlled.

General characteristics determined by the processor include the total number and type of devices (e.g., discrete, analog, peripherals) that can be controlled, whether or not I/O housings can be mounted both local to the CPU and at remote distances, and whether or not the controller can be configured in a communications network. In addition to these physical limitations, the processor also determines features such as the programming languages, instruction set, and processing speed. Table 3-1 is an abbreviated list describing major processor specifications.

While the items listed in Table 3-1 describe general specifications of PLC processors, those familiar with PLCs may also speak in terms of low-end controllers, mid-range controllers, and high-end controllers to imply inherent capabilities of the CPUs that fall into these classifications. These three classifications, used to categorize a PLC by the CPU capabilities, were introduced in chapter 1 and are covered in detail in chapter 13.

Table 3-1. Major Resources and Features of PLC Processors

PROCESSOR RESOURCE	DESCRIPTION
Input/Output Capacity	Maximum number of devices that can be monitored (inputs) and controlled (outputs).
Input/Output Types	I/O interfacing capability (*e.g., discrete, analog, positioning, thermocouple,*
Local/Remote I/O Capability	Ability to place input/output racks local to the CPU and at remote distances.
Memory Capacity	Total storage capacity for storing programs and data.
Networking Capability	Ability of CPU to communicate with several other PLCs on a local area network.
Processor Scan Rate	The average time in which the processor executes 1K (1,024) words of programmed instructions.
Programming Language	The language (s) used to create control programs (*e.g., ladder diagrams, sequential flowcharts, or high-level statements*).
Instruction Set	Available instruction types (*e.g., relay-type, arithmetic, data comparison, word transfers, block transfers, advanced arithmetic, sequencers, etc.*)
Arithmetic Capability	Available math functions (*e.g., addition, subtraction, multiplication, division, square root, trigonometric functions*).
Timers & Counters	Maximum number of software timers and counters available for control programming.
Data Formats	Determines how numbers are stored and the maximum and minimum values that can be represented (*e.g., Integers -32,768 to 32,767, BCD 0-9999, 32-bit Floating point*).
On-line Programming	The ability to insert or alter programs and data while the processor is in operation.
On-line Program Merging	The ability to download to CPU memory a library or newly created program segment and have it appended to the existing program.
PID Loops	The number of loops supported via a PID algorithm, integral to CPU firmware, or via intelligent PID I/O modules.

3-3 Principles of Processor Operation

The *processor scan,* illustrated in Figure 3-4, refers to the sequential process in which the PLC processor performs specific duties on a cyclical basis. Normal functions carried out on each scan cycle include reading the signals of connected input modules, processing the control program, and controlling the signals to connected output modules. In PLC terminology, reading inputs and controlling outputs are collectively referred to as the *I/O scan* or *I/O update.* Processing the control program is called the *program scan.*

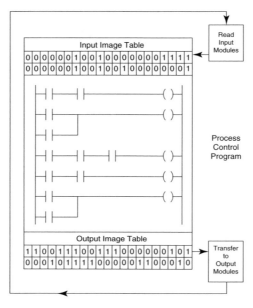

Figure 3-4. Illustration of the basic PLC scan

The Normal Processor Scan

In each processor cycle, the processor begins by reading or "taking a snapshot" of the status of the devices connected to input modules and storing the ON/OFF states of each in a special area of memory called the *input image table.* Each device has a unique place in the image table, where a 1 denotes the device is ON and a 0 denotes the device is OFF. These input states, held in the image table, will be used as conditions for driving logic in the control program segment of the processor scan. After the inputs have been read and stored in the input image table, the processor executes the control program.

During program execution, the processor evaluates the conditions of each statement by looking back at the input image table to see if the input conditions are met. If the conditions controlling an output are met, the processor immediately writes a 1 in a unique location in a special area of memory called the *output image table,* indicating that the output will be turned ON; conversely, if the conditions are not met, a 0 indicating that the device will be turned OFF, is written in the output image table. Each program statement is evaluated in this fashion until reaching the last program statement.

After evaluating the last program statement, the output image table will have been filled with 1s and 0s, reflecting the results of the programmed logic. The final step of the processor scan is to update the actual states of the connected output devices by transferring the output image table results to the output modules, thereby switching the connected devices ON (1) or OFF (0). The whole process may take a tenth of a second. Again, a new picture of the input signals is taken, the program is evaluated, the output signals are updated, and the processor scan repeats the cycle in this fashion continually.

The Processor Scan Rate

The *scan rate* is a processor specification given as the average time required to execute 1K (1,024) words of programmed memory. This specification provides a basis for determining the processor *cycle time* — that is, how long it will take for the processor to perform one complete cycle of the control program and I/O update. For instance, given a specification of *2ms/K*, an estimate of the cycle time is derived by multiplying the total amount of programmed memory (in units of 1K) by the scan specification (e.g., 16K times 2ms/K = 32 milliseconds).

Although the scan rate offers a rough means of comparing the processing speeds of different controllers, it is not a true unit of measure for determining the processor cycle time. To closely approximate the processor cycle time, other factors must be considered. For example, the published scan rate does not normally account for the update of the I/O image tables; this includes both local and remote I/O. If the I/O update is synchronous to the processor scan, the actual I/O servicing will increase dramatically for each local and remote I/O subsystem, especially as the remote distances increase.

The processor cycle also increases by a fixed overhead time required by the processor to perform routine housekeeping functions such as error-checking and communicating with its programming port or to other intelligent cards that may be installed in the CPU rack. Processor overhead time and remote I/O update times are generally given in the operations manual. Figure 3-5 gives a more complete illustration of the processor scan and an equation by which the average cycle time can be calculated.

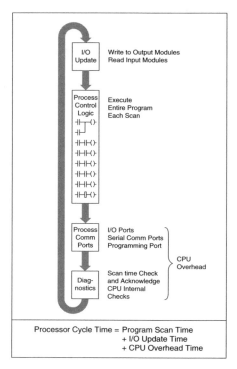

Figure 3-5. Functional components in determining the processor cycle time

Finally, the type of instructions used in a program will also affect the average cycle time. Consider the fact that the scan specification is based on 1,024 instructions. Although two programs may be of equal length in terms of memory usage, one may consist mostly of logic operations having fast execution times and the other may consist mostly of word operations having slower execution times. To allow users to make a more accurate estimate of the average scan time for a particular program, vendors publish a list of instruction execution times, as illustrated in Table 3-2. Typical program cycle times range between 10 ms and 100 ms.

Processor Response Time

The normal PLC processor operation involves the repetitive and sequential process of *reading the inputs, evaluating the program,* and *updating the output signals.* This method of processing the I/O only at the end of each program scan, as well as executing the program in a sequential and fixed fashion, may become inadequate where fast response is critical. Since the I/O status is only updated at the end of each cycle, output signals that need to be switched ON or OFF immediately upon certain conditions must wait until the end of scan.

Response time, or the time required to respond to an external signal and affect an output signal, is one of the most important characteristics of a programmable controller. Since the PLC processes the program in a cyclic manner, the response time is based on the cycle or scan time. As was shown in the previous discussion, the scan time includes one complete program cycle, the I/O update, and processor overhead time for error-handling and other functions. Since the exact occurrence of a signal is an unknown, it is not possible to make an exact determination of the response to a given signal. It is possible, however, to determine the best and worst case response.

Consider the best case, that is, an input signal change occurs just prior to the input image table being updated. When the program is executed the signal status would be current and the output could be updated all within one cycle. The worst case is when the input change occurs just after the input image table is updated. In this case, an entire cycle would transpire before the signal change would be transferred to the image table; another complete cycle would transpire before the particular statement was executed and the output was affected. Thus, given the normal processor scan, the best case response is one cycle and the worst case is two cycles. Since typical PLC cycle times are between 10 ms and 100 ms, most PLCs can respond within 20 ms and 200 ms. The next topic examines improving the response.

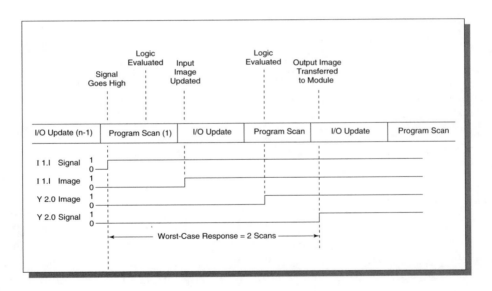

Figure 3-6. Illustration of the worst-case processor response time of two complete scans

Interrupting the Normal Scan

Several methods are used to improve PLC response time. The three methods introduced here involve altering the normal processor scan. One method is the use of an *immediate I/O update* program instruction, as illustrated in Figure 3-7. When an immediate input instruction is encountered, it causes the processor to immediately read an input status or to transfer new status to an output device, and then continue execution of the program. With this technique, critical inputs can be read immediately and outputs can be controlled before the end of scan. The response is therefore never more than one cycle.

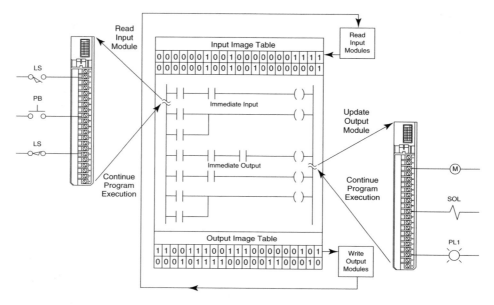

Figure 3-7. Interrupting the normal scan using immediate I/O update.

Hardware-interrupt Processing. Interruption of the normal scan is also possible in systems having hardware interrupt signals to the CPU. Critical response inputs are connected to a special *interrupt input module,* which energizes one of the interrupt signals to the processor whenever one of the input signals has a transition. The interrupt causes the processor to stop its normal scan and to jump to a user programmed subroutine. Each critical input signal is given an associated subroutine that, as illustrated in Figure 3-8, is immediately processed when that signal is generated.

When the service routine is completed, the main program resumes at the point at which it was interrupted. The interrupt input module is discussed in chapter 6.

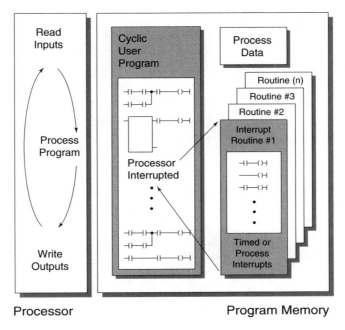

*Figure 3-8. Processing hardware and timed interrupts.
Each interrupt has a corresponding service routine*

Timed-interrupt Processing. In some mid-range and high-end controllers, a form of multitasking, referred to as *timed-interrupt processing*, allows the processor to process critical response tasks on a predetermined timed basis. In such systems, the user is able to create subtasks that can be executed at regularly scheduled intervals. This feature allows time-critical control tasks, such as high speed motions or machine fault detection, to be executed many times per second while noncritical tasks such, as switching indicator lights or data trending, run much slower. PID loops are typically processed using timed-interrupt processing.

Time-driven interrupt processing is similar to hardware-interrupt processing. However, time-driven interrupts involve timed clock pulses that interrupt the processor. The normal program scan continues its normal cycle and is interrupted based on the preprogrammed time-driven tasks. Timed interrupt tasks are serviced according to their timed interval and priority, and the remaining portions of the program are executed in so-called "spare time." In priority systems, a task of lower priority must wait if its time to be serviced occurs simultaneously with one of higher priority.

Flow-control Instructions. The normal scan method of executing the program in sequential order is also inefficient in some applications. For instance, some program sections such as arithmetic calculations or machine setup may require infrequent processing or processing only under certain conditions. To process every statement on each scan may result in an undue increase in program scan time. This practice would be undesirable in applications where fast response is critical. Some processors offer instructions that allow infrequently used portions of logic to be bypassed or executed only when required. These so-called *flow-control instructions* are discussed in detail in chapter 11.

3-4 Processor Modes of Operation

The *processor modes of operation* are the various operational states in which the processor can be manually or automatically placed. These operational states will affect program entry, program execution, the I/O system control and possible user interaction with the system. Typical operational modes include *STOP, RUN, RUN/PROGRAM, TEST*, and *I/O FORCE*.

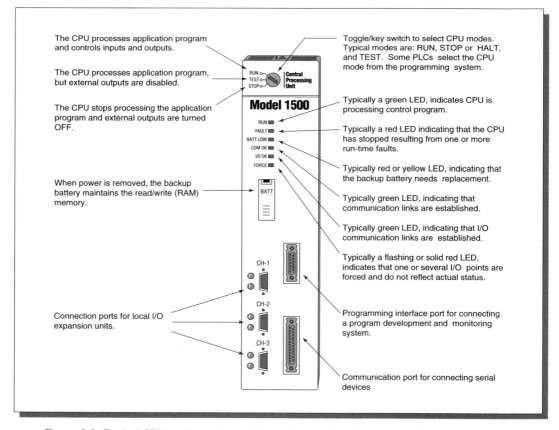

Figure 3-9. Typical CPU modes of operation and associated status and fault indicators

Processor modes, depending on the controller, may be selected from a key or slide switch located on the face plate of the processor module or the CPU casing, or via a software selection using the programming unit. Some controllers might even allow CPU modes to be remotely accessed using the command codes for each processor mode. This type of access allows processor modes to be determined or controlled over a communications network from an external device such as a host computer.

STOP Mode

Selecting the *STOP mode* sets the processor to a state in which the control program execution is halted. When the program is halted, controlled outputs are all automatically set to the OFF state. Program entry and modifications are allowed — however, execution of the application program is stopped and control of the outputs is disabled. Monitoring input device status is still possible in this mode; however, controlling output states usually will require use of an *I/O FORCE mode*, if available. (See I/O FORCING Mode later in this chapter.)

The operational functions of the STOP mode are mainly to allow new entries or modifications to an existing control program, as well as static testing of connected inputs and outputs during initial start-up or troubleshooting. Dynamic program testing in this mode is not possible since the control program is not being processed.

RUN Mode

The *RUN mode* is the normal operational mode of the PLC processor when the controlled system is on-line and under automatic control or during dynamic testing of the control program and I/O. When placed in this mode, the processor takes full control of the connected machine or process by executing the stored application program. An LED indicator on the processor's front panel will normally signal when this mode is selected.

Whenever power is applied and the processor is switched to the RUN mode, the processor first performs its routine system start-up checks (e.g., memory, I/O communication), and if errors or malfunctions are detected, the Processor automatically switches to the *STOP mode*. If all tests pass, the processor scans the input modules, and upon completion, executes the control program from the first instruction to the last instruction. Finally, the processor updates the output modules and the process is repeated.

On-line program entries or modifications, if allowed, can normally be performed in the RUN mode unless the processor also has a RUN/PROGRAM mode in which on-line program changes are made. On-line program changes should always be performed with caution since in many PLCs changes take effect as soon as entered into memory. A *TEST* mode, if available, is more appropriate for logic changes, but if not available, necessary precautions should be taken or the CPU should be placed in a STOP mode before making changes. In most PLCs, a *MEMORY PROTECT* option prohibits program changes while the CPU is in the RUN mode.

RUN/PROGRAM Mode

In addition to the normal RUN mode, some controllers have a *RUN/PROGRAM* mode. In such a case, the RUN/PROGRAM mode operates exactly as the previously described RUN mode — the control program is executed, the I/O are updated, and on-line programming is allowed.

When there is a RUN/PROGRAM mode, the RUN mode essentially becomes a RUN ONLY mode, causing program execution and I/O update, but not allowing any on-line programming. Having a RUN/PROGRAM mode essentially separates the "on-line programming" function from the "execute program" function. The key would be removed while in the RUN position rather than in the RUN/PROGRAM position. The Run mode, then, is equivalent to a MEMORY *PROTECT mode,* which some systems use to disallow on-line program alterations.

TEST Mode

The *TEST mode,* if available, provides a useful program debugging tool, as well as a mechanism for safely implementing changes to the control program. The TEST mode may also be called the *I/O DISABLE mode.*

When the processor is placed in the TEST mode, the control program is scanned just as it would be in the RUN mode for normal machine or process operation. Inputs are scanned, the program is executed, and the outputs are updated. The difference, however, is that although the output image table is updated according to the control logic, the processor has issued a disable outputs command to the I/O system, which prohibits updating the real-world outputs. If an output is commanded to turn ON, its correct status is reflected on the programming unit in a status mode showing logic continuity although the device will not be activated. The TEST mode allows the effects of program changes to specific program outputs to be dynamically tested without affecting the field devices.

I/O FORCE Mode

Many processors offer a selectable mode of operation referred to as the *I/O FORCING mode.* FORCE mode is not an operational mode such as those previously discussed; nor is it generally selected from the processor key switch. The forcing function is a useful program and I/O diagnostic tool that allows the user to selectively override the actual status of connected input and output devices to aid in program debugging. Forcing is typically selected from one of the I/O monitoring functions of the programming unit.

I/O forcing is similar to temporary "jumpering" of a circuit element to test circuit operation or obtain a desired operation without having all circuit elements in the correct state to complete the circuit. If an input or output is forced, its logic state (1 or 0) is changed by the processor regardless of its actual ON or OFF state. For example, an input may be forced to logic 1 (ON) while its actual state may be logic 0 (OFF). The switch is not actually forced to open or close, but its status bit in the input image table is placed in a forced state. The processor uses the forced state in the control program. Likewise, outputs can be forced to a logic 1 or 0.

Forcing is typically used for dynamic (system running) program testing or during system start-up. It allows individual circuits to be tested even though all circuit elements may not be in the physical state required to generate the desired output signal. Signal states can be simulated without having to go out and open or close switch contacts. Output wiring continuity can also be tested during start-up by forcing each output ON and verifying that the correct device is activated.

Since FORCING I/O status is overriding actual device status, it does create a potentially dangerous operational mode. When a particular input or output is forced to a logic 1 or 0, it will remain held in the forced state regardless of its actual state or of the program results. All forced I/O must therefore, eventually, be cleared or "unforced." An LED indicator is normally on the processor module to signal when forced states exist and are overriding normal program operation.

3-5 Processor Diagnostics

Detecting and annunciating internal malfunctions is a primary responsibility of the PLC processor. It must alert the operator, other system components, and the control program of faults detected in any of the PLC components, including itself, or in the user program. To achieve this function, the processor performs two categories of tests, *start-up diagnostics* and *run-time diagnostics*, the results of which are normally signaled by LED indicators on the CPU and stored in a CPU status memory area.

Although often overlooked by users when considering a controller, good diagnostics can provide a level of security and system integrity that give one controller a distinctive advantage over one with lesser diagnostics. Since diagnostics performed by different controllers can vary from minimal to comprehensive, this aspect of a controller should be carefully evaluated along with other features.

Start-up Diagnostic Routines

Power-up diagnostics are system routines performed by the processor immediately upon each system power-up or whenever the CPU is switched from STOP to RUN. The purpose of these preliminary tests is to ensure the integrity of major system components (e.g., processor, memory, I/O, CPU rack) and the control program prior to going on-line with program execution.

The processor normally initiates start-up test by testing its own operation to assure the validity of the remaining tests. It tests data flow through the microprocessor and performs a test of the operating system memory. Functional and comprehensive tests on the user application memory ensure that data can be read from and written into each memory location. Data paths of the CPU rack are tested, I/O communication links are tested, and in some cases, an audit of the installed I/O modules is performed. If all the start-up tests pass, the processor will assume the selected operating mode (e.g., PROGRAM, RUN), otherwise the CPU will stop and the appropriate LED indicator will signal that a fault has been detected.

Table 3-3. Typical Processor Start-Up Tests.

- ❑ Microprocessor functional operation
- ❑ Operating System Memory test
- ❑ Processor Working Memory test
- ❑ User Memory read/write test
- ❑ Backplane bus operation
- ❑ Memory backup battery has correct voltage
- ❑ I/O communication links valid and operational
- ❑ Audit of installed I/O modules

Run-time Diagnostic Routines

To ensure system integrity and safety during system operation, the processor performs *on-line* or *run-time diagnostic routines*. These diagnostic tests, which examine various system components and control program operations while the program executes, are important to review when evaluating the PLC processor. Run-time hardware checks generally are a shortened version of the start-up diagnostics that test the PLC hardware components, as well as test for the correct operation of the control program. (See Watchdog Timer.)

Evaluation of run-time diagnostics should consider not only what tests are performed, but also, perhaps more important, an evaluation of the facilities that exist to allow the control program to make a graceful recovery in fault situations. That is, after a fault is detected, proper operation can be restored without causing the processor to halt the processing of the control program. In some cases, this may even mean operating with limited operations. For example all communications processors may continue operation, although all outputs are disabled.

Typically, run-time faults are classified as either a "major fault" or "minor fault," depending on their severity. In most PLCs, any occurrence of a so-called major fault causes the processor to cease execution of the control program and go into the STOP mode. While certain run-time errors may be critical enough to cause a system shutdown, less critical faults such as *scan time exceeded* and certain programming errors may not be as critical, depending on the application. In actuality, if the processor does not detect fault with itself, it could continue some operations if the operating system is designed as such.

In some controllers, deciding how less-critical faults are handled is left to the system designer. Further, in these more *fault-tolerant systems*, major faults are also classified as being *recoverable* or *non-recoverable*, depending on whether it is possible for the processor to restore order and allow the user to react to these faults in the control program. To allow a graceful recovery after a fault, the processor stores error codes of all fault conditions in an area of memory called the *system status area.* In the event of a recoverable fault, the user can gain access to fault information, take corrective action through a programmed fault routine in the control program, and continue with normal operation.

Table 3-4. Typical Processor Run-time Tests.

> ❑ Scan time within limit (Watchdog Monitor)
> ❑ CPU clock pulse monitor
> ❑ Validity of program instructions/parameters
> ❑ Validity of user program addressing
> ❑ User memory read/write test
> ❑ User memory parity checks
> ❑ I/O module time-out tests (module response)
> ❑ I/O communication links valid and operational

Watchdog Timer Routine

In addition to hardware-related diagnostics (i.e., memory, power, battery, etc.) the processor also performs a software diagnostic routine referred to as a *watchdog timer,* or *scan monitor.* This test monitors the user program scan for correct operation. The premise of the watchdog timer is that the scan cycle should always be completed within a maximum time based on the program size. The object is to alert the processor in the event the scan time exceeds its predetermined limits. Such a condition may result from faulty program logic that causes an endless program loop.

In normal operation, the watchdog timer is enabled when the CPU is placed in the RUN mode. The watchdog times during each scan and under normal conditions is reset at the end of each cycle. In the event the program scan exceeds the watchdog preset, the timer will not reset;it reaches its maximum limit and times out. This condition will result in a *scan time exceeded* fault, causing a subsequent signal to the CPU to perform an orderly system shutdown. The timer is reset only after the fault is corrected.

In low-end PLCs, the preset time for the watchdog timer is normally fixed for a worst-case scan time, based on a fixed amount of memory. Mid-range and high-end processors, on the other hand, allow this preset value to be programmed to allow for longer or shorter programs.

3-6 Optional CPU Configurations

The requirements of automation systems in some manufacturing facilities have evolved quite dramatically in comparison to the simple demands once placed on the PLC processor. At the same time, however, enhancements in PLC hardware and software technology have resulted in a multifaceted control system capable of handling many complex control, data processing, and communications tasks. Three configurations that enhance PLC performance in advanced applications include *multiple CPU, fault tolerant CPU* and *fail-safe CPU* designs. A fourth hardware solution is that of *intelligent I/O modules* that are capable of performing control, data processing, or communications functions independent of the CPU. Intelligent I/O are covered in chapter 8.

Multiple CPU Design

As with many computer-based systems, the available functionality in PLCs has resulted in control systems design that pushes a single processor to the extreme. Inherent problems in such situations are very large and complex programs and subsequent increased processor scan times that can degrade overall system response. Such programs are also difficult to diagnose when problems occur. Using multiple CPUs is one of several PLC architectures that allows system configurations that relieve the central processing unit from the burden of performing all processing task.

Multiple CPUs is a distributed processing technique that involves placing two or more CPU modules into one PLC rack. Each CPU has its own memory and programs, which operate simultaneously and independently. In such a configuration, the controller can perform multiple tasks, each of which can be started or stopped without affecting the other. Since the scan of each processor is parallel and independent, the total response time can be reduced by a factor roughly proportional to the number of processors.

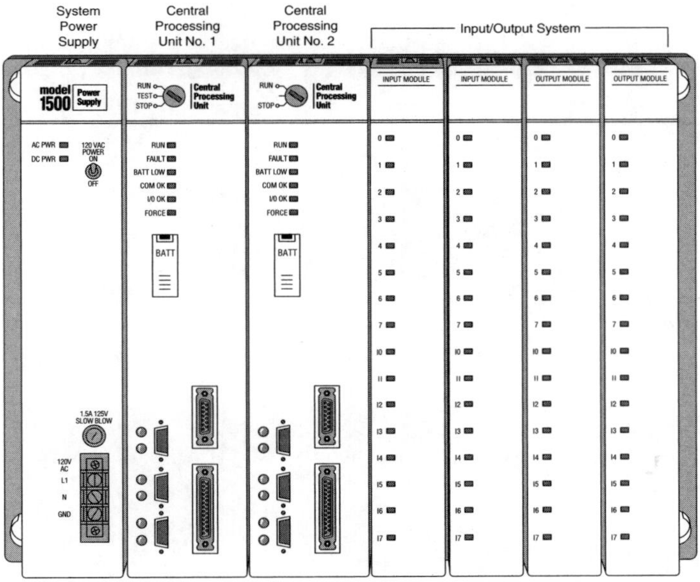

Figure 3-10. Multiple CPU configuration with two CPUs.
Dividing the task between two processors, can cut the cycle time in half

If dividing the tasks is practical, various strategies can result in better response times, increased reliability, and uncomplicated programs . One solution for dividing a large task might be to separate all control functions from data processing functions. Another approach might be to assign the control functions of individual sections of a machine or process into separate processors. An example of using multiple CPUs might involve a single system in which the control logic, alarm processing and annunciation, and data acquisition and reporting are handled by three separate CPUs.

Fault-tolerant CPU Design

The application of *fault-tolerant CPUs* is one solution for those areas of automation where costly downtime or the interruption of critical processes must be avoided at all cost. The goal of this design is to provide the maximum in system availability. An early evolution of the fault-tolerant CPU configuration is illustrated in Figure 3-11. This design approach, typically referred to as a *redundant system* or *hot back-up system*, involves two separate CPU racks, each having identical hardware and software and separate communication links to the same input/output system. A parallel cable connection allows high-speed communication between the two controllers.

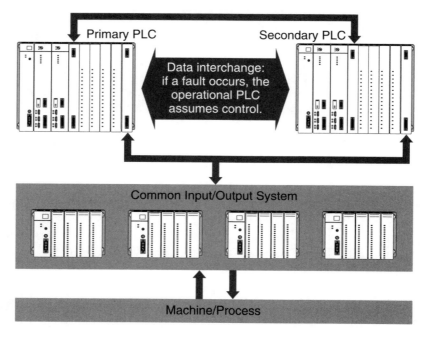

Figure 3-11. Redundant or hot-back up PLC system, with a common I/O system

In normal operation, one CPU acts as master or the *primary controller.* It scans the input signals, executes the control program, and controls the outputs. At the beginning of each cycle, the primary CPU also transfers a complete image of its own operating status, I/O status, and process data to the *secondary controller.* The secondary CPU, referred to as a *hot backup* or *hot stand-by,* is on-line and executing an application program identical to that of the primary controller; however, its link to the I/O system is disabled while the primary unit is in control.

The cycles of the two CPUs are somewhat synchronized but are out of phase by the transmission time required for the primary controller to update the secondary controller on each scan. If a fault is detected in the primary unit, an orderly transfer of control is passes to the secondary unit. A *bumpless transfer,* meaning one without interruption or loss of data and continuity of I/O status, is accomplished typically within a few milliseconds (e.g., 20-25ms). The malfunctioning primary controller would switch OFF automatically and could be serviced while operation continues under secondary control.

While original hot back-up systems performed diagnostics on PLC components only, evolution of these systems has resulted in fault-tolerant systems that diagnose the entire control system. Fault-tolerant designs enable the user to configure the PLC to diagnose all of the control system components, from the sensors to the final controlled elements. Fault-tolerant designs are available that allow the user to configure systems with redundant (two) or triple-redundant (three) CPUs, redundant I/O systems, redundant sensors, and redundant final actuators. To complement the redundant hardware, such designs incorporate software to diagnose faults involving discrepancies between identical components. If a disagreement exists between redundant sensors, the CPU performs a diagnostic test to determine which is at fault.

In configuring the fault-tolerant system, one must determine the level of redundancy actually required. In each system, some inputs and outputs are more critical than others. Naturally, a greater level of redundancy will mean greater costs. The cost of fault-tolerant systems, however, is generally insignificant when compared with the loss of production cost or the cost of raw materials lost due to an interruption in the process.

Fail-Safe CPU Design

The term *fail-safe* means that in a failure situation, whether encountered internally or externally to the PLC system, all controlled elements can be brought to a predictable and predetermined safe state. This also means that hazardous situations are precluded with absolute certainty. A fail-safe PLC system should be considered in those applications where safety has top priority, as well as where strict regulatory safety standards or approvals must be met. Typical applications include power plant systems, elevator systems, burner control, machine tools, or hazardous chemical processes.

Fail-safe systems, like the fault-tolerant configuration, may involve two or three CPUs, each having identical software, common or identical I/O systems, and a parallel communications link between the CPUs. The two or three units continually compare their input states and their program results and thereby preclude dangerous output responses to any deviations that may exist among them.

Like fault-tolerant designs, the fail-safe design enables the user to configure the PLC to diagnose all of the control system components, from the sensors to the final controlled elements. The fail-safe system also uses sophisticated diagnostic software to diagnose a fault when a discrepancy exists between identical components. In addition, routine on-line testing of all components is performed. Unlike the fault-tolerant system, which is aimed at avoiding a system shutdown, the fail-safe system's primary goal is to ensure an orderly and safe shutdown in the event of a detected fault or potentially unsafe condition.

3-7 The System Power Supply

The CPU power supply provides DC voltage sources for the processor, memory, and any other cards installed in the CPU rack. It converts higher- level line voltages to lower-level logic and control voltages (e.g., 5V, 12V, 24V) required by the PLC's electronic circuitry. CPU power supplies are mechanically packaged either with the CPU as an external unit connected to the CPU, or as a slot-mounted module installed in the CPU rack. See Figure 3-12.

Because of the important function of supplying reliable power to the CPU, a well-designed power supply is a critical element of the PLC system. A well-designed power supply is one that is (1) packaged properly to dissipate large amounts of heat, (2) capable of sustaining line voltage variations found in industrial facilities, and (3) meets one or more widely accepted standards for noise immunity — two of the most popular are NEMA ICS2-230 and IEEE-472.

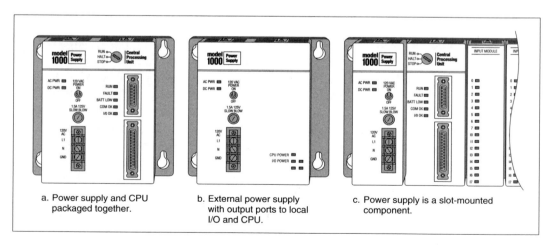

Figure 3-12. Illustration of typical PLC power supply packaging.

The Input Source Voltage

Usually, the PLC power supply operates from a user selectable voltage of 115 volts AC or 230 volts AC. Some small controllers may also operate from a 24-volt DC source. Each power supply is rated to provide a maximum current and therefore must be carefully selected to adequately supply the CPU modules and any I/O modules installed in the CPU rack (See *Power Supply Loading.*)

Since industrial facilities normally experience fluctuations in line voltage and frequency, PLC power supplies are designed to tolerate a variation in line conditions of, typically, plus or minus 10 percent of the nominal voltage. For example, a 120-VAC power supply with a tolerance of +/- 10 percent will still operate properly if the voltage source swings up to 132 volts or down to 97 volts. An LED indicator is normally on the front panel of the power supply to indicate when the power is within tolerance. If the voltage goes outside the specified tolerances for a predetermined duration, a signal will be given to the processor to start an orderly shutdown.

The PLC power supply, as illustrated in Figure 3-13, is normally connected to a separate transformer to electrically isolate it from noise-generating equipment. Power isolation also prevents the PLC from being subjected to nuisance shutdowns, resulting from line voltage variations caused by start-up or shut-down of heavy loads (e.g., large motors, air conditioning units, welding systems). Placing the controller on a separate transformer from the potential EMI generators will also increase system reliability. Other measures for ensuring a good clean power installation are discussed in chapter 15.

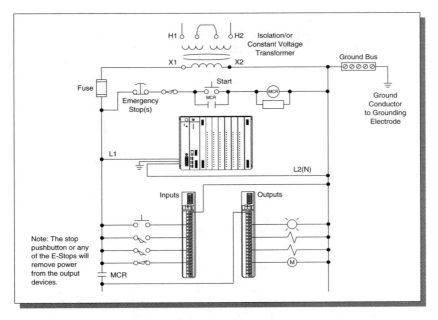

Figure 3-13. A typical PLC power supply connection, using an isolation transformer

Power Supply Loading

Each power supply, when installed in a CPU or I/O rack, distributes various DC voltage levels across the backplane to the installed CPU and/or I/O modules. Individual modules will have a unique current draw, and the total draw on the power supply is the sum of the current draw of the installed modules. However, since the power supply is rated to supply a maximum current at a given operating temperature, exceeding this maximum supply current causes overloading, which results in unpredictable operation or even failure of the I/O system.

Most vendors offer two or more power supply ratings to accommodate various I/O current requirements. Generally, the lower-rated power supply is sufficient to handle a general mix of commonly used I/O modules, such as the discrete type. The problem of overloading, however, generally arises when several modules having a high-current consumption, such as analog and intelligent modules, are placed in one rack. Such an installation may require a heavy-duty power supply of a higher current rating or the installation of parallel supplies, an option offered by some vendors.

Because the power supply overloading condition is often a function of the I/O devices that are active at a given time, its presence could appear intermittently and not under static load conditions. Specifying a sufficiently rated power supply for each rack requires determining the current consumption of each installed module, based on its worst-case condition. For example, output modules draw more current when the outputs are energized. The worst-case value for each module would be based on the greatest number of circuits that will be active at any given time. An example of power supply load calculation is illustrated in Figure 3-14.

Module Slot	Module Type	Power Consumption (mA)
0	16 PT 110 VAC Input	150
1	16 PT 110 VAC Input	150
2	16 PT 110 VAC Input	150
3	16 PT 110 VAC Input	150
4	16 PT 24 VDC Input	200
5	16 PT 24 VDC Input	200
6	16 PT 110 VAC Output	450
7	16 PT 110 VAC Output	450
8	16 PT 110 VAC Output	450
9	16 PT 110 VAC Output	450
10	16 PT 110 VAC Input	150
11	16 PT 110 VAC Input	150
Total Power Supplied	**5700 mA**	Total Power Consumed
		3250 mA

The total power consumed is less than the power supplied, therefore the configuration can be supported by the power supply.

Figure 3-14. Power supply loading or power budget computation

4

THE PLC'S APPLICATION MEMORY

Introduction

Application Memory Types

Memory Structure and Capacity

Application Memory Organization

Memory Addressing and Mapping

In most computer-based systems, the interaction that users have with memory (i.e., storage/retrieval of programs and data) at the application level is a transparent process. For the most part, there is little or no concern for how and where things are stored. Most interactions merely involve storing or recalling programs or data files by name. With PLCs, however, a working knowledge of how memory is arranged and utilized is vital. Moreover, its relationship to the I/O system is a prerequisite to the creation and interpretation of the user program, data storage, and any on-line interaction with the controller.

In this chapter, we will examine the organization and structure of the PLC memory, the various memory types and the applications to which they are best suited, and finally, memory addressing and its mapping to the I/O system.

4-1 Introduction

Back in chapter 1, we said that the most distinguishing feature of the programmable controller is its programmability. This feature makes it flexible with respect to the types of applications to which it can be applied, as well to the ultimate tailoring or changes typically made during design, installation, or expansion of a particular application. Such changes are made to the PLC's application memory using the PLC programming device.

The application memory is that part of the programmable controller's central processing unit that provides storage for all user-generated programs and data. Application memory is typically installed on 1) the processor module, 2) on one or more modular slot-mounted cards installed in the CPU rack, or 3) on small submodule plug-in type cartridges installed into the processor module.

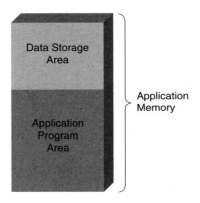

Figure 4-1. Application memory stores the control program and process data

The application memory consists of two basic sections, as illustrated in Figure 4-1; the *data storage area* and the *application program area*. The data table stores various types of data required by the control program and in some cases by the CPU. The application program area, is employed by the system programmer for implementing the control program. In this area are stored the step-by-step instructions for controlling the sequence of operations for a particular machine or process. The following sections examine various application memory types, storage capacity requirements, storage of various data types, and addressing schemes.

4-2 Application Memory Types

There are two major considerations regarding the memory type for your application program. Since application memory is responsible for retaining a control program that will be run each day, volatility should be the prime consideration. With the loss of the program, the day's production may be delayed or forfeited. The affects are usually costly. A second concern should be the ease of altering the program when required. Ease in altering the memory is important since the memory is ultimately involved in any interaction that goes on between you and the controller. This interaction begins with program generation and continues through with program changes, system start-up, and ultimately on-line program changes.

The following discussions describe various types of memory and how their inherent characteristics affect the manner in which programmed instructions are retained or altered within the PLC. The unique needs of each application will dictate what type of memory is best suited.

Volatile and Nonvolatile Memory

Table 4-1 lists the four types of memory used in programmable controllers, along with a summary of their characteristics and applications. These four memory types can be placed in two general categories: 1) those that are *volatile* and 2) those that are *non-volatile*. Volatility relates to the ability of the memory type to be modified and maintain its programmed contents.

Table 4-1. Memory types Used in Programmable Controllers

MEMORY TYPE	VOLATILITY	ADVANTAGES/DISADVANTAGES
RAM	Volatile	- Easily programmed - Easily modified - Loses contents if battery backup is lost
EPROM	Nonvolatile	- Maintains contents without battery backup - Tamper proof - Must be erased with UV-light (15-20 min.)
EEPROM	Nonvolatile	- Maintains contents without battery backup - Electronically erased - Tamper proof
NOVRAM	Nonvolatile	- Maintains contents without battery backup - Combines RAM and EEPROM technology - Tamper proof - Not available in many systems

Volatile memory types lose their programmed contents if all operating power is lost or removed. Like the onboard memory of personal computers, if a program file is loaded and power is lost or removed, the program will not be in memory when power is restored. The program would have to be reloaded. With PLCs, however, volatile memories are supported by back-up batteries that maintain the memory contents if power is removed. Most back-up batteries have operational lives of one year or more.

Nonvolatile memory types will retain their programmed contents even if operating power is completely lost. They require no type of backup. Examples of nonvolatile memory include storage media such as floppy disk, hard disk, and magnetic tape, all of which do not require power to maintain their programmed contents. However, nonvolatile memory types used in PLCs and discussed here are solid-state memories.

Random Access Memory (RAM)

Random Access Memory is the most commonly used memory type for PLCs. It allows programs to be easily inserted and later modified. The term random access means that the individual storage locations of RAM can be addressed and accessed randomly and directly without having to address or access preceding addresses. RAM is also a read/write memory, which means that data can be written into or read from any location — a location is changed by simply writing over the previous contents. These characteristics allow fast access that results in faster program execution and access for reading or making on-line program changes.

RAM is a volatile memory; therefore, in PLC systems, long-life lithium or nickel-cadmium type batteries are used to provide backup if the normal source of power is lost or removed. A notable point is that in some systems the back-up battery is installed on the memory board while in others it may be incorporated in the power supply. A battery installed on the power supply would result in loss of battery support and memory contents should the power supply or memory module be removed from the rack. Battery-backed RAM is sufficient in most applications; in fact, it is the most commonly used memory configuration. In many applications, however, it is desirable to have a nonvolatile memory as a backup to the RAM system.

Erasable Programmable Read Only Memory (EPROM)

EPROM is a nonvolatile memory that, once programmed, cannot be modified without first completely erasing the chips and then reprogramming. Erasure is accomplished by exposing the window of the chips to an ultraviolet light source for approximately 15-20 minutes. For this reason, EPROM memory may also be called *UV PROM*. EPROMs are normally programmed using a special EPROM programming device, but in some cases, the PLC programming device incorporates an EPROM programming facility.

EPROM provide a means for permanently storing a fully developed and tested program. It is widely used as a primary memory to safeguard against inadvertent changes or program loss due to power loss, or as a secondary or back-up system to battery-supported RAM. In this latter case, the tested RAM program is loaded into the EPROM. If for some reason the RAM contents are lost or if program alterations result in subsequent misoperation, the EPROM will always have the original program and can be simply installed until the RAM is corrected.

In some applications, EPROM serves as the primary memory if the installation calls for such security. However, because EPROM is a read-only memory as opposed to a read/write memory, once programmed it can be read (or examined) but not be changed. This means it can be executed by the processor or monitored by the user, but it will not allow on-line program changes. Such a requirement would require that a RAM (a read/write memory) be used to make the necessary changes and before reloading the program to the EPROM. EPROM is often used as the primary memory in systems developed by original equipment manufacturers (OEMs).

Electrically Erasable PROM (EEPROM)

EEPROM is an EPROM that can be erased and reprogrammed through electronic circuitry. Developed in the mid-1970s, this technology is a non- volatile memory that offers the ease of programming RAMs. Unlike EPROM, the EEPROM does not require a ultraviolet light eraser, but instead is erased electrically, typically via the programming device. While many low-end PLCs operate solely from EEPROM, it is offered as an option with others, including mid-range and high-end controllers. EEPROM technology is suitable in applications that require program security, as well as a less time-consuming means for making program changes and allowing on-line program changes.

Nonvolatile RAM (NOVRAM)

NOVRAM, is an enhancement of the conventional volatile RAM technology. It is designed to maintain its programmed contents if power is removed. NOVRAM, although proven technology, is still not widely used in PLCs. This memory device is comprised of a foreground static RAM, constructed against a background EEPROM — all on a single chip. Each bit within the RAM section of the chip has a corresponding adjacent bit within the EEPROM. Data can be transferred electronically between the two memories, giving this technology the easy read/write benefits of RAM and the nonvolatility of EEPROM.

NOVRAM, although not as widely used as the other memory types, has the makings of the perfect memory combination. When entered, the user program is written directly into RAM and is also executed from RAM, allowing faster program entry and execution by the processor. The program is automatically duplicated into the EEP-ROM. When power is removed from the controller, the RAM contents are lost but are automatically restored from EEPROM to RAM upon restoration of power. NOVRAM is an excellent memory technology for industrial applications. It offers easy reprogramming, like RAM, and protects against program loss resulting from power loss or by accidents, like EPROM.

4-3 Memory Structure and Capacity

Bits, Bytes, and Words

A graphic view of the memory arrangement in programmable controllers is typified by the array of cells in Figure 4-2. Each cell represents a *bit* location, which is capable of storing a value of 1 or 0. A bit, which is the smallest unit of memory, gets its name from the fact that it stores a single binary digit — 1 or 0. Ones and zeros are not actually in each cell; instead, a voltage charge present at the cell is represented by a 1 and no charge is represented by a 0. As we will see later, each bit can be addressed and is considered ON if it contains a value of 1 and OFF if the cell contains a value of 0.

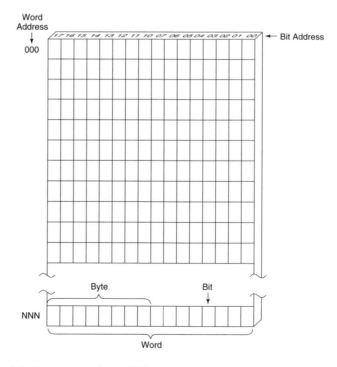

Figure 4-2. The basic units of PLC memory; bits, bytes, and words

The _byte_ is the second structural unit of memory, consisting of eight bits treated as a group. Since a byte is a group of eight positions, it is capable of storing binary numbers and codes. Just as the decimal number system requires more than one digit position for representing numbers larger than 0 to 9, a group of binary digits will allow expression of numbers greater than 0 to 1. Typical use of the byte is to store ASCII characters, which can be represented in eight bits.

The third and final unit of memory, also a grouping of bits, is called a _word_. PLC words typically consist of two bytes or a total of sixteen-bits. Like the byte, a word can be used to store numbers and codes, or simply store sixteen individual pieces of information (e.g., the status of sixteen-digital inputs). Since the sixteen bits of a word are handled simultaneously, a word stores twice as much information as the bytes and can store numbers twice as large. Our discussion of the memory data table will shed more light on how memory words are used.

Memory Capacity

The amount of memory available for storing programs and data in a particular controller is a processor specification defining the maximum number of storage locations (See Figure 4-3). Memory capacity is an important prerequisite for determining whether a particular processor is suitable for handling the storage requirements of the specific application.

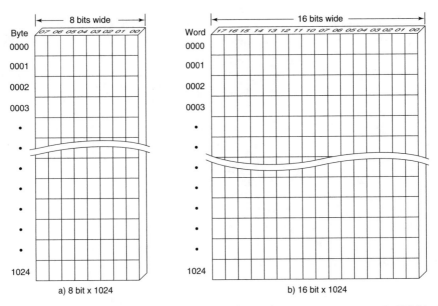

Figure 4-3. PLC memory, may be specified in units of bytes (8 bits) and words (16 bits)

Memory capacity is generally stated in units of (*K-bytes* or *K-words*) depending on whether the PLC has a *word-structured- memory* organized in sixteen-bit storage locations or a *byte-structured memory* organized in eight-bit storage locations. In either case, 1K is equivalent to 1,024 storage units. Figure 4-3 illustrates both a word-structured memory and a byte-structured memory with 1,024 locations. Note that since the byte unit is one-half the size of a word unit, a 16K-byte memory has one-half the storage capacity of a 16K-word memory.

Memory size normally varies, depending on the controller, as a function of input/output capacity. Low-end controllers with 64 I/O typically have memory capacities in a range of 4K to 8K words. This amount is generally adequate for controllers that are primarily relay replacers and use memory primarily for storing logic instructions. Mid-range and high-end controllers typically have expandable memories, in which memory segments can be added as needed in increments of 16K, 32K, or 64K up to the maximum capacity.

Determining Capacity Requirements

For some, deciding on the amount of memory to purchase might be guesswork while for others it may be a judgment based on experience or meticulous calculation. Although no rules exist for making this decision before the program is created, it's vital to make a judgment based on some predetermined criteria. The idea is to avoid extra expense and delays while allowing for sufficient expansion.

Knowing how memory is used to store instructions for a particular processor is the best way to estimate memory needs. *Memory utilization* defines the number of words required to store each programmed instruction. Most product specifications provide a list showing each instruction and its storage requirement. With this type of information, it is possible to make a rough estimate prior to generating the program.

Simple contact and coil instructions, including their addresses, typically require one word of memory while timers and counters may require three to six words. It is important to remember that more complex programs, with arithmetic, data manipulations, and other high-level functions, will require substantially more memory. An estimate of how much memory is needed can be based on the number of outputs to be controlled and an estimate of contacts per rung required to control the output (e.g., ten contacts/output). An estimated number of timers, counters, and other block functions, with the estimated logic for each ladder network, would also be added.

4-4 Application Memory Organization

As mentioned earlier, the application memory is that portion of the PLC's memory dedicated to storing the control program and any associated data. Normally, the CPU's memory specification refers to this storage space, which is intended for application use. A thorough understanding of the application memory, it's organizational structure, addressing, and uses, will enhance your understanding of program generation and the interaction between the memory and I/O devices.

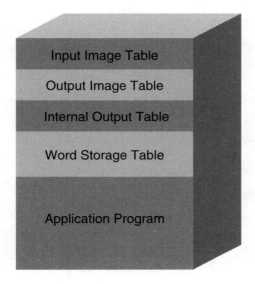

Figure 4-4. Typical application memory segments

Application memory can be divided into the five areas as shown in Figure 4-4 although in some controllers, the input and output image tables may be considered part of the system memory. This latter detail has no important consequences in the context of this discussion.

The Input Image Table

The *input image table* is that part of the application memory allocated to storing the ON/OFF status of connected discrete inputs. In a given PLC, a maximum number of discrete inputs that can be connected. Each input requires one bit storage location in the input image table to store its status; therefore, the input image table size generally corresponds exactly to the maximum number of discrete inputs.

A controller having a maximum of 128 discrete inputs, would require a 128 bit storage locations for the input image table — a total of eight sixteen-bit words, as illustrated in Figure 4-5. For each connected input, there is a unique bit location whose address in the input image table corresponds directly to the terminal to which the device is connected. These addresses are used in the control program to reference each input when examining its ON/OFF state.

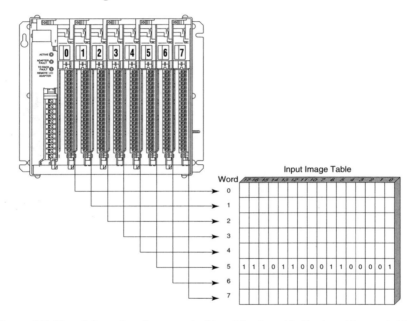

Figure 4-5. The status of each connected input is stored in the input image table

As described earlier in the discussion of processor scan, a snapshot of the status of all of the input signals is taken on each processor scan, and the actual ON/OFF states of each device is stored in its corresponding location in the input image table. If the input is ON (voltage present), its corresponding bit in the image table is set ON (1); if the input is OFF (no voltage), its bit location in the image table is turned OFF (0). The input image table, which is used by the control program, is constantly being updated on each scan to reflect the latest status of discrete input devices.

The Output Image Table

The *output image table* is that part of the application memory allocated to storing the actual ON/OFF status of connected discrete outputs. As with inputs, each PLC allows a maximum number of discrete outputs to be connected. Each output requires one bit storage location in the output image table to store its status; therefore the output image table size corresponds exactly to the maximum number of discrete outputs.

Given a PLC having a maximum of 128 discrete outputs, a total of 128 bits are required in the output image table — a total of eight sixteen-bit words, as illustrated in Figure 4-6. For each output device, there is a unique bit whose address in the output image table corresponds directly to the terminal to which the output device is connected. These addresses are used to reference each device in the control program to control its ON/OFF state.

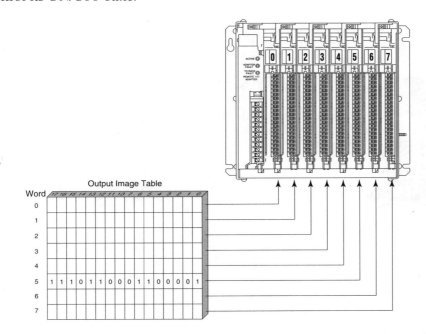

Figure 4-6. The status of each connected output is controlled by a bit in the output image table

As described in the discussion of processor scan, bits in the output image table are controlled by the logic sequences programmed for each output. On each cycle of the program, as the logic is evaluated, the resultant ON/OFF states of each device are stored in their corresponding location in the output image table. If the logic driving an output is TRUE, its bit in the output image table is set ON (1); if the logic driving an output is FALSE, its bit in the image table is turned OFF (0). At the end of each program scan, the current status bits of the output image table are used to command each output to turn ON or OFF, based on its image table status of 1 or 0.

The Internal Output Table

Internal outputs are ON/OFF signals generated by programmed logic. Unlike discrete outputs, internal outputs are not directly associated with a connected real-world output device. However, internal outputs are for internal logic uses such as interlocking various logic circuits. Internal outputs, often referred to as *internal storage bits* or *internal flag bits,* are to the ladder language, what control relays are to a hardwired relay circuit and what flags are to a computer programming language.

As an example, in hardwired relay circuits, a control relay is often used to generate a signal that is used in many other circuits. When the relay is energized, its contacts (normally-open or normally-closed) can be used for providing that signal in other circuits. Similarly, in computer programs, flags are used to signify some event having occurred. Likewise, internal outputs are used in PLC programs to detect and signify some occurrence. An internal output, like real or external output signals, have normally-open and normally-closed contacts that can be used throughout the program. How internals are used in PLC programming is discussed in further detail in Chapter 14.

Being ON/OFF type signals, internal outputs are single-bit storage locations in memory and are addressed as such. Internal outputs are programmed just as standard outputs, with an output symbol referenced by one of the bit addresses allocated in the internal output table. When the logic driving the internal output is TRUE, the referenced bit address is turned ON or set to 1. The number of internal outputs available is system dependent but generally increases as the number of real I/O increases. Figure 4-7 illustrates an internal output table with 2,048 internal outputs, which is equivalent to 128 sixteen-bit data table words.

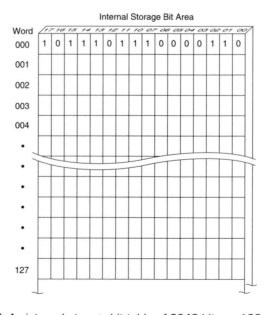

Figure 4-7. An internal storage bit table of 2048 bits — 128 sixteen-bit words

The Word Storage Table

The *word* or *register storage table* is an allocation of sixteen-bit memory locations set aside for the purpose of storing various forms of numerical data. The data types discussed thus far — for instance, discrete inputs, discrete outputs, and internal outputs — were all ON/OFF type information that could be represented using single-bit locations in which a binary 1 or 0 was stored. Word storage, however, implies that sixteen-bits are handled as a unit and therefore can be used to represent numeric or other types of data that cannot be represented by a single-bit location.

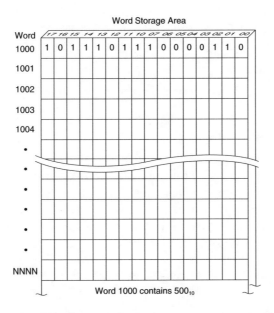

Figure 4-8. Word data locations store data that represents various process quantities (See Table 4-2)

Word locations are required to store variable and constant data, such as raw numbers used in arithmetic calculations, high and low limits, timer and counter presets, and timer and counter accumulated values. Word locations are also required to store data incoming to the controller through input modules, such as analog inputs, whose varying input signal is represented by a numeric value. They are also required for data outgoing from the controller through output modules such as a stepper motor output that require a numerical value to drive connected devices. Table 4-2, on the following page, lists typical variable and constant data that are stored in word locations.

In some controllers, the use of the word storage area is entirely user definable; that is, all available word locations can be used for storing whatever type of data the system programmer decides. However, the word storage area in many controllers is subdivided into separate blocks of words dedicated to handling specific types of data. Such an organization may allow data requiring special processor manipulation to be handled accordingly and perhaps more efficiently.

Table 4-2. Typical Variable and Constant Word Data

CONSTANT DATA	VARIABLE DATA
Timer Presets	Timer Accumulated Values
Counter Presets	Counter Accumulated Values
Loop Setpoints	PID Data
Other Setpoints	Computation Results
Analog Alarm Limits	Analog Input Data
Decimal Tables	Analog Output Data
Recipe Data	BCD Input Data
ASCII Characters	BCD Output Data

The Application Program Area

The *application program area* is that portion of the application memory reserved for storing the user-generated control program. The control program will determine the exact sequence of operations for a given machine or process. As illustrated in Figure 4-9, when the controller is switched to the RUN mode, the processor begins program execution and interprets each instruction while using and manipulating the data stored in the various data table areas to perform its operations.

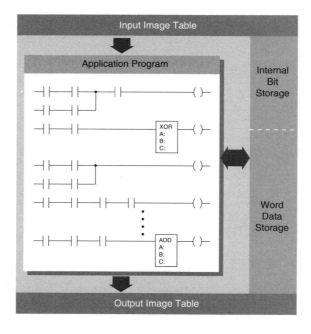

Figure 4-9. The application program area stores the control program. The program interacts with other parts of the memory

The amount of memory available for user program storage depends on the particular processor and on how memory is allocated for that controller. The memory areas described thus far, including the *input image table, output image table, internal flags, and word storage area,* are generally considered part of the application memory. However, in some cases, these areas may be considered internal to the controller and come as part of the system. In such a case, the application program area is usually considered separate and may be added as required.

In general, the actual amount of space available for program storage will be a function of the overall size and capability of the PLC. Memory size is usually fixed somewhere between 8K and 20K for low-end processors while expandable up to some maximum amount for middle to high-end processors — typically between 48K and 96K for mid-range controllers and up to 640K for high-end controllers.

4-5 Memory Addressing and Mapping

Thus far, we have described the basic structural units (i.e., bits, bytes, words) of memory, the various segments of application memory and the types of data stored in each. What remains, is an explanation of the techniques used to reference these areas throughout the control program. An understanding of these techniques, which are generally quite common in all PLCs, will simplify the task of working with different controllers.

Memory addresses are the numbers used to reference each location in memory. As a user, you will be concerned with addressing input and output devices, internal output coils, and numeric values stored in the word storage table. Addresses for these areas will allow you to access and manipulate these locations in the control program, or through the use of the PLC programming device.

Addressing Word-structured Memory

The application memory of most PLCs is organized in what can be referred to as a *word-structured memory*. Each word is sixteen bits wide and has a unique number that allows the location to be referenced and accessed as a sixteen-bit grouping. Figure 4-10 illustrates a 2K (2,048 decimal) data storage area. There are a total of 2,048 words, but if they are numbered in octal, the first location would be numbered 0000 and the last location would be numbered 3777. To examine the contents or store a value in any of these locations involves specifying the desired word address. Typical data types that would be referenced using word addresses were listed in Table 4-2.

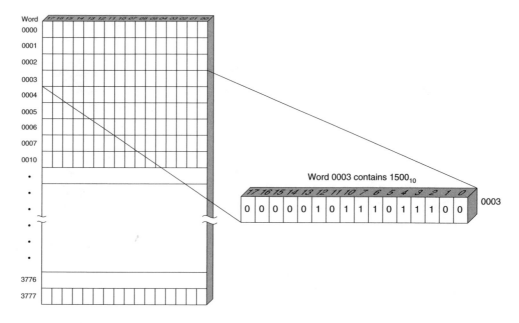

Figure 4-10. The contents of word address 0003 is shown in binary. The decimal equivalent is 1500

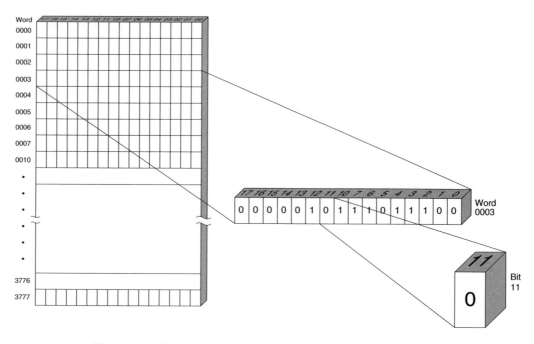

Figure 4-11. Illustration of bit address 003.11 — word 003, bit 11

Note that across the top of the memory table, the bit positions are also numbered in octal — 00 through 17. Some PLCs may number the positions 0 through 15 decimal. These bit positions are numbered the same for each word location, hence a specific bit location of any word has a unique address which is derived by prefixing the bit number with the word address. As illustrated in Figure 4-11, bit position 11 of word 003 has a unique address of 003-11. Normally, a bit address is written or specified in the program with the word location and bit location separated by a hyphen or period (e.g., 003-11 or 003.11). Connected discrete inputs and outputs, and internal outputs would be referenced in such a manner in the control program.

Addressing Byte-structured Memory

In systems that use a *byte-structured memory,* all addresses are based on the byte unit. As previously mentioned, byte-organized memories specify the total memory in units of K-bytes. As with word-structured addressing, byte-structured addressing also uses decimal or octal numbering.

Given an example data table, of 2K-bytes (2,048 decimal) as illustrated in Figure 4-12, each byte is numbered with a unique address. In octal, the first byte address is 0000 and the last byte address is 3777. Each bit position of any byte will be numbered 0 to 7. Hence, a specific bit location of any byte has a unique address that is derived by prefix-

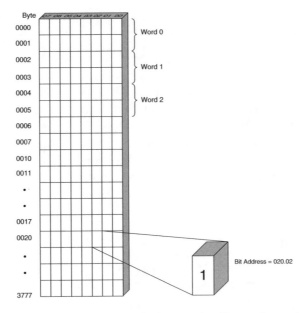

Figure 4-12. Addressing bits in a byte-organized memory is the same as for word-organized memory

ing the bit number with the byte address. As illustrated in Figure 4-13, bit position 02 of byte 020 has a unique address of 020-02 (typically written 020-02 or 020.2).

Although addressing words in a byte-structured memory is not as readily apparent in a word-structured memory, Figure 4-13 shows how this is generally accomplished by linking to bytes to form a sixteen-bit word. Generally, in this type of arrangement, each word is composed of two consecutive bytes — an even-byte address and an odd-byte address. For instance, byte 0 and byte 1 form the first word in the table; byte 2 and byte 3 form the second word. As illustrated below, the odd-addressed byte is normally the least-significant byte and even-addressed byte is the most-significant byte of the word.

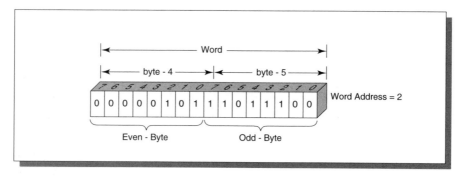

Figure 4-13. Byte-organized memory in some PLCs assign word addresses based on the starting byte address (e.g., word 0004 is made up of bytes 4 and 5)

Various techniques are employed for addressing words in a byte- structured memory. However, the most typical approach is the one previously described. When any of these addresses are referenced using a word instruction, the processor handles the two consecutive bytes as a word. And, of course, individual bits are accessed using bit-oriented instructions and referencing the location with the byte address and bit position. In addition, the instruction set will allow access to individual bytes for accessing byte-oriented data (e.g., one ASCII character is stored in a single byte).

Memory Mapping

In the two previous discussions, we examined the basic approach to addressing the PLC application memory, based on word-structured and byte-structured organization. Regardless of whether a memory is structured using bytes or words, the general ways in which PLC memory are arranged and numbered will appear quite similar for all controllers, from the user's standpoint. Whatever the minor differences are, however, they are easily understood by becoming familiar with the *application memory map*.

In our first examination of the application memory, we saw that it was segmented for different uses, with a fixed space allocated for each segment. To fully understand the structure and addressing of the application memory for a particular processor, a *memory map* is needed. A memory map is a detailed outline of how the Application memory is arranged, showing the allocated address range of segments and how each segment is used. In Figure 4-14 shows a memory map of a 6K-word application memory. There are a total of 6,144 (decimal) word locations, numbered 00000 through 31777 octal. An explanation of this memory map is given in the following example.

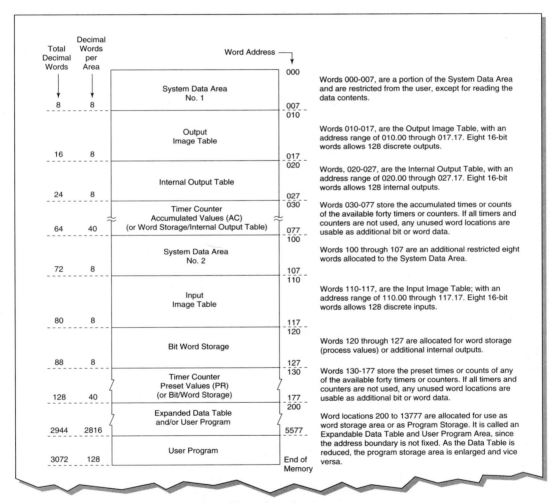

Figure 4-14. 6K-word application memory map

5 INPUT/OUTPUT SYSTEM OVERVIEW

Basic Components

I/O Housing and Power Supply

Input/Output Interface Modules

Local and Remote I/O

Input/Output Addressing

Having been an area of constant improvement and innovation for many years, input/output systems of PLCs now encompass a complete range and variety of digital, analog, positioning, communications, and special function interfaces. The result is easier interfacing to most standard sensing, actuating, and intelligent peripheral devices, as well as programmable controllers that can be applied to practically any type of control task.

In this chapter, you will learn the basic components of the PLC input/output system, as well as how most PLCs address the devices connected to the various input/output modules.

5-1 Basic Components

The programmable controller's *input/output (I/O) system* provides the means by which physical connection is made between the field devices and the PLC processor. By combining the proper components of an I/O system with your selected processor, a complete programmable controller system is formed.

Through various *input interface modules*, the controller is able to sense status conditions such as device OPEN or CLOSED, EXTENDED or RETRACTED, as well as measure process quantities such as temperature, pressure, flow, speed, and position. Using information gained from input modules and through execution of the control program, the processor issues commands to *output interface modules* that in turn will control various devices such as valves, motors, and alarms. In short, the input/output system provides the sensing and actuating abilities through which the processor exercises control over any machine or process.

In the remaining discussions of this chapter, the following basic components and configurations of the I/O system are introduced.

❑ I/O Housing and Power Supply
❑ Input/Output Interface Modules
❑ Local and Remote I/O
❑ Input/Output Addresses

In chapters 6, 7, and 8, a more in-depth discussion of the input/output system will examine the operation and application of *discrete*, *analog*, and *intelligent I/O*, respectively.

5-2 I/O Housing and Power Supply

The I/O Housing

The *I/O housing*, also referred to as *I/O racks* or *I/O mounting bases* is the most basic element of the input/output system. It provides the actual mounting structure in which various user-selected I/O modules are installed. These housings are normally available in different sizes, based on the number of module slots, which is typically between eight and sixteen. The number of slots will determine the capacity of the rack, which is typically 32, 64, 128, or 256 input/output channels. Figure 5-1 illustrates typical I/O housings. Each system will support some maximum number of I/O racks or mounting bases.

At the inside back of a typical I/O rack is a printed circuit board called the *backplane*. The backplane has plug-in type connectors that accept interface modules in each slot. These connectors form an *electrical bus* for allowing communication between the installed I/O modules and the CPU, as well as for distribution of power to the modules. In most PLCs, the backplane connectors of individual module slots can be keyed so that the slot will accept only certain module types. Keying allows a slot to be designated for a particular module type and thereby prevents replacement of a defective module with the incorrect module type.

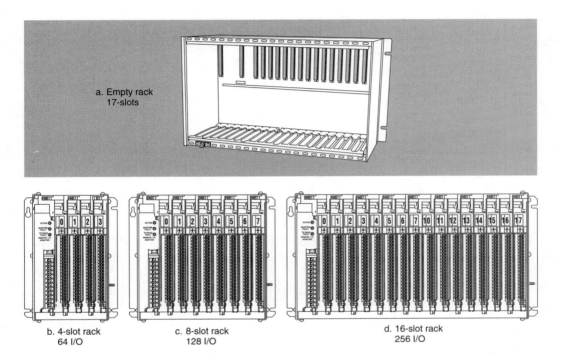

Figure 5-1. Example I/O module housings

In most PLCs, the I/O system utilizes a "private" or *proprietary bus*, allowing only the modules of a particular vendor to be installed in the rack. Other I/O systems may utilize a *standard bus*, allowing any modules designed to be compatible with the standard bus connections to be installed in the I/O rack. Examples of standard bus architectures include Motorola's *VME bus* and Intel's *MultiBus*. Use of a standard bus allows compatible I/O products manufactured by many companies to be utilized by the PLC's I/O system.

The I/O Power Supply

Each I/O rack requires its own power supply unless it is provided power by another rack connected in tandem. This power supply converts the main supply voltage to the internal DC levels required by the I/O modules. With some systems, one power supply is capable of supplying power to two or more racks. I/O system power supplies are often plug-in modules installed in one of the rack slots or externally attached to the rack. They may also be installed in a separate wall-mounted unit.

The I/O power supply does not supply power to the machine or process devices, but instead supplies power to the internal logic circuitry of the modules installed in each rack. Hence, the I/O power supply must be carefully selected to support the power consumption of the installed modules. Power supply loading is discussed in more detail in chapter 3.

5-3 Input/Output Interface Modules

Input/output (I/O) interface modules are the hardware components of the I/O system that allow various external devices to be connected to the PLC system. A given I/O system may have many different interface modules. These components are referred to as modules because of their modular nature with respect to mechanical design and. Each module is an encased circuit board designed to plug into an I/O rack and to interface with a specific category of devices (e.g., discrete, analog, communications) to the PLC.

Generally, interface modules are classed into two major categories: *input* and *output modules*. Each module typically contains 2,4,8,16 or as many as 32 input or output circuits. Module with 16 or 32 circuits are called *high density modules* since they double or quadruple the number of circuits on a card approximately the same size as the standard eight-point module. The number of circuits — or points, as they're called — determines the number of field devices that can be connected to the module. Some typical I/O modules are shown in Figure 5-2.

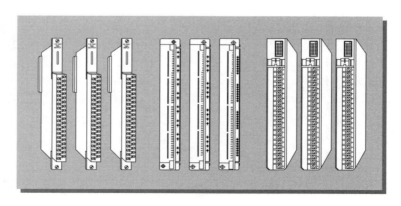

Figure 5-2. Input/output modules interface the machine or process to the PLC

Input Modules

Input modules, as the name implies, allow information to be sent to the controller from various field devices. The type of device determines the type of information and dictates what type of input module is required. Input modules contain circuitry that allows the processor to sense the status of digital signals such as those generated by pushbuttons and selector switches, as well as to measure the value of analog signals such as those generated by pressure or temperature transducers. The main functions of an input module are to

1) provide a place for terminating field input devices
2) accept and convert incoming field signals to signals compatible to and usable by the PLC processor.
3) provide isolation between field voltages and the PLC system and
4) provide LED status indication for each input device.

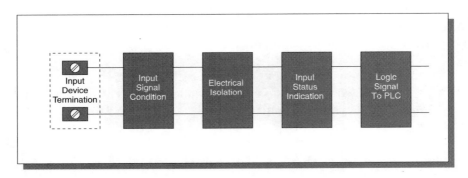

Figure 5-3. Block diagram of input module functions

Output Modules

Output modules, are used to output or send information from the controller to field devices. Again, the type of device determines the type of output information and what output module is required. Output modules contain circuitry that allows the processor to control the ON/OFF status of digital signals such as those required to switch devices like motor starters and solenoids. Others may vary a continuous analog voltage or current required to control devices such as electric drives or proportional flow valves. General functions of an output module are to

1) provide termination point for connecting field output devices
2) accept data from the Processor and perform conversion to appropriate signals required to control field devices
3) provide isolation between field voltages and the PLC system, and
4) provide LED status indication for each output device.

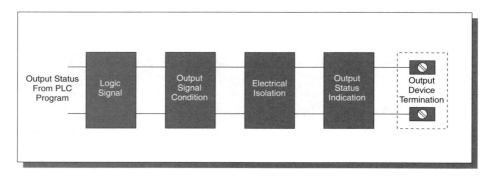

Figure 5-4. Block diagram of output module functions

I/O Module Classifications

As stated above, input modules allow data to be input to the controller while output modules allow data to be output from the controller. Input/output modules, however, can be further classified based on the type of signals they process and, consequently, on the type of devices they allow to be connected to the controller.

To achieve the objectives of this book, I/O modules have been grouped into three functional classes, each of which is discussed in the following three chapters. These classes of I/O interfaces, along with their functions, are listed in Table 5-1.

Table 5-1. Input/Output Module Classes

MODULE CLASS	PURPOSE
Discrete I/O	- Processing ON/OFF voltage signals
Analog I/O	- Processing continuous current or voltage signals
Intelligent I/O	- Pre-processing special signals and processing I/O functions independent of the PLC processor

5-4 Local and Remote I/O

The two basic configurations for placement of I/O chassis in the field are 1) *local I/O*, which is restricted to within a short specified distance from the CPU and 2) *remote I/O*, in which I/O chassis can be located long distances from the CPU. Depending on the PLC model, possible configurations may allow local I/O only or a combination of both local and remote I/O. Generally, low-end PLCs are limited to local I/O, whereas mid-range and high-end units allow both configurations. Each application will dictate whether local or remote I/O is best suited.

Local I/O Configuration

Although I/O is considered local if it is installed in the same rack housing as the CPU, here the reference to local I/O is regarding the restriction of the placement of I/O chassis to within a short distance of the CPU. Normally local I/O restrictions confine it to the same enclosure as the CPU. Typically this distance is distance ranges between 8 and 50 feet away from the CPU.

The local I/O configuration, also referred to as *centralized I/O*, is typical in applications involving a single machine or process having 256 or fewer I/O devices located in a limited area. In such a case, the I/O chassis and CPU enclosure are placed in a central location that minimizes the wiring runs for each device back to the I/O chassis. Local I/O connections between the CPU and the expansion racks typically use a parallel cable link, allowing high-speed communication for the I/O update. A typical local I/O arrangement is illustrated in Figure 5-5.

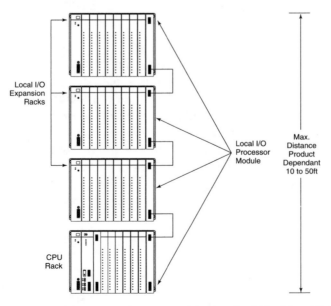

Figure 5-5. A local I/O configuration typically puts the I/O within 10 to 50 feet of the CPU

Remote I/O Configuration

Remote I/O, also called to as *distributed I/O*, refers to the ability to place I/O chassis long distances from the CPU. Typical distances range from 500 to 10,000 feet, with data rates from 32 kilobaud to 1.2 megabaud. This capability is usually found in medium to high-end controllers (i.e., capacity of 512 I/O or greater). An example remote I/O configuration is illustrated in Figure 5-6.

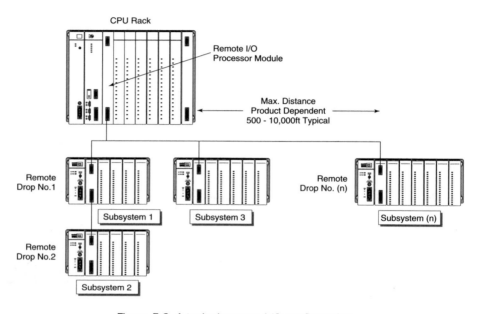

Figure 5-6. A typical remote I/O configuration

Tremendous savings on wiring and labor costs can be realized for large systems in which the field devices are in clusters at various spread-out locations, but centralized control is preferred (a single PLC). The I/O devices of several subsystems of a single machine or process can be connected with short wire runs going to a remote I/O rack located near each machine. With the CPU located in a central area or main control room, only the communications link — instead of hundreds of field wires — is brought back to the CPU. Distributed I/O also offers the advantage of allowing subsystems to be installed and started independently, and in some cases, allowing maintenance on individual subsystems while others continue to operate.

Local and Remote I/O Communications

Once placed in an operational mode, a constant communication involving the exchange of I/O data takes place between the processor and the input/output system. At the end of each program scan, the processor sends out to each I/O rack the latest status of outputs (based on the program results) and receives back the latest status of the connected input devices. This process is called the *I/O scan* or *I/O update*.

The actual hardware link required to maintain communication between the processor and each I/O chassis depends on whether the I/O chassis is mounted local to the CPU or in a remote location. In the case of local I/O installed in the same chassis as the CPU, communication with the processor takes place directly via the chassis backplane. Communication between the CPU and separate local and remote chassis requires a physical link. The components used to make this link include *I/O processor modules* and I/O *communication cables*.

I/O Processor Modules

The term *I/O processor modules* refers collectively to any of the modules used to configure interconnections between the CPU and I/O racks. Generally, this set of modules includes a *local I/O processor module*, installed in each local rack, and a *remote I/O processor module*, installed in each remote rack. At the CPU end, a *local I/O scanner* is installed to communicate with the local processors in each local rack, and a *remote I/O scanner* communicates with the remote I/O processors in each remote rack. The block diagram in Figure 5-7 illustrates I/O processor links.

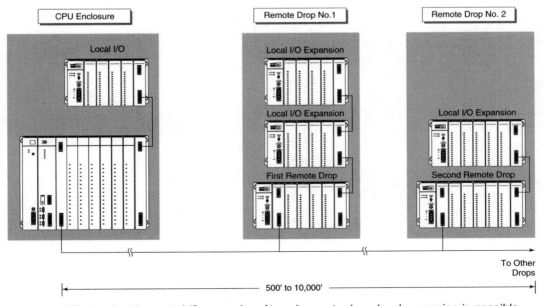

Figure 5-7. Local and remote I/O expansion. At each remote drop, local expansion is possible

Functionally, I/O processor modules must all transmit I/O status, receive I/O status, decode I/O addresses, and perform error checking. At the CPU end, local and remote I/O processors must accept output signal status from the CPU, send it to the appropriate racks, receive back the status of input signals from each rack, and relay it back to the CPU. At the rack end, local and remote I/O processors must accept output signal data from the CPU and determine whether it is addressed to itself or should be passed on to another rack (in daisy-chain configuration) and send input status data back to the CPU.

Because the integrity of I/O data is critical, error checking routines are incorporated in the continuous communication between the processor and each I/O chassis to confirm the validity of the data transmitted and received and to confirm if the communication link is intact and ready. Diagnostics are normally reported on LEDs at each I/O processor module and at the CPU, indicating whether an I/O rack is functioning correctly or has failed. A common practice with many I/O systems is to provide error status bits for each rack that can be accessed and utilized by the control program.

Local and Remote Connections

The communication conductors for connecting I/O racks to the CPU are typically *shielded twisted pair conductors*, *fiber optic cables*, or *coaxial cables*. The cable type may vary with connection configurations, communication method (i.e., serial or parallel), and increased distances from the CPU. I/O data is normally transmitted serially over a single shielded pair of conductors to remote racks; local racks, located within shorter distances, may use parallel cable links.

Local racks are generally linked to the CPU in a *daisy-chain* as illustrated in Figure 5-5. In this configuration, the local I/O scanner in the CPU connects to the local I/O processor of the first local rack and from there to each additional rack until reaching the last rack. The last rack is typically restricted to within a certain distance from the CPU.

Remote configurations normally allow a group or cluster of racks to be placed in several distinct locations, as illustrated in Figure 5-7. Each location is referred to as a remote drop. A single remote I/O scanner can normally link several drops. At the *remote drop*, racks are then daisy-chained like a normal group of local racks, using a parallel communication link. Each remote drop is then connected back to the CPU over a serial communication link between the remote I/O scanner in the CPU rack and the remote I/O processor of the first rack in the drop.

5-5 Input/Output Addressing

After determining the I/O racks and modules to comprise a system, the system designer or programmer generally has to define the I/O addresses. Defining the I/O addresses, in a manner of speaking, specifies what numbers are to be used to reference each connected device in the control program. Once the addresses are assigned to each I/O module, the assigned numbers will always be used to reference (monitor inputs or control outputs) devices connected to the modules. The addressing process may involve hardware switch settings or software configuration depending on the controller.

Each PLC has a predefined range of addresses that accommodate the entire I/O capacity. This address range coincides with the area in memory set aside for retaining the status of I/O devices (See chapter 4). This one-to-one correspondence between specific memory addresses and addresses of physical I/O terminals is referred to as the *I/O mapping*. When the designer assigns the I/O addresses, he or she in essence tells the CPU which I/O addresses are used and where they are located (i.e., in which racks and slots modules are installed). Three commonly used addressing methods are examined in the following discussions.

Fixed-slot Addressing

Fixed-slot addressing is an addressing method typically used with low-end PLCs. This method addresses the I/O circuits on each module based on the exact slot in which the module is installed. A typical approach for systems using this method is to have assigned a fixed number to each slot of a rack (in octal or decimal), starting at 0 with the slot closest to the central processing unit and progressing until reaching the last possible slot. An example system, illustrated in Figure 5-8, has a capacity of 256 digital I/O and uses sixteen-point modules; hence it will fill sixteen slots. The slots are prenumbered $0\text{-}15_{10}$.

In this example, individual circuit terminals on each digital input or output module are always numbered $0\text{-}15_{10}$. A unique address is therefore established for each I/O circuit by prefixing each circuit number with its slot number.

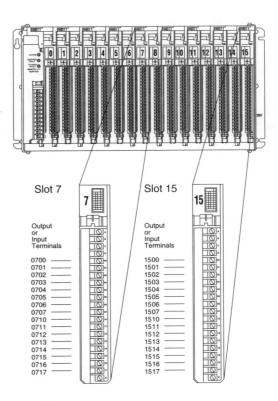

Figure 5-8. Fixed-slot addressing determines addresses based on the slot position

Typically, the slot and circuit numbers are separated by a period or hyphen. For example, an address of 12.6 designates circuit-6 of slot-12. All other addresses would be derived in the same manner; hence, the total address range for all 256 I/O circuits would be 0.00 (slot-0, circuit-0) to 15.15 (slot-15, circuit-15).

An illustration of a typical memory mapping for this type of addressing is shown in Figure 5-9. Note that since it is possible to have a maximum of 256 digital inputs and outputs in any combination, both the *input image table* and the *output image table* require 256 bit locations or an equivalent of sixteen words for each memory area.

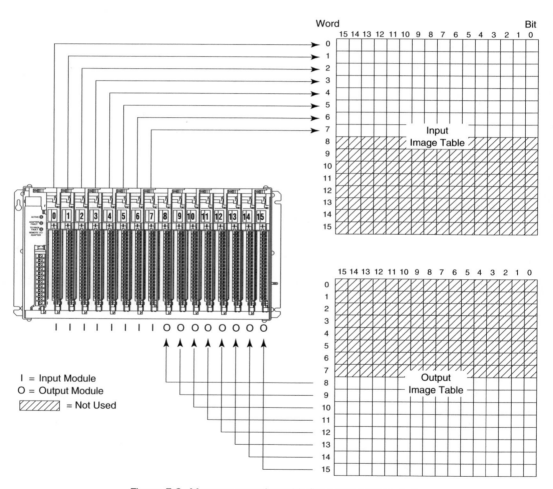

Figure 5-9. Memory mapping with fixed-slot addressing

The word locations in each table are numbered from byte-0 to byte-15 — essentially a fixed-word address for each of the sixteen slots. The sixteen bits of each byte are numbered 0-15. Since either input or output modules can be placed in a slot, the normal address is prefixed with an "I" for input modules and "Y" for output modules to distinguish the module type. A sixteen-point output module installed in slot-14 would have addresses Y14.0 through Y14.15. Note in the output image table where the status of these points would be stored, the corresponding addresses for an input module (I14.0 through I14.15) would go unused since slot-14 is taken by an installed output module.

Variable-slot Addressing

Variable-slot addressing, is a method in which the addresses of each I/O module are user-defined. Unlike fixed addressing, in which the addresses of each module are based on a fixed-slot address, the addresses of each module are set using a software configuration mode or via hardware settings. A variety of hardware methods are used for setting the module addresses including, a bank of switches on each module, a bank of switches for each slot on the backplane of the I/O racks, or address switches for each slot on the I/O processor module installed in each rack.

In either case, a *starting-word address* is defined for each I/O module slot. The starting-word address defines the location in the I/O memory map at which I/O data is stored for a particular module. The address is referred to as a starting word since the module may require one or more words of I/O data. For example in the case of a 32-point digital I/O module, two words of the I/O image table are required. This module, given a start address of 2, would actually use word-2 and word-3, for a total of 32 bits. The individual circuit addresses would be addressed as they were in our example of the fixed-slot addressing.

If the installed module had been an analog input or output module having eight or sixteen channels, a start address is still specified. However, each channel would use one complete word to store the analog I/O data. The next available starting-word address on each analog I/O module would depend on the number of channels on each preceding module and the last word address used. Typical addressing for analog I/O modules is illustrated in Figure 5-10. See chapter 7, *The Analog I/O System*.

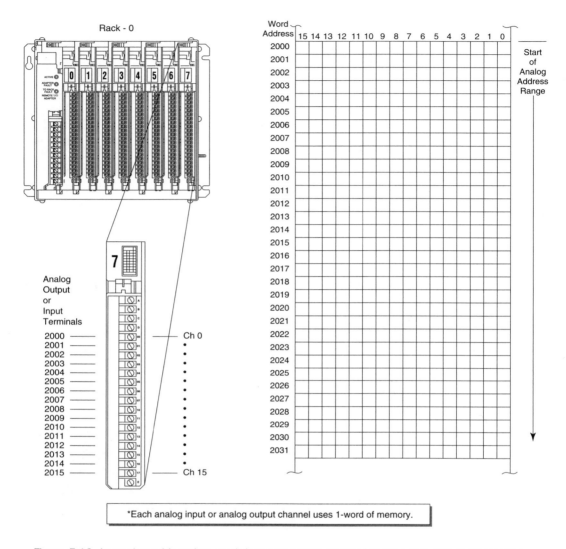

Figure 5-10. In analog addressing, each input or output channel is stored in one word location

Rack-based Addressing

In this method of addressing, the addresses of each module will depend on the rack and slot in which it is installed. This technique involves assigning an identifying number to each I/O rack that distinguishes it and its installed modules from all other racks. Rack addresses are set either through a software configuration mode or by setting a bank of rocker switches, typically located on the backplane of each rack.

Rack-based addressing is similar to how houses are addressed in a city. Each I/O rack number is somewhat analogous to the city name, whereas the rack slots (and the inserted module) are numbered streets. The input/output circuits on each module are like houses. This particular scheme, used in many PLCs, is illustrated in Figure 5-11. Note that the module slots in each rack are numbered $0-7_8$, and the circuits on each module are always numbered 00 through 17_8. The rack number is what gives each individual circuit a unique address.

In this illustration, the system has a maximum of 512 digital I/O and uses modules with sixteen points. Each rack has eight slots and therefore can hold 128 I/O points. A total of four racks, numbered 0 through 3 are required to hold 512 I/O. The actual address of a specific terminal is determined, as shown in Figure 5-11, by combining the rack number, slot number, and module terminal number. Terminal-5 in slot-4 of rack-3 is 34.05; an address of 37.17 designates rack-3, slot-7, terminal-17.

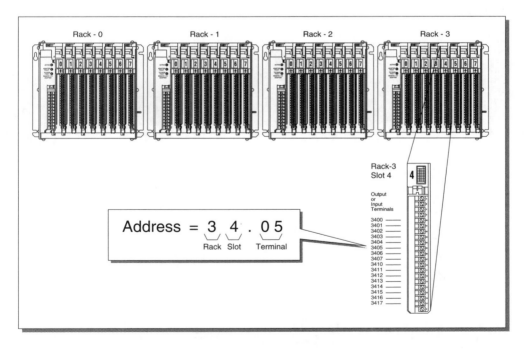

Figure 5-11. Illustration of rack-based addressing

Figure 5-12 is a memory map illustrating how the physical addresses of Figure 5-11 might be mapped to the I/O image table. Each of the four racks that hold 128 I/O are mapped to a group of sixteen-bit words of the image table. Words 0 to 07 store rack-0, words 10 to 17 store rack-1, 20 to 27 store rack-2 and 30 to 37 store rack-3. Each of the eight words per group corresponds to one of the eight slots of a rack, and the bits (00 to17) of each word store the sixteen circuits of each slot. The mapping of individual I/O terminal addresses is such that the first digit of a word address coincides with a rack number, the second digit coincides with a slot, and, finally, bit locations 00 to 17 represent the I/O terminals. Hence, the status of I/O address 33.00 (rack-3, slot-3, terminal-00) is stored in word-33, bit-00.

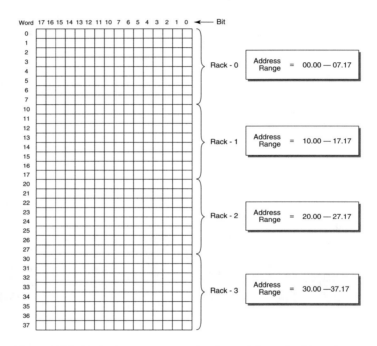

Figure 5-12. Typical memory mapping for rack-based addressing

6 DISCRETE INPUT/OUTPUT MODULES

Discrete input and output modules are the oldest and most common class of programmable controller interface modules. They provide the CPU with the ability to sense and control the two possible states of virtually all discrete sensing and actuating devices. With a variety of voltage ratings ranging from 5 volts DC to 230 volts AC and DC, these interfaces, combined with basic programming instructions, allow combination and sequential logic functions that effectively replace conventional electromechanical control systems.

The previous chapter introduced the basic functions of the I/O system, input and output modules, and the major I/O module categories. This chapter will focus entirely on the discrete I/O category. Here, we will explore the operation, application, and connection diagrams of standard and special purpose discrete module types. Finally, a review of discrete I/O specifications will aid in properly matching field device requirements with the correct interface module. It may be helpful to review the previous chapter, as well as the Input/Output Image Table sections in chapter 4, if you have not already done so.

6-1 Discrete I/O Application

Discrete I/O modules allow the PLC to interface with field signals that will always assume one of two states — such as ON/OFF, OPEN/CLOSED — or that are equivalent to a switch closure. To a discrete input module, any input device is seen as a switch that is either open or closed. On the other hand, discrete output modules allow the PLC to switch devices between two states, such as ON or OFF, EXTENDED or RETRACTED, RUNNING or STOPPED. Table 6-1 lists typical devices that are interfaced to the PLC using discrete I/O modules.

Table 6-1. Typical Discrete Input/Output Devices

DISCRETE INPUTS	DISCRETE OUTPUTS
Pushbuttons	Motor Starters
Selector Switches	Solenoids
Limit Switches	Alarm Horn
Proximity Switches	Pilot Lights
Photoelectric Eyes	Fans
Relay Contacts	Control Relays
Float Switches	Pumps
Starter Contacts	Buzzer Device

Since all discrete inputs and outputs either generate or are controlled by a particular on/off voltage level, selecting the appropriate discrete I/O module should pose little problem. The specific electrical characteristics of the device, however, and the power source to which it is connected, will determine the specific discrete I/O module that is needed. In the following discussions, we will examine the various types of discrete I/O, their application, operation, and field connections.

Basic on/off control and sequencing of discrete I/O devices are accomplished using *Relay Logic Instructions*, or equivalent *Boolean Operations*. This basic category of PLC instructions is discussed in chapter 11. Various programming examples for examining the status and controlling the state of discrete I/O devices are covered in chapter 14.

6-2 Standard Discrete Inputs

Discrete input modules act as on/off sensors for the PLC's processor. The basic function of the discrete input module is to determine the presence or absence of an incoming signal (e.g., 115V AC, 230V AC) from a connected input device and convert it to a logic-level signal that is passed along to the CPU. Generally, an input module contains two or more identical input circuits (e.g., 2,4,8,16 or 32). Although actual input circuitry may vary for different input modules, functional requirements and operation are the same. Table 6-2 lists standard discrete input modules.

Table 6-2. Standard Discrete Input Modules

INPUT MODULE RATING	DISCRETE INPUT APPLICATION
5V TTL	TTL Input Devices
24V AC	Low Voltage AC Input Devices
120V AC	General Purpose AC Input Devices
220/240V AC	General Purpose AC Input Devices
24V AC/DC	Low Voltage Inputs AC or DC
48V AC/DC	Medium Voltage Inputs AC or DC
120V AC/DC	General Purpose Inputs AC or DC
240V AC/DC	General Purpose Inputs AC or DC
24V DC	Low Voltage DC Input Devices
12-24V DC	Low Voltage DC Input Devices
24-48V DC	Medium Voltage DC Input Devices
48-60V DC	Medium Voltage DC Input Devices
Isolated Inputs	Devices With different power sources

AC/DC Input Modules

A functional block diagram of an AC or AC/DC input circuit is shown in Figure 6-1. Each input circuit has two primary parts. The *power section*, interfaces directly with the field input signal and performs required signal conditioning; the *logic section*, which interfaces with the I/O bus via the backplane of the I/O housing, relays the input status to the CPU. The power and logic sections of each circuit are normally coupled using an optical isolator or pulse transformer, which physically isolates and protects the I/O bus circuitry from field voltages. This isolation is referred to as *galvanic isolation*.

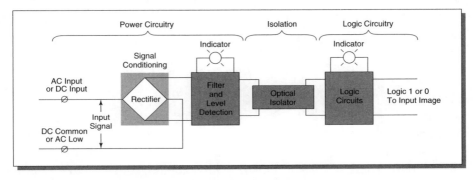

Figure 6-1. Functional block diagram of AC/DC inputs

The power section first converts the incoming field voltage (e.g., 115V, 230V), to a DC voltage level compatible to the module's circuitry. The rectifier element performs the function of converting AC or DC voltages to the proper DC level. Next, filtering is performed to ensure that transient noise does not enter the circuit and be falsely interpret it as a valid signal. This filtering introduces a delay in processing input signals that is typically 9-25 msec. Finally, threshold detection determines if the incoming signal has reached the proper voltage level for the specified input rating. If the input signal exceeds and remains above the threshold for a duration of at least the filter delay, it is recognized as a valid input.

When the circuit's power section eventually detects a valid voltage level, an ON signal passes through the optical isolator, thereby completing the isolated transition from a field voltage level to a logic level. A logic 1 is maintained at the output of the logic circuit until a new value is produced by a change of state at the field device. In the meantime, the data is read by the processor and stored in the input image table during the I/O scan. Since inputs are scanned on every cycle, the latest status is always reflected in the input image table. Figure 6-2 illustrates typical circuits on an AC input module.

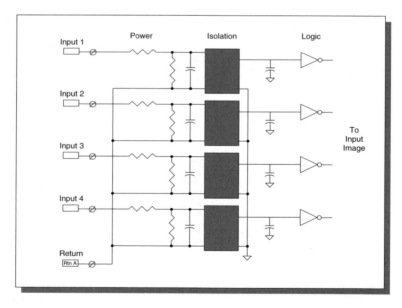

Figure 6-2. Simplified AC/DC input module circuits — typically module circuits are identical

As a diagnostic aid, each circuit on the input module, contains an LED indicator, referred to as the *status* or *power indicator*, that illuminates when power is present at the circuit's input terminals. Also as shown in the diagram, some modules will include an additional LED, called the *logic indicator*, that illuminates when power is applied and if a logic 1 is seen at the output of the logic circuit. With both a power and logic indicator, the correct operation of both sides of the circuit is clearly identified when both LEDs are illuminated.

Figure 6-3 shows a typical AC input module connection. Given a pair of normally-open or normally-closed contacts of a device, one side of the contacts is connected to the "hot side" of the AC power, the other side to one of the input terminals of the input module. Unless the module is an isolated type (See *Isolated Discrete Inputs*), a single terminal is provided on the module for connecting the "neutral" or "low-side" of the user power supply.

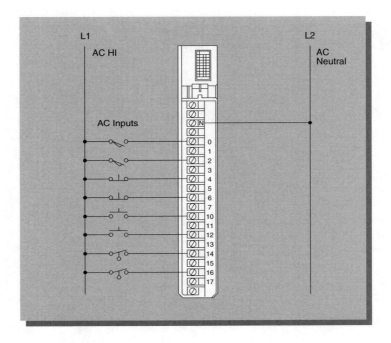

Figure 6-3. AC input device wiring, with all circuits sharing the same AC return

DC Input Modules

The DC input module allows the PLC to accept input signals in the range of 5-60V DC from DC-powered devices such as pushbuttons, proximity and photoelectric switches. The internal configuration and operation of each circuit is much like the AC/DC input, providing voltage reduction where necessary, optical isolation from field signals, filtering circuitry that protects against contact bounce and noise on the input lines, and LED status indication for each input circuit.

DC input modules are normally available in *current-sourcing*, or *current- sinking* configurations to allow connections to either current-sourcing or current-sinking devices. A device is said to be current sourcing if it provides current to a circuit when it is enabled; it is current sinking if it receives current from the circuit when it is enabled. In the same manner, DC input modules can be either a sourcing or sinking type. Hence, if a device sources current, it will require connection to a sinking module; conversely, if the device sinks current, it will require connection to a current-sourcing module. Generally, an input module is designed to interface only with sourcing or sinking devices; however, some allow each input type to be selected.

The connection diagram in Figure 6-4 illustrates current flow in four DC input circuits, two set for current-sourcing and two set for current-sinking operation. For modules that do not offer this selectable feature, the direction of current flow is fixed and the devices will have to be selected for proper operation. Sinking devices require current-sourcing modules and sourcing devices require current-sinking modules. If the direction of current flow is selectable, each circuit need only be set to suit the field device.

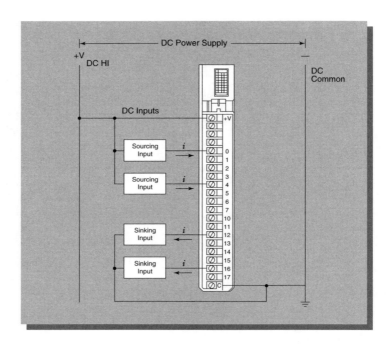

Figure 6-4. DC input device wiring to DC input module with sink/source selectability

TTL Input Module

The TTL (*transistor-transistor logic*) input module allows the controller to accept signals output from various TTL-compatible devices, including solid-state controls and sensing devices. Typical TTL input devices include proximity and photoelectric sensors, output interfaces from intelligent devices, weighing systems, and bar code scanners and readers. While TTL input devices are available with open-emitter (current-sourcing) and open-collector (current-sinking) outputs, TTL input modules typically recommend devices having open-collector outputs.

Generally, TTL devices generate a voltage between -0.2V DC and +0.8V DC when in the OFF state, and between 2.4V DC and 5.25V DC when in the ON state. Devices that are at the higher of the two potentials when in the ON state are referred to as being *Active-High*. Conversely, *Active-Low* devices are at the lower logic voltage when in the ON state. Although most TTL input modules are designed strictly to handle TTL voltages, some may also accept input from other types of DC inputs ranging up to 30 VDC.

To handle both types of TTL signals, the TTL input module allows the module to be set for active-high, also called *High=True Logic*, or for active-low, also called *Low=True Logic*. When set for active-high, an incoming signal at the higher voltage level produces a logic 1 in the input image table, indicating an active device — a low incoming signal produces a logic 0. If the input device is active-low, an incoming signal at the lower voltage produces a logic 1 in the input image table. The higher voltage would produce a logic 0 in the input image table.

Figure 6-5 illustrates a typical TTL input connection. Generally, the TTL input device (open-collector type) will have an internal pull-up resistor to minimize the affects of the small leakage current when in the OFF state. In addition, the resistor provides better noise immunity and faster turn-on/turn-off times. If the pull-up resistor is not internal, it should be connected at the output of the device or at the input terminal. TTL specifications generally recommend use of shielded cable connections.

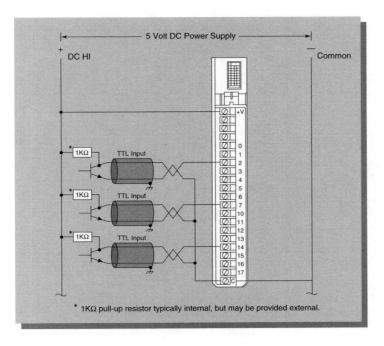

Figure 6-5. Typical open collector input connection to TTL input module

Isolated Discrete Inputs

Isolated input modules derive their name from the fact that they contain input circuits that are electrically separated from one another. This design of input circuits provides greater immunity to noise and allows devices having different power sources or AC phase relationships to be interfaced using the same input module. The term isolated, used here should not be confused with optical isolation, which protects the I/O bus circuitry against high field voltages. Instead, the term as used here refers to isolation between module circuits relative to one another and their respective ground reference.

Input circuits are usually isolated by individual circuits, as shown in Figure 6-6a, or in groups of two or more circuits, as in Figure 6-6b. If all circuits are individually isolated, each circuit will be separated from all other circuits and will have two connection terminals, one for connecting the input signal of each device and a second for the connection to the AC or DC return (ground). If isolation is in groups, a separate ground terminal would be provided for each group of circuits. In Figure 6-6c, the circuits are isolated in groups of four inputs. Devices from four different power sources could therefore be connected.

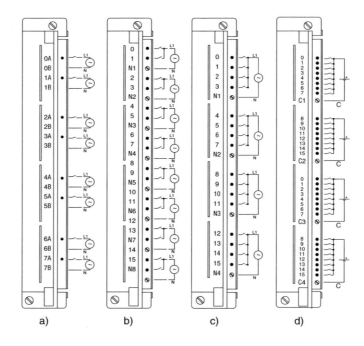

a)   b)   c)   d)

Figure 6-6. a) 8-point 115 VAC input, individually isolated b) 16-point 115 VAC input, isolated in groups of two c) 32-point 24 VDC input, isolated in groups of eight

Unless specified as isolated inputs, discrete input modules are considered "nonisolated," and individual input channels on a module are not electrically separated from one another. On the nonisolated input module, a single return line (common) internal to the module ties all input circuits together. Hence, input devices connected to the module must share the same power source. The design and operation of isolated AC and DC input modules are otherwise no different than their nonisolated counterparts.

6-3 Standard Discrete Outputs

Discrete output modules act as power switching circuits for the PLC's processor. The basic function of a digital output module is to accept a turn ON or turn OFF command from the CPU in the form of logic 1 or logic 0 taken from the output image table and to switch the appropriate control voltage (e.g., 24V, 115V) that controls the on/off state of the connected device. A given output module generally contains two or more identical output circuits (e.g., 2,4,8,16, or 32). Table 6-3 lists standard discrete output modules.

Table 6-3. Standard Discrete Output Modules

OUTPUT MODULE RATING	DISCRETE OUTPUT APPLICATION
5V TTL	TTL Load Devices
24V AC	Low Voltage AC Load Devices
120V AC	General Purpose AC Load Devices
220/240V AC	General Purpose AC Load Devices
24V DC	Low Voltage DC Load Devices
48V DC	Medium Voltage DC Load Devices
12-24V DC	Low Voltage DC Load Devices
24-48V DC	Medium Voltage DC Load Devices
48-60V DC	Medium Voltage DC Load Devices
10-60V DC	General Purpose DC Load Devices
Isolated Outputs	AC or DC Loads on different power sources

AC Output Modules

A block diagram of the typical *AC output* circuit is shown in Figure 6-7 on the following page. Like AC inputs, each AC output circuit has two parts, a *power section* that interfaces directly with the field device, and a *logic section*, that interfaces to the I/O bus via the backplane of the I/O housing. The power and logic sections of each circuit are normally coupled using an optical isolator. This isolation that physically and electrically separates the two circuits thereby isolates the PLC from possible damage caused by electrical transients.

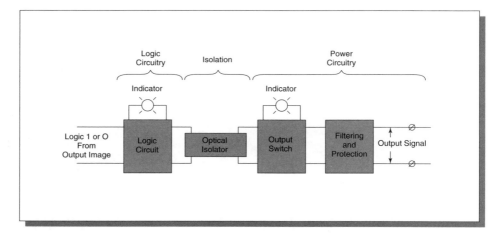

Figure 6-7. Functional block diagram of AC outputs

In operation, the control program commands an output circuit to switch ON or OFF, by placing a logic 1 or logic 0 in the associated location in the output image table. The ON or OFF signal is reflected at the input of the logic circuit. A logic 1 signal activates the circuit's switching device (e.g., *triac*) of the power section, thereby switching the field supplied control voltage. The data output from the logic circuit holds the output signal at the input of the power circuit until new data is received from the processor, thereby maintaining the output device in either the ON or OFF state until a change occurs in the output image table.

The power section contains the circuit switching element, typically a triac, and filtering to protect the triac from damage that might result from transient spikes or inductive feedback generated when inductive loads are switched off. This protection is normally provided by limiting circuits such as RC (resistive-capacitive) and *surge suppression networks* as shown in Figure 6- 8. Most AC output modules also place a fuse in each circuit to protect against overloading and short-circuiting. If fuses are not included, they should be provided externally for each circuit.

The LED indicator normally incorporated in each output circuit is a "logic indicator" that illuminates when the circuit has been commanded to turn ON. A logic indicator signals only that the circuit was commanded to turn ON, however the output triac, if malfunctioning, would not be ON as indicated by the LED. Hence, some AC output modules also include a "power indicator" that illuminates if the power side of the circuit has been activated. When the module is operating correctly, both logic and power indicators will be ON or OFF simultaneously.

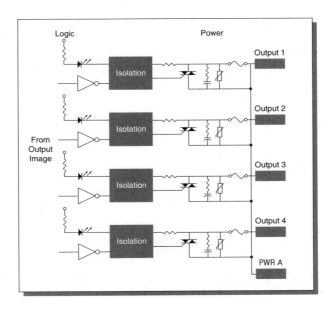

Figure 6-8. Simplified AC output module circuits — typically module circuits are identical

Figure 6-9 shows a typical connection diagram for AC output modules. One side of the device is connected to the "low side" of the AC power, the other side goes to one of the output terminals of the output module. Unless the module is an isolated type (See *Isolated Discrete Outputs*), a single terminal is provided on the module for connecting the "highside" of the user power supply.

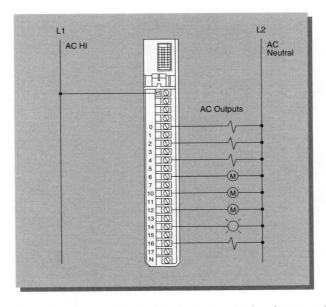

Figure 6-9. AC output device wiring, with all circuits sharing the same AC source

DC Output Modules

DC output modules, like their AC counterparts, provide output device switching in the 5-60V DC range, but for DC loads. Functional operation and configuration is much like that shown in Figure 6-7 for AC outputs. However, the switching element is typically a power transistor. Optical isolation between the logic and power sections of each circuit electrically separates the PLC from harsh field signals. A *free-wheeling diode* across the load protects the output transistor from feedback transients. DC output modules also incorporate protection against short circuits and reverse polarity connections.

Like the DC input module, DC output modules are also available with *current-sourcing*, or *current-sinking* operation. If the module provides current to the load device when energized, it is said to be sourcing current. If the module receives current from the load when energized, then it is said to be current sinking. Since there are both sinking- and sourcing-output devices, DC output modules with this feature generally allow each circuit to be set for either. If the load provides current, then the module is set for sinking current; conversely, if the load accepts current, then the module should be set for sourcing current.

Figure 6-10, illustrates current flow in four DC output circuits, two sets for current-sourcing and to for current-sinking operation. Some DC output modules do not offer this selectable feature and the direction of current flow is fixed. Hence, the devices will have to be selected for proper operation. Sinking devices require sourcing modules, and sourcing devices require sinking modules. If the direction of current flow is selectable, then each circuit need only be set accordingly to suit the connected field device.

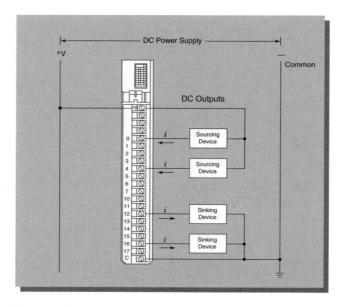

Figure 6-10. DC output device wiring to DC output module with sink/source selectability

TTL Output Module

The *TTL output module* allows the controller to drive various TTL-compatible devices or simply allows the PLC to output signals to devices requiring TTL input, such as integrated circuits, LED displays, and various other 5V DC devices.

Like TTL input devices, TTL output devices are operated by two well-defined voltage levels. Typically, a TTL device is turned ON at a voltage between 2.4V DC and 5.25V DC and turned OFF when the voltage is between -0.2V DC and .8V DC; hence, the TTL output module is generally designed to output a voltage within these two ranges. TTL devices activated by the higher of the two voltage ranges are referred to as being *Active-High*. Some devices, however, may be *Active-Low* and are turned ON by the lower voltage range (i.e., -0.2V DC to .4V DC).

To handle both types of TTL devices, the TTL output module allows the user to set the module to drive either active-high or active-low devices. When a module is set for active-high, a logic 1 in the output image table for any of the referenced outputs causes the device to turn ON; logic 0 causes a device to be switched OFF. If the module is set for active low, the connected output devices will be switched ON whenever logic 0 is in the output image table location that corresponds to the connected devices. Logic 1 would cause a device to be switched OFF.

Figure 6-11 illustrates a typical TTL output connection diagram. As with TTL inputs, maximum noise immunity is obtained with shielded cable connections.

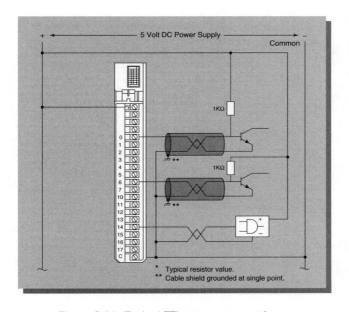

Figure 6-11. Typical TTL output connections

Isolated Discrete Outputs

Isolated output modules, like their input counterparts, contain some combination of output circuits electrically separated from one another. This design allows devices having different power sources or AC phase relationships to be connected using the same output module. Generally, an isolated output module will have half the number of circuits as a nonisolated module of the same type. Because there are fewer circuits on the module, isolated outputs are also applied to high-current loads such as large motors and heavy-duty solenoids.

Isolated output modules will usually isolate circuits individually, as shown in Figure 6-12a, or will have groups of circuits, as in Figure 6-12b, c, and d. If all outputs are individually isolated, each circuit will be separated from all other circuits and will have two connection terminals, one for connecting the output signal and the other for the high side of the AC or DC output. If isolation is by groups, a terminal for the hot side of each power source would be provided for each group of outputs. In Figure 6-12c, the circuits are isolated in groups of four outputs — outputs from four different power sources could therefore be connected.

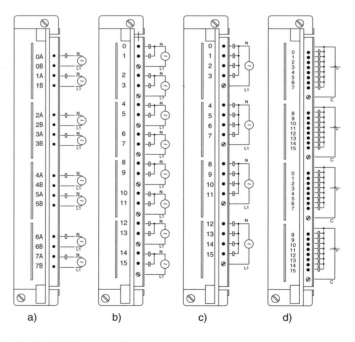

Figure 6-12. a) 8-point 115 VAC output, individually isolated b) 16-point 115 VAC output, isolated in groups of two c) 32-point 24 VDC output, isolated in groups of eight

Unless specified as isolated outputs, output modules are considered *nonisolated* and output channels on a module are not electrically separated from one another. On the nonisolated output module, a single terminal is provided for the hot side of the AC or DC power source for all of the output channels; therefore output devices connected to the module must share the same power source. Otherwise, the design and operation of isolated AC and DC output modules are no different than for their nonisolated counterparts previously discussed.

6-4 Special Function Discrete I/O

In most cases, the discrete signals generated by the I/O devices listed in Table 6-1 can be detected and processed by one or more of the standard discrete I/O modules listed in Table 6-2. The supply voltage along with a few other basic electrical specifications is enough to determine a suitable interface module. In certain situations, however, there may be application requirements such as fast response; device signal requirements or characteristics, such as pulse duration, output current; or retriggering; requirements that will demand special discrete I/O.

To satisfy special cases, some programmable controller systems provide a variety of discrete I/O modules designed to process on/off signals that have special signal or other interfacing requirements. These special-purpose discrete I/O modules offered by some product lines are given in Table 6-4 and are described in the following discussions.

Table 6-4. Special-purpose Discrete I/O Modules

MODULE TYPE	MODULE APPLICATION
Interrupt Input	- Immediate response to input signal changes
Voltage Comparator Input	- Analog setpoint comparison
Latching Input	- Detecting signals of short duration
Fast Input	- Non-contact (electronic) DC input devices
Rapid Response I/O	- Provides fast input/output response
Relay Contact Output	- High-current switching & signal multiplexing
Wire Fault Input	- Wire break and short circuit detection

Interrupt Input Module

The term *interrupt* refers to a processing technique whereby the PLC processor temporarily discontinues its normal processing (hence the term interrupt) and performs a specific task considered more important at that precise moment. This is a useful feature in applications where critical process events must be acknowledged immediately and the appropriate action taken without delay.

An *interrupt input module* is like any other discrete input module except that when an input is activated, it interrupts the PLC processor's normal scan. By causing an interrupt directly to the PLC's microprocessor, the main program is temporarily suspended, thereby eliminating the delay due to normal program processing and completing the current processor scan. When the connected field signal causes an interrupt, the processor discontinues cyclic processing and takes up processing of a specific user program, as illustrated in Figure 6-13.

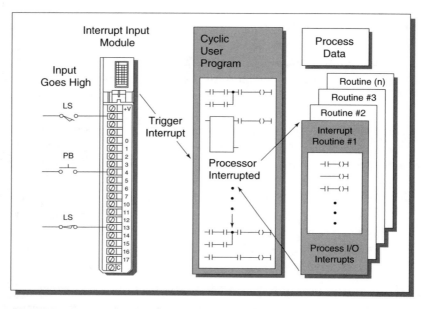

Figure 6-13. Interrupt input modules allow process signals to interrupt the CPU's normal scan

When an interrupt occurs, a special portion of the user program called an *interrupt service routine* is processed. In the control program, each interrupt input would have an associated service routine, executed whenever the corresponding interrupt is triggered. After completing a service routine, the processor returns to the main program and resumes program execution at the point where the interrupt occurred. Typically, interrupts can be assigned a priority number that will determine the order in which interrupts are serviced if two or more occur at the same time.

Voltage Comparator Module

The *voltage comparator input* module is also referred to as a *level detector* or *analog set-point* module. Its function is to accept an analog voltage signal from some process and to compare it with a reference voltage that is either input to the module from an external source or provided internal to the module.

Whereas standard analog input modules are able to measure the change in an analog signal over its entire range, the voltage comparator module simply monitors the input signal for two set levels — for example, greater than or less than a set reference voltage. Two logic signals are generated that alert the processor when the process signal goes below or above the reference. This limited analog functionality makes this module an inexpensive analog solution when all you need to know is when the process signal goes above or below the setpoint.

Figure 6-14 illustrates a typical configuration of one channel of a voltage comparator module. Each input channel has two input lines and two logic outputs. Input line A accepts the process signal and line B is for an external reference voltage. One logic output turns ON if the input voltage goes above the reference voltage. The second logic output turns ON if the input voltage falls below the reference voltage. Each of these logic outputs is generally an internal output that has an address that can be referenced by the control program to control real outputs.

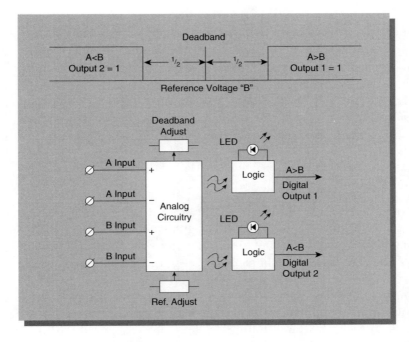

Figure 6-14. Functional block diagram of an voltage (analog) comparator input module

The exact configuration and operation of the voltage comparator may vary depending on the particular system. For instance, some modules may compare for greater than the reference and for less than the reference, as in Figure 6-14. Others may compare for greater than or equal to the reference, and less than or equal to the reference. A dead-band adjustment on some modules allows the module to be set so that no output response is generated if the deviation from the setpoint is less than a set percentage of the full voltage span. This feature will avoid "banging" of the output as the input signal fluctuates above and below the setpoint.

Latching Input Module

The *latching input module* is used to interface with devices that generate signals having very short pulse duration — typically on the order of 100 microseconds to 5 milliseconds. The ON state of these signals is much shorter in duration than one scan cycle of a typical PLC processor and consequently cannot be detected by standard discrete input modules.

Fast input signals are normally generated by certain electronic DC devices such as incremental encoders and proximity and photoelectric switches. To accommodate such devices, the input voltage range is generally between 5 and 30 volts DC. Features selectable by the user that allow the module to be tailored for the signal typically include current-sourcing or sinking operation, leading or trailing edge triggered, and minimum pulse width. The minimum pulse width selection allows the circuit to be adjusted for the typical input pulse duration.

In operation, the input circuitry latches and holds the input signal until it is read during the normal I/O scan. After the state of the input is read and stored in the input image table, the latch is reset and ready to detect another change of state of the input. Exactly how the module is reset and how fast it can recover to capture a new signal is an important point for consideration. The minimum time between the occurrences of the signal will also have to be known. If your application requires capturing signals that are shorter than the processor's normal scan, you should consult with the vendor for alternative solutions.

Fast Input Module

The *fast input module* offered by some vendors performs a function similar to that of the latching input module; however, it is significantly different. This module shortens the normal filtering delay of standard input circuits required for interfacing mechanical switches or devices with hard contacts; however, the circuitry does not latch the signal.

By minimizing the delay due to filtering, the module can respond faster to electronic or DC signals from noncontact type devices such as photoelectric eyes and proximity switches. Such devices do not require the long delay required to filter out the *contact bounce* exhibited in mechanical switches. An input delay of 1 millisecond is typical for the fast input module. An important criterion, however, since the signal is not latched, is that when it turns ON it must stay ON for at least the duration of one full scan cycle, otherwise the input signal will not be recognized. Signals shorter than the typical scan would require the latching input module.

Rapid Response I/O Module

The *rapid response I/O module*, a unique interface module found only in some controllers, is both an input and output module. Like the *latching input module*, this module is capable of sensing digital signals having very short pulse durations (typically a minimum of 1 millisecond). An added output section, however, allows the module to instantaneously energize an enabled output when the input signal is detected; hence, the name rapid response. The fast input/output ability allows this module to be applied in critical situations where an immediate output action is needed whenever the connected input condition occurs.

A block diagram of a rapid response module is shown in Figure 6-15. Note that for the output to energize, its corresponding address has to be enabled according to programmed logic and its triggering input on the module has to be activated. In this fashion, ultimate control of the output is dependent on the control program and not on the triggering input alone.

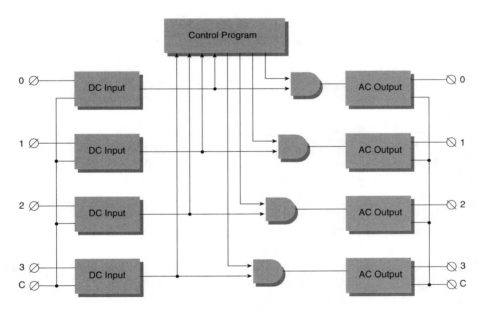

Figure 6-15. Functional block diagram of a rapid response I/O module

The achievable response time (from input to output) of a fast response module will depend on the functional characteristics of the module and on the CPU. For instance, depending on the system, the response may or may not be independent of the controller scan. If it is dependent on processor scan the worst-case response will be the delay of the module added to the worst-case processor scan.

Relay Contact Output Modules

The *relay contact output* module is a discrete output module having electromechanical relays as the switching elements as opposed to solid-state output elements such as triacs or transistors. These modules generally contain two or more output circuits with some combination of normally-open and normally-closed contacts that can be used to switch either AC or DC loads. Typical operating ranges for these modules are 5-30 VDC and 20-265 VAC. A block diagram of the relay output module is illustrated in Figure 6-16.

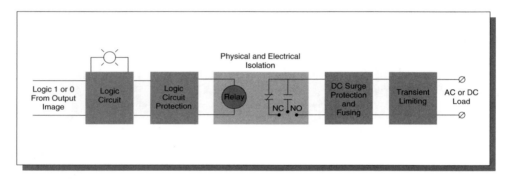

Figure 6-16. Simplified block diagram of a relay contact output

Because of the electrical characteristics (i.e., power, voltage, current) of the relay contacts, the relay output is suitable for switching heavy inductive or capacitive loads. In general, the relay output is selected for high-current applications and in cases where inrush or surge currents of inductive loads are higher and the continuous output current requirements are much greater than the typical 1 or 2 amps supplied by solid-state AC and DC outputs. The relay output module can also be used for handling loads on isolated circuits and where leakage currents cannot be tolerated.

Some I/O systems also offer a so called *low-power relay output module* generally used for switching small AC and DC currents at low voltages. Typical applications for the low-power relay output include multiplexing of low-level analog and instrumentation signals and low performance communications lines. A typical relay output connection is shown in Figure 6-17.

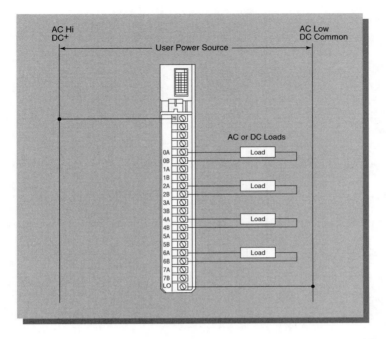

AC Hi
DC+

AC Low
DC Common

User Power Source

Hi

AC or DC Loads

0A · Load
0B
1A
1B
2A · Load
2B
3A
3B
4A · Load
4B
5A
5B
6A · Load
6B
7A
7B
LO

Figure 6-17. Relay output device wiring — loads may have different AC or DC sources

Wire Fault Input Module

The *wire fault input module*, like other discrete inputs, senses the ON/OFF state of a discrete input device and sends it to the processor, which in turn places the status in the input image table. It also detects an open or shorted circuit to ground between the module and the user input device power circuit. The wire fault input, which accepts signals from DC input devices having normally-open or normally-closed contacts, offers an economical alternative in critical situations where redundant inputs might normally be used to detect a device or wiring fault.

Figure 6-18, on the following page, illustrates the wire fault input module. Like standard DC input modules, it has filtering and optical isolation to protect against noise and accepting false signals. In operation, the module generates a monitoring current of 20 mA through the field wiring, the input device contacts, and the shunt resistor in each input circuit whenever an input is activated. When the contacts are opened, this current drops to 6 mA. A shorted or open circuit causes the monitoring current to drop considerably below 6 mA, which is detected as a fault (open or short circuit) by the module. The fault, which is detectable by the user program, is also indicated by an LED indicator.

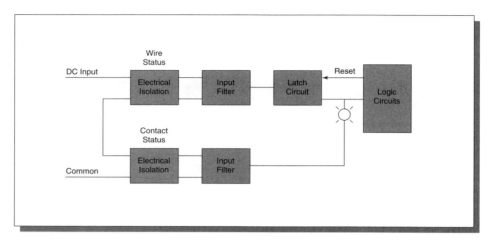

Figure 6-18. Simplified block diagram of a wire fault input circuit

A typical connection diagram for the wire fault input is shown in Figure 6-19. Typically, the wire fault module accepts DC input devices powered from a user supply between 15V DC and 30V DC. Some important points about the shunt resistor are that its value is selected according to the power supply voltage (e.g., 3.3k, 1/2 watt for 24V DC), that it should be connected as close as possible to the device terminals, and that all unused input circuits should have a shunt resistor placed in line with the positive terminal of the power supply.

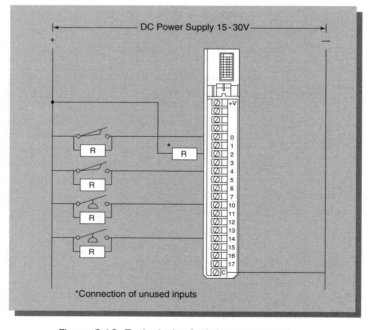

Figure 6-19. Typical wire fault input connections

An important consideration of the wire fault input connection is that the "total wire resistance" of the field wiring from the power supply (+ side), through the input device, to the module input terminal and back to the power supply (- side) should be less than the maximum allowable value for a given supply voltage. The maximum allowable wire resistance at 24V DC, for instance, is 100 ohms. The total resistance is computed by multiplying the wire length by the wire resistance in ohms per foot, which is a function of the wire size (e.g., #14 AWG, 0.002525 ohms/ft.). Although it is unlikely, if the maximum resistance is exceeded, a heavier wire gage or an increase in power supply voltage will be required.

6-5 Parallel Discrete Input/Output

In the Chapter 2 discussion of numbering systems, *binary-coded decimal (BCD)* was described as a method of coding each of the decimal digits (0-9) in a fashion that is easily handled and interpreted by both digital machines and humans alike. In more practical terms, this coding performs a conversion that allows us to deal only with numbers represented by 0 through 9 while the PLC uses its familiar values of 1 and 0. This interaction takes place through the use of parallel discrete input/output modules.

From Table 6-5 we see that the number 9, the largest decimal symbol, requires four binary digits to be represented. If each of these four positions were to be represented by an ON/OFF signal indicating a binary value of 1 or 0 at that position, four signal wires would be required. Since the remaining numbers, 0- 8, can all be represented using four or fewer signal wires, a minimum of four signal wires is required to represent any of the decimal numbers 0-9. This is the basis for the four digits in the BCD code and for the way decimal numbers are input to or output from the PLC in parallel.

Table 6-5. Decimal to BCD Encoding

DECIMAL	BINARY	BCD
0	0	0000
1	1	0001
2	10	0010
3	11	0011
4	100	0100
5	101	0101
6	110	0110
7	111	0111
8	1000	1000
9	1001	1001

A thumbwheel switch, shown in Figure 6-20a, is a typical BCD input device. It produces four binary digits at its output that correspond to the decimal number selected on the switch. The conversion from a single decimal digit to four binary digits is performed by the device. A seven-segment LED display, illustrated in Figure 6-20b, is a typical BCD output device. On the face plate of each segment of the device, it displays a decimal number that corresponds to the BCD value it receives at its input. Again, the conversion of four binary digits to a single decimal digit on the display is performed by the device. The following discussions describe how BCD I/O devices are interfaced with PLCs.

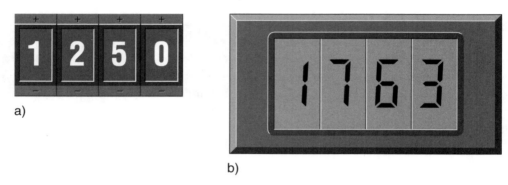

a)

b)

Figure 6-20. a) A four-digit BCD thumbwheel device b) A four-digit BCD 7-segment display

Parallel (BCD) Inputs

Input from devices, such as thumbwheel switches (TWS) or bar code readers that generate a decimal number coded in binary (BCD), can be accomplished using standard discrete input modules. This type of input is referred to as *parallel input* since the binary data on the input lines are read together as a group that represents a number.

Since four input lines are required to accept each BCD digit, input modules having sixteen or 32 input lines are generally used for this purpose. The voltage rating of the input module will depend on the specifications of the input device, which is typically between 5 and 30 volts DC. As illustrated in Figure 6-21a, sixteen input lines will allow input of a four-digit BCD value; 32 input lines would allow input connection of eight BCD digits.

While the most common application of parallel input is for entering numeric data from thumbwheel switches and bar code readers, it can be applied to any device that outputs parallel data, such as BCD, Gray code, or other binary-coded data.

Table 6-6. Devices Interfaced with Parallel Inputs

- ❏ Thumbwheel switches
- ❏ Bar code readers
- ❏ Weigh scales
- ❏ Position encoders
- ❏ Analog-to-digital converters
- ❏ Any device with BCD or parallel data output

Standard discrete input modules used for parallel input operate the same as when connected to devices that generate a single on/off input. The only real difference is that the sixteen input signals are treated as a group that can be interpreted as a number in the user program. The sixteen-bit pattern of 1s and 0s that represent a four-digit BCD number can be read from the module using the appropriate instruction in the user program and placed in a specified word storage location. Figure 6-21b illustrates how data is typically read from a parallel input module.

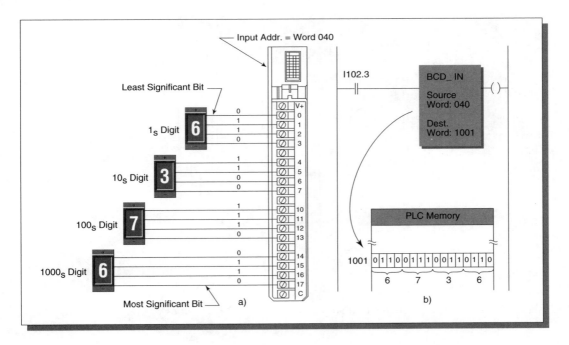

Figure 6-21. a) BCD input wiring to a standard discrete input module b) Reading BCD input data

Multiplexed Parallel Inputs

In applications handling parallel data input from several devices, the *multiplexed parallel input module* offers and enhanced an economical solution over using standard digital input modules. Using standard discrete input modules having sixteen or 32 input lines limits connection of only one or two four-digit TWS devices to the controller. The multiplexed BCD input module uses a strobing (or enabling) technique that allows a single module to interface as many as four or eight sets of four-digit TWS devices or up to 32 BCD digits.

The multiplexed parallel input module generally has 16-32 input lines that accept input voltages in the range of 5V to 30V DC. It also has some number of strobe inputs (typically four to eight) that determine how many groups of signals can be multiplexed to the module. A simplified connection of a typical multiplexed BCD input module is shown in Figure 6-22. This module accepts four groups of sixteen parallel inputs, all of which are wired in parallel, to the sixteen input lines of the module. The four strobe inputs select which group of sixteen bits is to be read at any time.

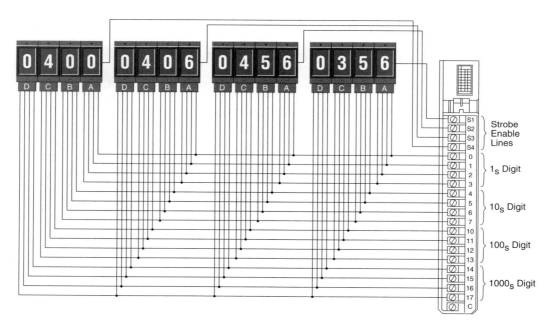

Figure 6-22. BCD input modules with strobe inputs allow several groups of BCD inputs to be read

In operation, each group of sixteen signals is referred to as a channel; hence, in Figure 6-22, the module accepts four channels of parallel inputs. Each of the four strobe (enable) inputs is associated with one channel and allows the user program to select the channel from which input data should be read. For instance, if strobe 1 is enabled, the data on the sixteen lines will be read from channel 1. Generally, the strobe signals may be triggered externally by user-connected inputs to the strobe lines, or they may be controlled internally by the processor. In the latter case, the strobes are enabled sequentially.

Typically, when the strobes are internally controlled by the parallel input module, the module channels are scanned asynchronous to the PLC scan and the data for each channel is stored in onboard buffer memory. All channels can be read from the module using the appropriate instruction in the user program. The data is generally placed in consecutive word storage locations (e.g., the data from four channels are stored in locations 2000 through 2003).

Parallel (BCD) Outputs

Numeric data output to devices such as seven-segment LED displays can be accomplished using standard discrete output modules. This type of output is referred to as *parallel output* since the binary data on the output lines is output as a group that represents a number. Since four output lines are required to output each BCD digit, output modules having sixteen or 32 output lines are generally used for this purpose. As illustrated in Figure 6-23a, sixteen output lines will allow output of a four-digit BCD value; 32 lines would allow output of eight BCD digits.

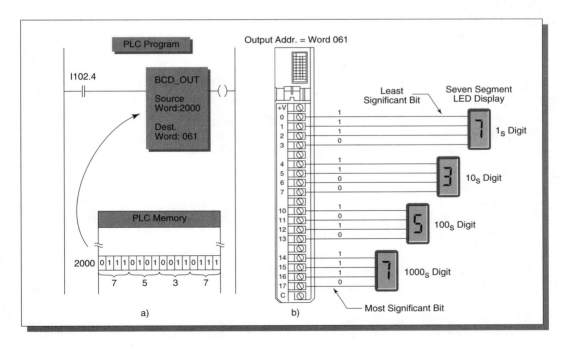

Figure 6-23. a) Writing BCD output data b) BCD output wiring to a standard discrete output module

While the most common application of parallel output is for controlling seven-segment LED displays, it can be applied to any device that is driven by parallel output data such as BCD, Gray code, or other binary-coded data. Supply voltages for such devices are typically between 5 and 30 VDC; therefore, the appropriate module should be selected.

Table 6-7. Devices Interfaced with Parallel Outputs

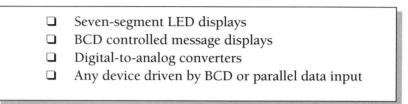

- ❏ Seven-segment LED displays
- ❏ BCD controlled message displays
- ❏ Digital-to-analog converters
- ❏ Any device driven by BCD or parallel data input

Standard discrete output modules used for parallel output operate the same as when connected to devices that are controlled by a single on/off signal. The only real difference is that the sixteen output signals are treated as a group that reflects a numeric value output from the control program. Figure 6-23b illustrates how data is typically output to a parallel output module. The sixteen-bit pattern of ones and zeroes represent a four-digit BCD number taken from a word-storage location and output to the module using the appropriate instruction in the control program.

Multiplexed Parallel Outputs

The *multiplexed parallel output module* offers an enhanced and economical solution over standard digital output modules for handling parallel data output to several devices. Using standard discrete output modules having sixteen or 32 outputs, only one or two four-digit, seven-segment display devices can be interfaced to the controller. The multiplexed BCD output module uses a strobing technique that allows a single module to interface as many as four or eight sets of four-digit, seven-segment display devices.

The multiplexed parallel output module generally has sixteen or 32 output lines, rated for a range of 5V DC to 30V DC. The module also has some number of strobe lines, that determine how many groups of parallel outputs can be controlled by the module. A simplified connection of a typical multiplexed parallel output module is shown in Figure 6-24. This module controls four groups of sixteen parallel outputs, all of which are wired in parallel to the sixteen output terminals of the module. The four strobe outputs determine which group of sixteen bits is to be output at any time.

In operation, each group of sixteen signals is referred to as a channel; hence, in Figure 6-24, the module controls four channels of BCD outputs. Each of the four strobe lines, is associated with one channel and determine which channel should output data onto the sixteen output lines. For instance, if strobe 1 is enabled, the data output on the sixteen lines will affect the device connected to channel 1.

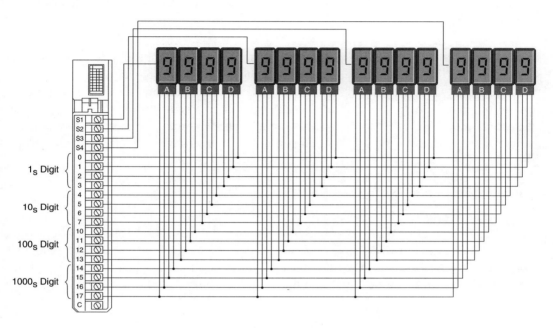

Figure 6-24. BCD output modules with strobe outputs allow several groups of BCD output devices to be controlled

Controlling the manipulation of the multiple channels of a parallel output module is somewhat different than for the multiplexed parallel input module. Although actual operation may differ for different products, the principle is similar. Each module has a number of sixteen-bit word-storage buffers equivalent to the number of multiplexed channels. Data sent to these buffers is controlled by user-assigned data words in the control program and are sent to the module using the appropriate output instruction. Generally, one or all channels can be updated with a single instruction.

Whereas the use of external strobes lines is arbitrary with the multiplexed input module, external strobe lines are generally required with the multiplexed output module and are controlled by the module rather than by the program. This approach ensures that the correct data is sent to each output device. On each module update, the module strobes each channel sequentially, thereby cycling the data from each of the storage buffers onto the sixteen data lines for output to their respective devices.

6-6 Discrete I/O Module Specifications

Selecting a particular I/O module requires matching the characteristics of different input and output devices with the unique signal characteristics of a variety of I/O modules. It is also important to consider factors peculiar to the application that may influence the type of modules used. If not properly matched with regard for more than just the nominal input or output voltage, I/O devices may fail to operate at all or may lead to faulty operation.

An important prerequisite to selecting the appropriate I/O modules for a particular application is that of understanding the various specifications associated with each module. This section introduces general module specifications as well as electrical operating characteristics that define conditions under which discrete I/O modules are designed to operate safely and correctly. Other specifications, such as those related to temperature, humidity, vibration, noise immunity, or agency approvals, are provided in the Appendix.

Specifications Common to Discrete I/O

Points Per Module. This specification defines the number of input or output circuits contained in a single module. Most commonly, a module will have 8, 16, or 32 circuits; however, low-end controllers may have modules with two or four circuits. A module is normally referred to as a *high-density module* if it contains sixteen or more circuits. As a rule, the fewer number of outputs a module has, the greater its current handling capacity.

The number of points per module has three implications. First, the fewer the number of circuits per module, the greater the total space requirement; second, the higher the density, the less likely the total I/O count can be closely matched with the hardware. For example, if the module contains 16 points and the application requires an additional seventeen, two modules must be purchased resulting in a total of fifteen extra inputs or outputs. A third implication, is that the fewer circuits per output module, the greater the current handling capacity — a point to consider if the connected devices will draw high currents.

Acceptable Conductor Size. A specification of acceptable or recommended wire size and type is not always given, but may be of importance to some users. Such specifications will normally state the largest acceptable wire size and the number of wires per terminal (e.g., Two - #14 AWG). Other designations may include requirements for shielded or unshielded cable and maximum wire lengths to the field device.

Electrical Isolation. Discrete I/O module circuitry is typically electrically isolated to protect the low-level circuitry of the PLC (i.e., CPU and backplane) from the high voltages that could be encountered from the field device connections. Recall that each circuit of an I/O module has two sides — a power side that accepts and conditions the field signal and a logic side that interfaces to the PLC's I/O bus.

The power and logic circuits are typically isolated using an optical coupler or switching transformer, which physically and electrically separates the field wiring from the PLC system. The specification for electrical isolation, typically 1500 or 2500 volts AC RMS, defines the module's capacity for sustaining an excessive voltage at its input or output terminals. If the module is subjected to a voltage exceeding this breakdown voltage, the logic circuitry and consequently the PLC bus is protected. However, the power side of the module may be damaged. Modules having this electrical isolation may also be referred to as *floating modules,* those without it are called *nonfloating modules.*

Sink or Source Module. DC and some AC I/O modules will normally specify whether a module is designed for interfacing with current-source devices or current-sink devices. If the module is a current-sourcing module, then the connected input or output device must be a current-sinking device. Conversely, if the module is specified as current-sinking, then the connected devices must be current sourcing. Some modules allow the user to select whether the module will act as current sinking or current sourcing, thereby allowing it to be adjusted to whatever the devices require.

Module Load. *Module load*, also referred to as the *operating current requirement* or *module current consumption*, specifies the amount of current that a particular input or output module's circuitry draws from the system power supply. This is a critical value when determining the total current consumption that a particular combination of modules will place on an installed PLC power supply and, consequently, the required power supply current rating.

When calculating the total load, it is important to note that output modules consume more current as each individual circuit is energized. Normally, specification tables will provide a static load current for when the module has no energized circuits — as well as a value to add for each energized output.

Discrete Input Specifications

Input Voltage. The *input voltage* is a nominal value defining the magnitude (e.g., 5V, 24V, 230V) and type (AC or DC) of user supply voltage that a module is designed to accept, and, consequently, the type of field devices the module interfaces to the PLC. Input modules are typically designed to operate correctly and without damage within a range of plus or minus 10 percent of the input voltage rating. This range defines the minimum and maximum operating voltages. With DC input modules, the input voltage may also be expressed as an operating range (e.g., 24-60 volts DC) over which the module will operate.

Input Threshold Voltages. This input module specification normally specifies two values: a minimum ON-state voltage that is the minimum voltage at which a logic 1 is guaranteed; and a maximum OFF-state voltage, which is the voltage at which a logic 0 is guaranteed. These values are important since field devices change ON/OFF states at different rates and do not always have well defined ON/OFF states (i.e., voltages at which the device is considered ON or OFF). The threshold voltage specifications, although not specified by most PLCs, alert the user to the values that the input circuit will be guaranteed absolutely ON or absolutely OFF.

Input Current. This input module specification is normally expressed as a minimum value and defines the necessary current (at the rated voltage) that must be seen at the terminals of an input circuit before the signal will be recognized as a valid input or a logic 1. The specification may also state a current value at which the module circuit will produce a logic 0. The input current value, in conjunction with the input voltage, functions as a threshold to ensure against detecting noise or leakage currents as valid signals.

Minimum Input Impedance. In both AC and DC input modules, a logic 1 state saturates the filtering and switching circuitry, an effect partially accountable for off-delay time. When the circuit switches, all of its energy discharges through the path of least resistance. Since digital input modules must sense current and voltage through their internal circuitry, if the minimum specified resistance is not seen across the input, much of the current will discharge through the input device and will not be sensed by the module's filtering circuitry. Consequently, the input would not turn off.

Input ON/OFF Delay. These values specify the maximum time required by an input module's circuitry to recognize that a field device has switched ON (*input ON-delay*) or switched OFF (*input OFF-delay*). These time delays, which are normally on the order of a few milliseconds, are due to the module's filtering circuitry. The main purpose of filtering on discrete inputs is to ensure that electrical noise generated when mechanical contacts open and close is not mistaken for true signals. The *input delay* is independent of the processor scan and therefore must be taken into account when determining the overall response time for a particular circuit. The input ON-delay indirectly specifies the minimum duration for which an input must be present at the input before being recognized as a valid signal.

Discrete Output Specifications

Output Voltage. The *output voltage* is a nominal value defining the magnitude (e.g., 5V, 115V, 230V) and type (AC or DC) of user supply voltage at which a module is designed to operate, and, consequently, the type of field devices that the module interfaces to the PLC. Output modules are typically designed to operate correctly and without damage within a range of plus or minus 10 percent of the nominal output voltage rating. This range defines the maximum and minimum operating voltages. With DC outputs, the output voltage may also be expressed as an operating range (e.g., 12-48 volts DC) over which the module will operate.

Output Current. The *output current rating* defines the maximum current that a single output circuit can safely deliver to a device while energized. A device drawing more than the rated output current results in overloading, causing the output fuse to blow. Standard digital output circuits are rated at 1 or 2 amps per channel at an operating temperature range of 0-60 degrees C. This rating, which is a function of the module's electrical and heat dissipation characteristics, will normally be derated if the operating temperature exceeds 60 degrees C.

The output current rating may also be specified as the amount of current that can be supplied by the entire module; for instance, a module with eight circuits delivers a total of 7.5 amps. Although individual circuits may be capable of supplying 1 amp continuously, this value would be derated depending on the number of outputs energized at one time. Other names for the output current rating, are *maximum continuous current* and *maximum load current*.

Inrush Current. An *inrush current* is a momentary surge of current that an AC or DC output circuit usually encounters when energizing inductive, capacitive, or filament loads (e.g., large motors, solenoids, contactors, fluorescent lights).

The inrush current specifies the maximum current and the duration for which a module's output circuit can safely conduct while exceeding its maximum current rating. Typically, one or more values are specified along with the duration for which the inrush current can be sustained (e.g., 20 amps. for .01sec. or 10 amps. for .1 sec.). This specification is normally specified as nonrepetitive, meaning that the circuit can only sustain one such occurrence during a specified period (e.g., 10 seconds). For some AC output modules, the inrush current may be stated as a maximum current for some percentage of the AC cycle (e.g., 5A for 50 percent of an AC cycle).

Leakage Current. This value defines the amount of current still conducted through an output circuit even after the output has been turned OFF. Leakage current, a characteristic exhibited by triacs and transistors, is normally less than 5 milliamperes. This small current, which is rarely sufficient to falsely trigger an output device, may do so when switching very low currents. It may also give false indication when using a sensitive measuring instrument to check contact continuity. Leakage current must also be a consideration whenever a PLC output signal is input to an input module since the switching device in these modules does exhibit current leakage.

Short Circuit Protection. This specification defines the type of circuitry incorporated in AC and DC output modules to disable the output and protect the module's circuitry in over voltage or short circuit occurrences. Generally, this protection is provided by either fuses or some other current-limiting circuitry. The specification will also designate whether the particular module's design has individual fuse protection for each circuit or if fuse protection is provided for groups (e.g., four or eight) of outputs.

Although short circuit protection for the most part is included internally to output modules, this may not have been the case for some older systems. In such cases, fuses would have to be installed externally for each circuit. If installing or replacing fuses, manufacturers' specifications must be strictly adhered to. Fuse designations normally include fuse current, voltage, and tripping characteristics.

Output ON/OFF Delay. The *output ON-delay*, defines the response delay time for the output circuit to go from OFF to ON once the logic circuitry has received the command from the CPU to turn ON. Conversely, the *output OFF-delay*, defines the response delay time for the output circuit to go from On to OFF once the logic circuitry receives the turn OFF command from the CPU. As with discrete input circuits, the delay in output circuits is due to filtering. The ON and OFF delays are factors to be considered when determining the worst-case response when energizing or de-energizing a field device. Other names for this specification are *turn ON/OFF time* and *output delay time*.

7

ANALOG INPUT/OUTPUT MODULES

Analog I/O Application

Standard Analog Input Modules

Standard Analog Output Modules

Low Level Analog Inputs

Analog I/O Specifications and Features

This chapter, which is devoted to Analog I/O, will explore the application, operation and typical connection diagrams of both standard and low-voltage analog module types. Finally, a review of analog I/O specifications will aid in properly matching field device requirements with the correct interface module. It may be helpful, if you have not already done so, to review, the word storage table of chapter 4.

7-1 Analog I/O Application

The second general class of I/O interfaces are analog I/O modules. These modules allow interfacing to devices that either generate or are controlled by a continuous signal. Whereas digital signals of devices like limit switches and photoelectrics are either ON or OFF at any instant in time, and have no in-between values, analog signals are continuous in nature. As illustrated in Figure 7-1, analog signals have many different values over a given period. Such signals are characteristic when measuring or controlling physical quantities, such as temperature, speed, flow, or pressure, that may also vary with time.

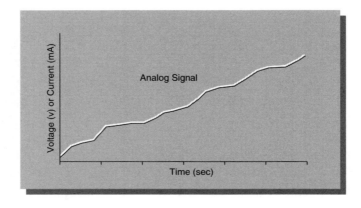

Figure 7-1 Analog signals represent continuous quantities such as speed and temperature

Analog signals are normally prevalent in continuous and batch processes where temperatures and flow rates must be measured, and on production machines where speeds and pressures must be constantly regulated. Just as there are digital sensors and actuators for detecting or controlling on/off states, there are also devices that measure continuous quantities and that require a continuous signal to regulate their operation.

Analog sensors measure a varying physical quantity over a specific range and generate a corresponding current or voltage signal. For example, a sensor may measure temperature over a range of 0-500 degrees C, and output a corresponding voltage signal that varies between 0 and 50 millivolts. Signals that vary over a range are accepted by analog input modules and processed so that they are usable by the CPU. Conversely, analog output modules accept numeric data from the CPU and convert it to a varying analog signal for controlling an analog actuator. Table 7-1 lists typical devices that are interfaced using analog I/O modules.

Table 7-1. Typical Devices Interfaced Using Analog I/O

ANALOG INPUTS	ANALOG OUTPUTS
Temperature Sensors	Analog Meters
Humidity Sensors	Chart Recorders
Pressure Sensors	Proportional Valves
Flow Rate Sensors	Variable Speed Drive Controllers
Load Sensors	Current-to-Pneumatic Transducers
Potentiometers	Voltage-to-Pneumatic Transducers

7-2 Standard Analog Input Modules

Standard ratings for operating signal ranges for analog input modules are listed in Table 7-2. These standard current and voltage ranges will allow PLCs to accept input signals generated from a variety of analog sensors. Input modules normally have multiple input channels, that allow four, eight, or sixteen devices to be interfaced to the PLC using one module.

As shown in Table 7-2, analog input modules accept both *unipolar* and *bipolar* signals. A unipolar input signal varies in the positive direction only (e.g., 0 volts to + 5 volts); bipolar signals swing between a maximum negative value and a maximum positive value (e.g., -10 V to +10 V). Most analog input modules can be configured via hardware switches or in software to accommodate different current or voltage signals. While some modules may allow individual channels to be configured, others require that signal ranges be selected in groups of channels.

Table 7-2. Standard Analog Input Module Ratings

LOW-VOLTAGE SIGNAL RANGES	VOLTAGE SIGNAL RANGES	CURRENT SIGNAL RANGES
0 to 50mV	0 to 5V	0 to 20mA
0 to 100mV	1 to 5V	4 to 20mA
0 to 500mV	0 to 10V	1 to 5mA
-50 to +50mV	-5 to +5V	10 to 50mA
-100 to +100mV	-10 to +10V	-20 to +20mA
-500 to +500mV		

The following discussions review basic operational principles of standard analog input modules listed in Table 7-2. Although the following discussions are applicable to all analog input modules, analog modules for interfacing low-level analog signals (i.e., signals in the millivolt range) are presented in further detail under *Low Level Analog Inputs*.

Analog Input Operation

A simplified block diagram of analog input module operation is shown in Figure 7-2. The basic function of this module is to accept the analog signals at its input channels and convert them to digital values usable by the CPU. Since analog signals vary between some minimum and maximum level with many values in between, the input circuits must accept the analog signal and present a continually changing digital representation of the signal to the CPU. This translation of an analog signal to digital values is accomplished by an *analog-to-digital converter (A/D or ADC)*, the main element of the analog input module.

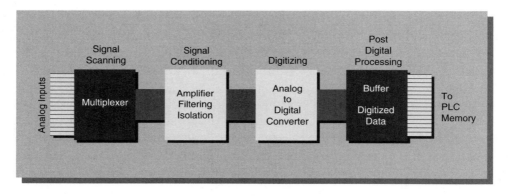

Figure 7-2. Simplified block diagram of an analog input module

Although some analog input modules may use an A/D for each channel, most use a single A/D with multiplexing circuitry. In operation, the multiplexer scans each input channel and sends the input signal to the A/D. The resultant digital values on each channel are forwarded one at a time to an onboard memory buffer for the specific channel address. The time to complete one such scan is referred to as the *module update time*. On most analog input modules, the module's update is asynchronous to the CPU scan and is repeated until a read request is made by an analog read instruction from the control program. The data for each channel is then sent to a sixteen-bit word in the PLC's data table.

The value output from the A/D is actually a binary approximation of the input signal. The closeness of the approximation depends on the converter's *digital resolution*. Resolution is based on the number of bits used in the digital representation, as illustrated in Figure 7-3. Most analog input modules have at least twelve-bit resolution.

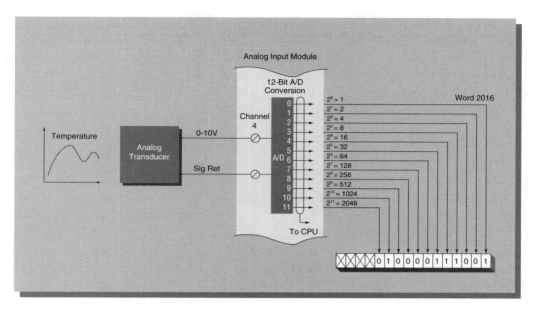

Figure 7-3. Functional diagram of analog input from signal input to the PLC memory

Twelve-bit resolution means that the full scale input is divided into 2^{12} or 4,096 parts. The A/D can measure a signal change as small as 1/4096, or 0.024 percent of full scale. A sixteen-bit resolution A/D converter would offer very close approximation of the analog signal — the full scale input is divided into 2 or 65,536 increments. This resolution would detect a signal as small as 1/65,536, or .15 millivolts on a 10-volt range. Table 7-3 lists several analog signal ranges and their corresponding signal resolution, resulting from twelve-bit A/D conversion. These values are obtained by dividing the signal span into 4,096 parts.

Table 7-3. Analog Signal Resolutions Based on Twelve-bit Conversion

ANALOG RANGE	SIGNAL SPAN	SIGNAL RESOLUTION
0 - 5V	5 V	1.22 mV
1 - 5V	4 V	0.98 mV
0 -10V	10 V	2.44 mV
0 - 20mA	20 mA	.0049 mA
4 - 20mA	16 mA	.0039 mA
-5V to +5V	10 V	2.44 mV
-10V to +10V	20 V	4.88 mV
-20mA to +20mA	40 mA	.0097 mA

Since analog input module designs are different, the influence of characteristics such as module update and resolution will have to be examined for each application. Temperature signals, for instance, may not require the fast update that may be required for pressure signals. Further details regarding these designs are presented in the discussion of Analog I/O Specifications. First, let's look more closely at how analog input signals are represented in a digital form usable by the control program.

Analog Input Data Representation

An analog input signal cannot be represented by a single binary digit as can a digital input signal whose two states are easily represented by a value of 1 or 0. Instead, the analog input module must produce a range of values between a maximum and minimum value to represent the analog signal over its entire span. The analog-to-digital converter, therefore, produces at its output a changing binary value representing the changing magnitude of the incoming signal. The data received by the PLC for each channel is stored in a sixteen-bit data word location as shown in Figure 7-4.

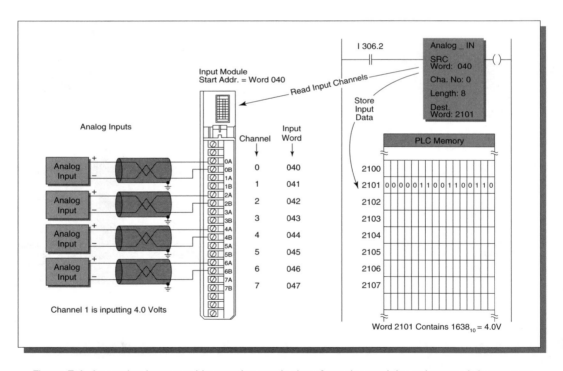

Figure 7-4. An analog input read instruction reads data from the module and stores it in memory

Each of the selectable input ranges on an analog input module have a corresponding range of numeric input data that is sent to the CPU to represent the analog input range. This range of values represents the full scale range of the analog input signal. Typically this range of values reflects raw (unscaled) binary output of the A/D converter that is represented in decimal, BCD, or some other number format. For instance, a module with twelve-bit resolution can produce a range of values from 0 to 4,095. In this case, a value of 0 represents the minimum input signal and a value of 4095 represents the full scale signal.

Table 7-4 illustrates the digital representation for an input channel having a unipolar input range of 0-10 volts. The module has twelve-bit resolution and a corresponding *binary output range* of 0-4095. This means that the signal range of 10 volts in this case is divided into 4,096 parts. Therefore, one count represents 10V/4096-counts (or .00244 volts/count). As the input signal varies up and down in units of 2.44 millivolts, the input data is being incremented or decremented in units of one count to reflect the changing signal. At a reading of 2.44 millivolts, the input data should read 1 count. At 50 percent of full scale or 5 volts, the input count to the CPU is 2,048.

Table 7-4. Twelve-bit Digital Representation of a 0-10V Input Signal

ACTUAL ANALOG INPUT (VDC)	DIGITAL REPRESENTATION IN DECIMAL COUNTS (0-4095)	PERCENT OF FULL SCALE (0%-100%)
0V	0	0%
1V	410	10%
2V	819	20%
3V	229	30%
4V	1638	40%
5V	2048	50%
6V	2458	60%
7V	2867	70%
8V	3277	80%
9V	3686	90%
10V	4095	100%

The data received by the PLC for each analog input channel is stored in a sixteen-bit word location. This data is accessed by the control program for a given channel by using an analog read instruction specifying the desired channel. Once the data is read, it is available for further use or manipulation by the control program. The expected digital word value resulting from a given voltage input, from the example above, is easily determined using the following equation.

$$\textbf{Digital Input Word} \text{ (DIW)} = \frac{Input\ Voltage}{10\ volts} \times 4096$$

The following general equation can be used to determine the expected digital input value for any current or voltage input signal:

$$\textbf{Digital Input Word} \text{ (DIW)} = \frac{Actual\ Input\ Signal}{\text{Signal Resolution}}$$

Bipolar input signals are handled in a similar manner. If the same module allowed a signal range of -5 volts to +5 volts, the digital representation might be as shown in Table 7-5. The binary output range is from -4,095 to + 4,095. In this case, the negative swing of the analog signal is represented by 0 to -4,095 while the positive swing is represented by 0 to +4095. Since the range is from -5 volts to +5 volts, the effective span is still 10 volts, as in the previous unipolar example. The signal is resolved, however, over 8,192 counts (-4,095 to + 4,095). This results in a signal resolution/count of 10/8192 or (.00122 volts/count). If the signal was resolved over 4,096 counts or from 0-4095, the resolution would be 10/4096 or .0024 V/count.

Table 7-5. Digital Representation of a Bipolar Input Signal

ACTUAL ANALOG INPUT (VDC)	DIGITAL REPRESENTATION IN DECIMAL COUNTS (0-4095)
5.0 V	+4095
4.0 V	+3279
3.0 V	+2459
2.5 V	+2048
2.0 V	+1639
1.0 V	+ 820
0.0 V	0
-1.0 V	- 820
-2.0 V	-1639
-2.5 V	-2048
-3.0 V	-2459
-4.0 V	-3279
-5.0 V	-4095

Since the PLC uses a sixteen-bit word for analog inputs, the twelve-bit value from the converter represents the signal and the remaining four bits are typically used to designate the sign of the data, an over or under range value, or other diagnostic data.

Analog Input Connections

Analog input devices are wired to analog input modules in two basic ways — *single-ended input* and *differential input* connections — as shown in Figure 7-5. The less expensive single-ended connections have the common leads of all the inputs electrically tied together. It is used in applications where noise is less likely or where all the devices are powered from the same source . Differential input connections measure the net difference between a positive and negative lead terminated on the module. This method allows any noise appearing equally on the two leads to have a canceling affect.

When placing I/O modules within the module housings, analog input modules should be grouped and kept away from AC modules or high-voltage DC I/O modules to minimize the effects of noise. If connecting voltage inputs, close adherence to vendor requirements regarding wire length is important to minimize signal degrading and the effects of noise induced along the connecting conductors. Current input signals, which are not as sensitive to noise, are typically not distance limited.

Shielded twisted pair cable is normally recommended for connecting analog input signals. It provides greater uniformity in line impedances and good common mode rejection. If the input signal is driven from an unbalanced (one side grounded) source, like in Figure 7-5a, then the shield drain wire should be grounded at the signal source. At the module end, the shield is typically not terminated but is cut away and insulated to prevent any electrical contact.

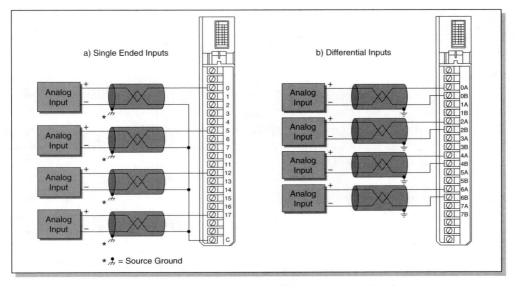

Figure 7-5. Illustration of single-ended and differential analog input connections

7-3 Standard Analog Output Modules

Analog output modules, like their input counterparts, come in a variety of standard ratings. These modules allow the PLC to interface to devices that are driven by a variable current or voltage signal. Each module normally has multiple output channels — typically four, eight or sixteen devices can be connected to a single analog output module.

Analog output modules also include both current and voltage ratings having both *unipolar* (positive swing only) and *bipolar* signal ranges (positive and negative swing). Individual output channels are configured using rocker switches or software to allow different current or voltage signals to be output from the module. For example, if a channel is configured for bipolar operation of +/- 10V, it can then output both positive and negative voltages within the range of -10 volts and +10 volts.

A listing of operating signal ranges commonly available for analog output modules is given in Table 7-6. On some modules, these range selections may be mixed to meet requirements of the application. The following discussions cover the basic operation of analog output modules.

Table 7-6. Standard Analog Output Module Ratings

VOLTAGE SIGNAL RANGES	CURRENT SIGNAL RANGES
0 to 5V	0 to 20mA
1 to 5V	4 to 20mA
0 to 10V	1 to 5mA
-5 to +5V	10 to 50mA
-10 to +10V	-20 to +20mA

Analog Output Operation

The function of the analog output is to accept a range of numeric values output from the PLC control program and to produce a varying current or voltage signal required to control a connected device. Output circuits on the module must accept this range of values and produce the appropriate analog signal between a specified minimum and maximum signal range. This translation from digital data to an analog signal is accomplished by a *digital-to-analog converter (DAC or D/A)*, the heart of the analog output module.

In operation, digital data is sent to an analog output module by using an analog output instruction and referencing the module by its address. The data is directed to the module's onboard memory buffers for each channel. From there the data for each channel is forwarded one at a time by the module to the D/A, which outputs the appropriate analog signal. The time the module requires to move the buffered data through the D/A for

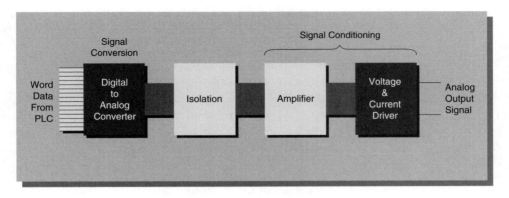

Figure 7-6. Simplified block diagram of an analog output circuit

all of the channels is referred to as the *module update time*. Unlike analog input modules, the update of analog output modules is typically synchronized with the CPU scan, and no new data is sent to the module's onboard buffers until a write request is made by the control program.

The actual level of the analog signal output to each channel is based on the digital value taken from a sixteen-bit data word associated with the channel, as illustrated in Figure 7-7. Typically, the data has been manipulated by the control program or is driven by an analog input signal. Whether the binary data is interpreted as decimal, BCD, or some other data format will depend on the module. The location from which the data is taken is normally determined by the user program but in some systems is predetermined by analog I/O memory mapping.

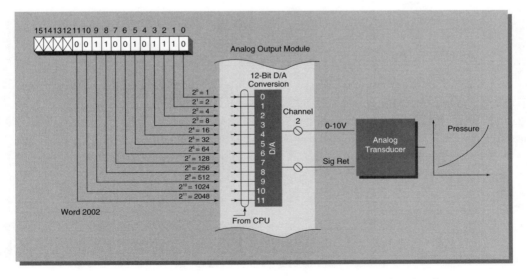

Figure 7-7. Functional diagram of analog output from memory to the signal output

The digital value output to each channel represents a percentage of the full scale analog range selected for that channel. As with the conversion of the analog input, the closeness of the actual analog output signal to the percentage represented by the digital value will depend on the *digital resolution* of the module's D/A. Like analog input modules, most analog output modules have twelve-bit resolution. As illustrated in Figure 7-7, resolution for the D/A defines the number of bits it accepts at its input as the digital representation. In the following discussion, we'll look at how a digital output value is determined to achieve a desired output signal.

Analog Output Data Representation

An analog output signal is a continuous and changing signal that is varied under the control of the PLC program. Whereas the digital output accepted a logic 1 or 0 to switch a control voltage ON or OFF, the analog output must accept a range of values from the CPU in order to vary the specified analog signal over its entire range. The digital-to-analog converter, which performs this function, accepts a digital value at its input and produces a proportional analog voltage or current at its output.

Each of the selectable signal ranges on an analog output module has a corresponding range of numeric data that allows the control program to vary the module outputs between 0 and 100 percent of the full-scale output. Typically, this range of values output to the D/A is represented in decimal, BCD or some other number format.

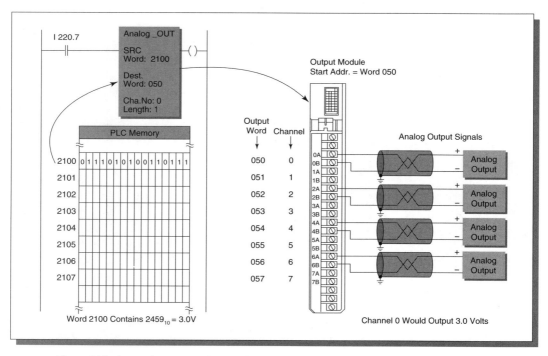

Figure 7-8. An analog output instruction uses the associated word from memory and directs it to the module to alter the desired current or voltage signal

For instance, a module with twelve-bit resolution can accept a range of unscaled decimal values from 0 to 4,095. In this case, a value of 0 represents the minimum output signal and a value of 4,095 represents the full-scale output signal.

Table 7-7 shows what the digital representation might be for an output channel having a unipolar output range of 4-20 milliamps. The module has twelve-bit resolution, and the corresponding *binary input range* to the module is 0-4095. This means that the signal range, in this case 16 milliamps (20-4), is divided into 4096 parts. Therefore, one count represents 16/4096 or .003907 mA. To vary the output signal up and down in units of .003907 mA the digital output data is incremented or decremented in units of one count. The minimum output of .003907 mA, is obtained when the digital output data is at 1 count. An output value of 2048 would generate an output signal at 50 percent of full scale or 12 milliamps.

Table 7-7. Twelve-bit Digital Representation of a 4-20mA Output Signal

DIGITAL REPRESENTATION IN DECIMAL COUNTS (0-4095)	PERCENT OF FULL SCALE (0%-100%)	ACTUALANALOG OUTPUT
0	0%	4mA
256		5mA
512		6mA
768		7mA
1024	25%	8mA
1280		9mA
1536		10mA
1792		11mA
2048	50%	12mA
2304		13mA
2560		14mA
2815		15mA
3071	75%	16mA
3327		17mA
3583		18mA
3839		19mA
4095	100%	20 mA

The data sent to each output channel from the application memory is done so on demand by using an analog output instruction to specify the appropriate source word locations and the desired output channel. The value to be output to a specific output channel to achieve a desired signal level is easily determined in this example using the following equation. Note that with a 4-20 mA signal, an offset of 4-mA must be subtracted from the desired output reading.

$$\textbf{Digital Output Word}\ (\text{DOW}) = \frac{Desired\ Current\ Reading - 4}{16\text{mA}} \times 4096$$

The following general equation can be used with any signal range to determine the digital output value for obtaining the desired output current or voltage signal:

$$\textit{Digital Output Word}\ (\text{DOW}) = \frac{Desired\ Output\ Signal - 4}{\text{Signal Resolution}}$$

Analog Output Connections

Analog output modules can be grouped along with analog input modules in the I/O housing, but they should be kept away from AC modules or high-voltage DC I/O modules. The signal wiring should also be kept separate from power wiring. This arrangement will help minimize the effects of noise generated by high-frequency switching. If connecting voltage inputs, close adherence to vendor requirements regarding wire length is important to minimize signal degrading and the effects of noise induced along the connecting conductors.

Shielded twisted pair cable should be used to transmit the analog signal to the output device. Since the best ground termination point for cable shielding is the point at which the signal originates, for analog output signals this would be at the module end, as illustrated in Figure 7-9. If shield terminals are not provided on the I/O module, the shields can be terminated at a central enclosure ground. At the load end, the shields should not be terminated but should be cut away and insulated to prevent any electrical contact.

Finally, an important consideration when planning the wiring for analog output modules is that of *loop output resistance* of the output circuit. This parameter, which is influenced by the series resistance of the connected device and by the length and type of wire, is discussed later under *Analog I/O Specifications*.

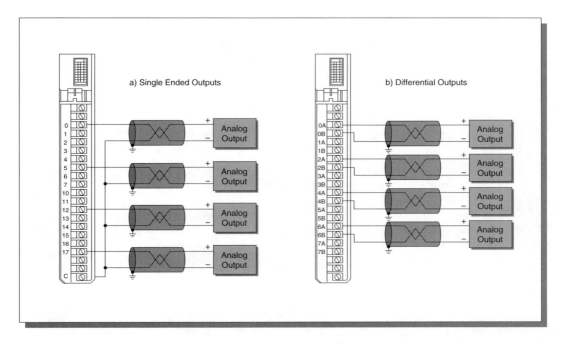

Figure 7-9. Illustration of single-ended and differential analog output connections

7-4 Low-level Analog Inputs

This section takes a look at analog modules used by PLCs to allow interfacing of very low-level signals. Such signals, which are typically in the 0-250 millivolts range, are generated by devices such as the *thermocouple (T/C), resistance temperature detector (RTD), strain gauge, load cell,* and *thermistor.* An advantage of these modules is that signal conditioning such as amplification, linearization, and special noise filtering are performed on the interface module, allowing direct connection to the PLC.

Thermocouple Inputs

Thermocouples (T/C) are the most widely used temperature measuring devices in industrial applications. They are very rugged and inexpensive when compared to thermistors and RTDs. Thermocouples come in a wide selection of types suited for a variety of applications, ranging from -250 degrees C to 2,300 degrees C. Different T/C types are also suited to different environments; for example, some are very resistant to corrosion. Table 7-8, on the following page, lists standard thermocouple devices and their temperature ranges.

Thermocouples operate on the principle that when two wires composed of dissimilar metals are joined at both ends and one end is heated, a continuous current will flow through the thermoelectric circuit. If the circuit is broken in the center, the net open

Table 7-8. Standard Thermocouples and Temperature Ranges

T/C TYPE	TYPICAL RANGE (DEG. C)
E	-270 to 1000
J	-210 to 760
K	-270 to 1372
T	-270 to 400
B	400 to 1820
R	-50 to 1768
S	-50 to 1768

circuit voltage, known as the Seebeck voltage, will vary based on the junction temperature and the composition of the two metals. Hence, a change in temperature can be sensed. Typical output from a thermocouple is about 7-to-40 microvolts for every one degree C change in temperature.

Different metals can be used for thermocouple construction, and the choice of metals will influence the size of the voltage produced, as well as the temperature range over which the thermocouple can be used. Therefore, standard types of thermocouples have been defined by standards organizations such as ANSI. The different types are designated by a unique letter, as seen in Table 7-8. Type J, for example, consists of an iron wire and a constantan (copper-nickel alloy) wire.

In temperature measuring applications, thermocouples actually measure the difference in temperature between two junctions, the so-called *hot junction,* which is located in the process, and the *reference junction,* which is located at the measuring device. In this case, the reference junction, which is also called the cold junction, would be at the PLC thermocouple input module. Since the connection to a measuring device introduces another dissimilar metals junction, the temperature at this junction would be sensed and would distort the actual reading. In older measuring systems, the temperature of the reference junction was held constant at 32 degrees F (0 degrees C) by immersion in melting ice. Modern measuring systems are usually equipped with *cold junction compensation,* an electrical method that simulates the maintenance of 0 degrees C.

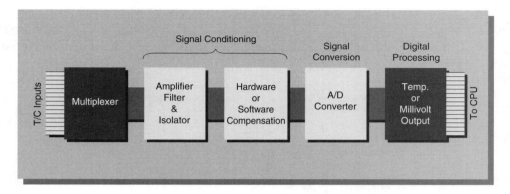

Figure 7-10. Simplified block diagram of a thermocouple analog input module

Thermocouple Input Module

Typically the thermocouple input module is designed with eight or sixteen individually isolated input channels that accept direct input from standard thermocouples, including E,J,K,T,B,R, and S. Because of their usual input voltage range of 0-100mV, these modules may also accept input from other devices that output signals in this range. Configuring the module to accept a specific thermocouple type or for other millivolt signals is usually done through software or using hardware jumpers or rocker switches.

The thermocouple input module performs much like the standard analog input modules. It scans each channel and passes the signal to an analog-to-digital converter, which translates the signal to its digital equivalent and buffers the result in a binary format. Since the thermocouple signal is not linear with respect to temperature, an onboard microprocessor takes the buffered data and produces a linearized output based on the selected thermocouple type. The converted data, which the module outputs to the PLC then represents an actual temperature value in degrees Centigrade or degrees Fahrenheit, depending on how the module was configured. The data is stored in sixteen-bit word locations just like standard analog input signals.

Thermocouple input modules must also provide cold-junction compensation to eliminate measuring errors resulting from the effect of ambient temperature at the point where the thermocouple wires are connected to the module. Typically, this compensation is provided internally to the module's wiring connector. The module automatically corrects the temperature by subtracting the ambient temperature from the temperature measured at the machine or process. The result is the actual temperature value that can be used for comparison against some process setpoint.

Unlike other analog input modules, where signal ranges may be mixed, this is not normally the case with thermocouple inputs since each T/C type requires different linearization and compensation. Some typical thermocouple input connections are illustrated in Figure 7-11.

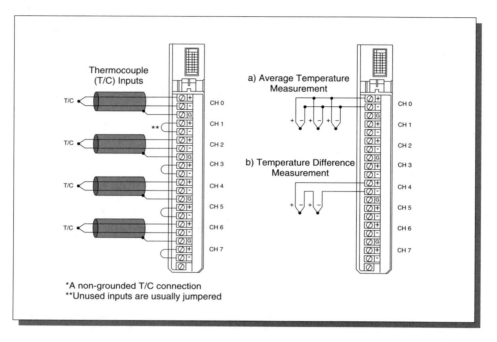

Figure 7-11. Typical thermocouple input connections

RTD Inputs

The resistance temperature detector (RTD) is a another widely used temperature measuring device. While the thermocouple is considered the most versatile of the temperature transducers, the RTD is considered the most stable. Its operation is based on the principle that all metals produce a known change in resistance when subjected to a positive change in temperature. For the resistance to be sensed, the RTD requires an accurate excitation current or voltage source. In its most common construction, the RTD consist of a small coil of platinum, nickel, or copper protected by a sheath of stainless steel, glass, or ceramic.

RTDs have several advantages, especially platinum RTDs and in particular, the 100 ohm platinum type (PT100, 100 Ohms at 0 degrees C). It has a wide range of -200 degrees C to 850 degrees C, it is extremely stable and accurate, it is highly resistant to adverse conditions, and, unlike the thermocouples, it does not need cold-junction compensation. However, the RTD does need linearization for accuracy. RTDs also have a relatively small resistance such that the resistance of the copper lead wires can create severe measurement errors unless special care is taken. Several configurations of the RTD, however, reduce this problem.

The simplest RTD has two leads. With this device, temperature is determined by applying a small current to the RTD and measuring the voltage drop across it. Long leads directly contribute to the measurement error for this type of RTD. The three-wire RTD uses the third wire to cancel the error due to lead wire resistance. There is still an error, however, due to the matching of one lead wire to the other. Since the wires are normally in a pair that is manufactured together, the matching is very close, making the three-wire RTD an acceptably accurate device for most applications at a reasonable price. The four-wire RTD is used where the best possible accuracy is required. The reference current flows through one set of wires to the RTD while the voltage drop is measured across the other two wires.

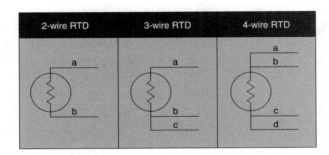

Figure 7-12. RTD two-wire, three-wire, and four-wire lead configurations

Although it is more linear than the thermocouple, the RTD still requires curve fitting to achieve measuring accuracy. There are two different compensations for RTDs. They are distinguished by alpha, the factor that measures the change in resistance with change in temperature. The most common is the European curve, which has an alpha of 0.00385. The less common RTD has an alpha of 0.00392. The alpha coefficient actually represents the average slope of change in resistance with respect to change in temperature. For example, the alpha of platinum wire is 0.00385. For a 100 ohm wire, this corresponds to +0.385 ohms/degree C, which represents the average slope from 0 degrees C to 100 degrees C.

RTD Input Module

The RTD module is designed to make direct connections to resistive temperature devices, including three- and four-wire RTDs. Like the thermocouple input module, the RTD input module is still performing analog-to-digital conversion, yet it is an intelligent analog input module that preprocesses the measured signal and sends temperature data to the CPU. While most modules specify the commonly used PT100, one or more other RTD sensor types can generally be configured as inputs to the module.

For those RTD modules that accept several RTD types, each channel must be configured for the type of RTD input, whether the input to the PLC will be reported directly in ohms or converted to degrees C or degrees F, and for the format of the data (e.g., BCD, fixed point). Channel configurations are set in either hardware or software and can normally be set individually or the same for all channels. Different configurations are only possible with those modules that provide linearization for different alphas. Using different RTDs on the same module, however, is not generally recommended since it is very easy to get the RTDs mixed up.

For operation, the RTD sensor requires a small excitation current, which is typically supplied by the RTD module. The current is passed through the RTD device, thereby providing a voltage drop that can be measured by the input circuit. This voltage, which is directly proportional to the RTD resistance, is used by the module to determine the RTD resistance to current flow, which of course, is temperature dependent.

When connecting RTD inputs, the same practical precautions that applied to standard analog inputs and thermocouple inputs apply. Use shielded twisted pair conductors, avoid stress and kinks in the shielding, use heavy-gauge extension wire, and keep good documentation. Since the operating principle of the RTD module is based on the measurement of resistance, it is important to select cable that has a consistent impedance throughout its length. It is also vital to keep input cable lengths as short as possible since the length will directly affect the overall impedance. The RTD module will generally specify maximum cable lengths based on a maximum impedance. Typical RTD connections are shown in Figure 7-13.

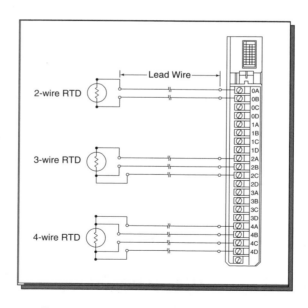

Figure 7-13. Typical RTD module connections

7-5 Analog I/O Specifications and Features

Selecting the appropriate analog input or output modules and applying these modules correctly requires an understanding of their electrical and operating specifications. It is important to understand the unique signal characteristics and requirements of the input and output devices to be interfaced. Finally, you must consider factors peculiar to the application that may influence the type of modules used or any special wiring considerations. The following specifications define general analog I/O module features and electrical operating characteristics.

Common Features and Specifications

Channels Per Module. Whereas individual circuits on digital I/O modules are referred to as points, circuits on analog I/O modules are sometimes called channels. These modules normally have four, eight, or sixteen channels. In those cases, where an analog input or output module allows either *single-ended* or *differential connections*, twice as many connections are possible if single-ended connections are used. For example, if the module normally allows sixteen single-ended connections, it will generally allow eight differential connections. Normally, all channels on the module must be set for the same connection configuration.

Single-ended/Differential Connections. The most accurate analog I/O cards will not give good results unless the inputs are connected appropriately for the given application. The biggest problem encountered is *ground loops*. Ground loops are created when an unexpected voltage drop results from current flowing in a ground wire. The best way to eliminate this problem is to use isolated I/O modules. Because of cost, the next best alternative, "differential inputs," is often used. Differential inputs use a separate positive and negative terminal for each channel. Less expensive designs use "single-ended inputs," which have a single ground terminal for all channels or for a group of channels.

Optical Isolation. Like digital I/O modules, analog I/O circuitry typically provides optical isolation to protect the logic side of the PLC (i.e., CPU and backplane) from transient voltage spikes that may occur between the channel connections and system ground. This specification may also be referred to as *channel-to-ground isolation* or *galvanic isolation*. The isolation voltage, which ranges between 1000 and 1500 volts RMS, defines the module's capacity to sustain an excessive voltage at its field terminals. If the module is subjected to a voltage exceeding this breakdown voltage, the PLC bus is protected; however, the module's circuitry may be damaged. Modules having this type of isolation are referred to as *floating modules,* those without it are called *nonfloating modules.*

Isolated Channels. Individually isolated I/O channels provide extra protection for the analog I/O signal by minimizing cross-channel interaction. Each channel provides a separate signal and ground lead, which allows connection of devices on different power sources and helps to simplify connections by greatly reducing ground-related problems. Isolated I/O modules are typically applied in areas where high noise levels are anticipated or where the influences of a noisy environment cannot be tolerated on the input lines. These modules, which provide protection between individual channels, referred to as *channel-to-channel isolation*, create a protective separation barrier of typically 1000 volts between channels.

Module Load. Module load, also referred to as the *operating current requirement* or *module current consumption*, specifies the amount of current that a particular input or output module's internal circuitry draws from the PLC's power supply. Each module's current requirement adds to the total current consumption that a particular combination of modules will place on the PLC power supply and consequently the required current rating. While some system power supplies are designed to handle any combination of modules within a rack, with others this may be an important consideration when specifying the I/O rack power supply.

Module Update Time. This specification defines the time required for an analog I/O module to scan all of its channels. This duration, which is also referred to as the *module scan time*, is that time required for all channels on an input module to be sampled, converted, and buffered or for new data output from the control program to be converted and output to all channels on an output module. The update time, consequently, affects how long it takes for recent changes of a particular analog point to be recognized. This value, which affects the time required to respond to field conditions, is also influenced by elements of the circuit design, such as input filtering or whether or not the module utilizes a single A/D or D/A converter instead of the more expensive design, that uses a converter for each channel.

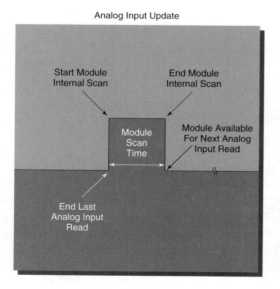 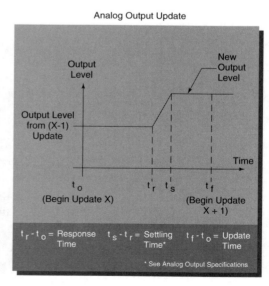

Figure 7-14. Illustration of analog input and analog output module update

Accuracy. The accuracy of an analog I/O module is an important specification in open-loop measuring and monitoring applications. It defines the maximum deviation in the actual reading and the expected reading at one or more operating temperatures. This value is given as a percentage of the full scale signal. For instance, given a 0-10V signal range and an accuracy of +0.1 percent of full scale at 25 degrees C — a reading should be in error by no more than 0.1 percent of 10 volts. Since accuracy is expected to degrade with temperature deviation, it is generally specified for different temperatures. Sometimes, accuracy is also specified over the full operating temperature range (e.g., .1 percent at 0-60 degrees C). With this measure, you can determine if the module offers the accuracy required for the application.

Signal Scaling. Analog I/O modules normally allow the analog input or output signal to be linearized to engineering units corresponding to the particular application. This process is referred to as *signal scaling*. The data normally read into or output from the PLC without any scaling is called unscaled or raw data. Unscaled data is the specified binary range input from an analog input module or is sent to an analog output module. For example, 0-4,095 on a unipolar range or -4,095 to +4,095 on a bipolar range. To scale an analog signal, you specify the lower and upper limits of the input or output data, which are referred to as the *minimum scaling value* and the *maximum scaling value*. These values are used to perform a linear translation to some engineering unit (e.g., gal./min., lbs./sq.in. or degrees C).

The purpose of scaling is to simplify the interpretation of analog input/output data by creating a one-to-one relationship between the units of the measured process variable and the input data or between the data output and the engineering units of the controlled variable. In the following example for instance, the minimum scale value of 100 and maximum scaling value of 1000 are selected to scale the input data to correspond to the upper and lower limits of the measured process input of 100 watts and 1000 watts. The scaling limits are specified in the analog input or output instruction.

Table 7-9. Example of Analog Signal Scaling

MEASURED PROCESS VALUE	ANALOG INPUT VOLTAGE	SCALED INPUT DATA (0-1000)	UNSCALED INPUT (0-4095)
1000 W	10V	1000	4095
900 W	9V	900	3686
800 W	8V	800	3277
700 W	7V	700	2867
600 W	6V	600	2458
500 W	5V	500	2048
400 W	4V	400	1638
300 W	3V	300	1229
200 W	2V	200	819
100 W	1V	100	410

Analog Input Specifications

The following discussion will define some of the most important analog input specifications. Since some of these may be referred to by different terminology, sometimes, wherever this is the case, alternative nomenclatures will be referenced. Figure 7-15 shows a typical specification data sheet for analog inputs.

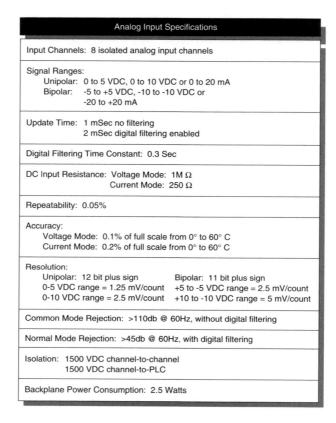

Figure 7-15. Typical analog input specifications

Input Current/Voltage Range(s). These are the voltage or current signal ranges that an analog input module is designed to accept. Typically, an input module will specify one or more unipolar or bipolar current or voltage ranges (e.g., -10V to +10V, 4 to 20 ma). When selecting analog input modules, the input ranges must be matched according to the varying current or voltage signals generated by the analog sensors. It is important to remember that the module's resolution is maximized when the input range is closely matched to the output of the input device.

For those input modules that only specify voltage signals, current signals may be connected by placing a resistor across the input. By applying Ohm's law, you can determine the required precision resistance value. For example, given a 5-volt scale and a maximum current of 20mA, the resistor value is determined as illustrated below.

$$\frac{5\ Volts}{20\ Amps} = 250\ Ohms$$

Analog-to-Digital Resolution. This specification determines the smallest measurable unit of current or voltage that an analog input module's A/D converter can detect and represent in digital form. For this reason, resolution is usually the first factor considered in selecting an analog input module. It determines if a module will be able to measure or monitor changes in the signal required by the application. Resolution, which is based on the number of binary digits used to represent the analog input signal over its entire range, is determined by dividing the given signal span by the number of counts that can be represented by the available binary digits. The table below shows selected ranges on an input module with twelve-bit resolution and the smallest signal for each.

Table 7-10. Twelve-bit Signal Resolution for Selected Signal Ranges

ANALOG RANGE	SIGNAL SPAN	SIGNAL RESOLUTION
0-5 V	5V	1.22mV
1-5 V	4V	0.98mV
0-10 V	10V	2.44mV
0-20 mA	20mA	.0049mA
4-20 mA	16mA	.0039mA
-5V to +5V	10V	2.44mV
-10V to +10V	20V	4.88mV
-20mA to 20mA	40mA	.0097mA

A/D Binary Output. The A/D binary output specifies the data format and range of numbers output from the analog-to-digital converter and sent to the PLC Processor. The data sent to the processor is usually in decimal or BCD, having a range determined by the binary resolution of the module. For example, a module having twelve-bit resolution may output numbers in decimal from 0 to 4,095 to represent bipolar signal ranges, and -4,095 to +4,095 might be used to represent all bipolar signal ranges. The A/D binary output for each analog input channel is stored as a numeric value in a sixteen-bit PLC data word.

Input Protection. Analog input circuits are usually protected against accidentally connecting a voltage that exceeds the specified input voltage range. The specification normally gives a maximum *RMS* voltage level that exceeds the nominal input voltage range and that can be applied to the input circuit continuously. If, however, this maximum level is exceeded for a continuous duration, the module will be damaged. An important point here is that while modules that also provide electrical isolation between the field connection and the PLC will prevent damage to the PLC, modules without this protection (*nonfloating*) may result in damage to the PLC.

Common-mode Rejection. Common-mode noise rejection only applies to differential inputs. A differential measurement is one in which two signal wires (i.e., +lead and -lead) are connecting the transducer and the system and the difference between the two is the measured value. *Common-mode rejection* is the quantification of the input circuitry's ability to measure only this difference while rejecting the components that both wires have in common (i.e., noise). Noise that is picked up equally in parallel wires is rejected because the difference is 0. Twisted pair wires are used to ensure that this type of noise is equal on both wires. CMR is normally expressed in decibels or as a ratio.

Normal-mode Rejection. Sometimes, instead of affecting both wires equally, noise affects one lead more than the other. This noise is called normal-mode noise. *Normal-mode rejection*, or filtering, is a measure of the input module's ability to attenuate transient changes in the normal-mode (the difference between two voltages). The most common source of normal mode noise is line frequency from the power lines (i.e., 50hz or 60hz), but the rejection can be characterized over a broad range of frequencies. Effective normal-mode rejection is generally achieved by filtering fast changes to the signal that can only come from external sources while allowing the real signal to pass through.

Analog Output Specifications

The following discussion will define some of the most important analog output module specifications. Since some of these may be referred to by different terminology, wherever this is the case, alternative nomenclatures will be referenced. A typical specification data sheet for analog outputs is shown in Figure 7-16.

Output Current/Voltage Range(s). This specification defines the current or voltage signal ranges that a particular analog output module is designed to output under program control. Typically, a given output module will specify one or more unipolar or bipolar current or voltage signals (e.g., 0 to 10V, -5V to +5V, 4-20mA). When selecting analog output modules, the output ranges must be matched according to the varying current or voltage signals that will be required to drive the analog output devices. Closely matching the output range selection to the requirements of the output device will maximize the module's resolution.

Analog Output Specifications
Output Channels: 8 isolated output channels
Response Time: 2 mSec total module (0.25 mSec per channel) (includes settling time)
Output Ranges: 0 to 10 VDC and 0 to 20 mA (sourcing)
Resolution: 12 bit (2.5 mV or 5 uA per count)
Isolation: 1500 VDC channel-to-channel 1500 VDC channel-to-PLC
Capacitance Drive: 0.01 microfarads
Load Resistance: Voltage: 10M Ω minimum, no maximum Current: 0 Ω to 500 Ω max. or u0p to 1000 Ω max. with an external 10 V power supply present in circuit
Voltage Accuracy: 0.1% of full scale from 0° to 60° C (over total load range)
Current Accuracy: 0.5% of full scale from 0° to 60° C (over total load range)
User Supply: 20 to 28 VDC @ 0.5 Amps (maximum ripple of 0.4 V)
Backplane Power Consumption: 1.7 Watts

Figure 7-16. Typical analog output specifications

Digital-to-Analog Resolution. This specification defines the smallest incremental unit of current or voltage that an analog output module's D/A can output as a step change. This value is determined by the number of binary digits the D/A converter uses to represent the analog output signal over its entire range. Resolution can be determined by dividing the given signal span by the number of counts that can be represented by the available binary digits. Refer back to Table 7-10 to see the effect of twelve- bit resolution on selected signal ranges.

D/A Binary Input. The D/A binary input specifies the data format and range of numbers that may be output from the PLC processor to the digital-to-analog converter of the analog output module. The data sent from the Processor is controlled by the control program and is usually in decimal (binary) or BCD, having a range determined by the binary resolution of the module. For example, a module having twelve-bit resolution might have a binary input range of 0-4,095. Bipolar signal ranges on the same module may use signed numbers (e.g., -4095 to +4095) to represent signals that vary in negative and positive directions.

Overload/Over-voltage Protection. *Overload protection* for the analog output module is a design measure taken to prevent the output channel circuits from being damaged in case the output wiring is shorted to ground. Some output modules also provide over-voltage and reverse-voltage protection. The *over-voltage protection* specifies a value to which the nominal range may be exceeded without causing damage and the *reverse-voltage protection* prevents damage that might be caused by accidentally reversing the polarity of the signal leads.

Output Current. The output current specifies the amount of current an output channel can deliver to the output circuit when in a voltage mode. This specification is important when the analog output must not only output a varying voltage level, but must also supply the current to drive a device such as a motor.

Settling Time. This output module parameter is the time required for the analog output signal to stabilize at a new desired level based on the latest output data received at the module from the control program. As illustrated in Figure 7-14 this value, which contributes to the total *module update time*, is the duration from which the module responds to the receipt of new output data to the time that the new level is reached.

Maximum Loop Resistance. This specification is typically given for the analog output when used in the current mode. Loop resistance for the output circuit is determined by the length and type of conductors, as well as by the series resistance of the connected loads. The loop resistance determines the maximum length of the field wires that can be used. Although the loop resistance is generally specified as a maximum value (e.g., 1200 ohms), some specifications may give a minimum and maximum resistance. In either case, if the loop resistance is not within these limits, the module will not operated correctly. Actual loop resistance for a given output channel may be determined using the following equation.

$$Loop\ resistance = (2 \times L_c \times R_c) + R_{fd}$$

where:

L_c = *cable length*
R_c = *conductor resistance (ohms/unit length)*
R_{fd} = *sum of resistance for all field devices*

In some cases, depending on the module, the maximum loop resistance can be increased by adding an appropriate power supply to the loop to maintain the accuracy of the module. Another alternative would be to change one of the other loop resistance factors.

8

INTELLIGENT INPUT/OUTPUT MODULES

Introduction to Intelligent I/O

Computer Coprocessor Modules

Networking and Serial Communications

Closed-loop Process Control

Position and Motion Control

Process-specific Modules

Artificial Intelligence Modules

One of the most innovative areas of development for programmable controllers is that of specialized I/O modules known as "intelligent I/O." Intelligent I/O modules are microprocessor-based I/O modules that in many cases perform their specific tasks independent of the main CPU. Equipped with their own memory and a link to the CPU bus, these quasi-standalone processors allow PLCs to perform complex functions that once burdened the main CPU or were performed by separate dedicated control systems. This chapter introduces the various categories and types of intelligent I/O, and presents some of the ways in which these modules are applied.

8-1 Introduction to Intelligent I/O

The emergence of *intelligent I/O* was largely a result of ever-increasing performance demands placed on industrial automation control systems and of the continuing desire of PLC users to integrate entire control functions using PLC technology. Control tasks that were typically performed outside the controller, or only partially by the PLC, included closed-loop PID for both batch and continuous processes, as well as high-speed motion, position, and speed control in certain machine control applications. These applications often required extensive programming that increasingly burdened the CPU and consequently degraded overall system response.

In Chapter 3, our discussion of multiple CPUs suggested intelligent I/O as a means of relieving the CPU of complex tasks that require repetitive processing, consume large amounts of memory, increase development time, and complicate troubleshooting. Packaging specific functions in co-processor modules, frees up resources of the CPU and improves performance. Intelligent I/O also offers lower cost solutions that are thoroughly tested and easier to implement. In order to cover a variety of intelligent I/O, this chapter introduces the most common modules and to review their basic functions and common applications.

Definition and Application

Intelligent I/O are coprocessor modules that operate asynchronous to the CPU and are installed in the I/O housing like other I/O modules. An intelligent module normally performs a control function, some form of signal processing, or some other computing or communications task that would usually be done by the CPU in conjunction with standard I/O modules. These modules, which are widely used in both open- and closed-loop control, generally incorporate their own I/O circuits (e.g., digital, analog, serial ports). Figure 8-1 illustrates how intelligent I/O interact with the main CPU.

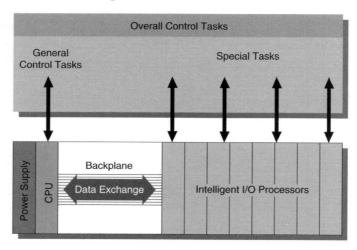

Figure 8-1. Intelligent I/O module interaction with the main CPU

Intelligent Module Classifications

Intelligent I/O modules are generally of two types: 1) those that perform special signal processing functions on analog or digital signals and 2) those that perform a special processing function or application that is usually handled by an onboard microprocessor. This first category of intelligent I/O was discussed in subsections of chapters 6 and 7, *Special Purpose Discrete I/O* and *Special-purpose Analog I/O*, respectively. The *thermocouple input* module is an example of an intelligent analog input module.

The second type of intelligent I/O involve modules that are computers in their own right. They incorporate their own microprocessor and memory and can be programmed to perform operations independent of the CPU. While many of these modules can operate in a stand-alone mode, they all have some form of backplane communication with the CPU that occurs automatically or is initiated via the control program. This communication will either involve direct memory access or a pseudo-direct memory access to the CPU for getting parameter assignments from the CPU or for communicating status or other information. Table 8-1 lists commonly available intelligent I/O modules.

Table 8-1. Typical Intelligent Input/Output Modules

INTELLIGENT MODULE CATEGORY	INTELLIGENT I/O MODULE
Serial & Network Communications	- ASCII Communication Module - Serial Communication Module - Loop Controller Interface Module - Proprietary Network Module - MAP Network Module
Computer Co-Processors	- PC/AT Computer Module - BASIC Language Module - I/O Logic Processor Module
Closed-Loop Process Control	- PID Control Module - Temperature Control Module
Position & Motion Control	- High Speed Counter Module - Encoder Input Modules - Stepper Positioning Module - Servo Positioning Module
Process Specific Modules	- Parison Control Module - Injection Molding Module - Press Controller Module
Artificial Intelligence Modules	- Voice Output Module - Vision Input Module

In the early years of development, modules such as serial communications, BASIC language, PID control, and others were primarily designed to meet general requirements. As the industry advanced, developments in application-specific intelligent I/O was aided by cost/performance improvements in microprocessor technology. These improvements also will allow more complex applications — for example, using voice and vision technology. Other tasks not usually thought of as input/output, but that are handled with intelligent I/O, are data acquisition, communication with host computers and operator interfaces.

8-2 Networking and Serial Communications

Although not usually considered as I/O in the classical sense, communications modules play key roles in the overall PLC control scheme. Generally, two types of communications links can be established between the PLC and other intelligent devices — including other PLCs. The first type of link, a *point-to-point serial link*, is with devices such as message displays, operator workstations, motor drives, bar code readers, computers, or another PLC. The second type of communication, a *Local Area Network* (LAN), supports communication among multiple PLCs and other devices. This section introduces serial and LAN communications modules.

ASCII Input/Output Module

The ASCII module was one of the first intelligent PLC modules. This serial communications module is used to handle bidirectional communications between the PLC and devices that either generate or use ASCII characters to perform their operation. Although the ASCII module can be used for bidirectional data communication, it is generally suited for relatively small data transfers (e.g., text strings, short messages, device command telegrams). Figure 8-2 illustrates applications of the ASCII module.

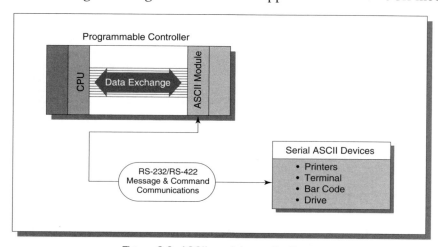

Figure 8-2. ASCII module applications

Typical input from the ASCII module to the PLC is from devices such as bar code readers, weigh scales and other electronic meters, data terminals, and keyboards. Typical output from the PLC via the ASCII module is to message displays, printers, and video terminals in applications involving operator prompting, alarm, and message reporting. Many of these same devices, such as the bar code reader and the servo controller, can also accept parameter setup from the ASCII module.

The ASCII module normally incorporates a microprocessor that handles communication with external devices and with the CPU memory to buffer data transfers, and one or more serial communications ports that use RS232, RS422, or 20 mA current-loop serial interfaces. A feature available in some ASCII modules is the ability to store a large number of messages that may be triggered by the PLC program for output to a message display or printer. Message formats typically include text only, text with embedded numeric values, and text with time and date fields.

Serial Communications Module

Serial communications modules are used to establish point-to-point connections with other intelligent devices for the purpose of data exchange. Such connections are normally established with computers, operator stations, digital drive controllers, process control systems, and other PLCs. While the serial communications module may be used in applications requiring data exchange with more than one other PLC, it is generally more efficient, cost effective and practical to establish a local area network where more than two controllers are involved.

For two devices to communicate, they must do so based on a common protocol. The protocol of the serial module is normally a proprietary protocol that varies with different vendors. A serial module installed in each controller is all that is required for two controllers of the same vendor to establish a point-to-point link. For controllers of different manufacture to communicate over a serial link, each must use its own serial module; however, one must adapt to the other's protocol. For this reason, some vendors offer software-loadable drivers to communicate with serial devices and PLCs of different manufacture.

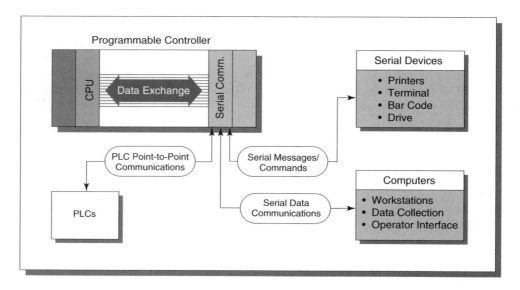

Figure 8-3. Serial communications module applications

The serial communications module handles data exchange with other devices autonomously, over an RS232C, RS422, or RS485 serial interface, at baud rates typically ranging between 110bit/sec and 19.2Kbits/sec. The RS485 interace is used for multipoint connections, such as the drives connection shown in Figure 8-3. The serial module receives data from the PLC and transmits it to the end device; it receives data from the device and sends it to the PLC. Normally, the serial module is able to read from or write to the PLC memory using some form of direct memory access (DMA).

Loop Controller Interface Module

The *loop controller interface* module, also called a *loop management module*, is a serial communications module designed to communicate with a specific model of single-loop controller. Usually the same vendor will have made the single-loop controller although it may have been made by a third party. The loop management module gives the PLC access to process data, alarm status, and operating modes of each loop controller. Such access allows the PLC to act as a supervisory controller over multiple loop controllers that are in turn controlling process variables such as temperature, pressure, or flow.

Features typically found in these modules include the ability to transfer a complete configuration to and from any loop controller, change loop settings (e.g., PID gain parameters, setpoint, operating mode, and alarm limits), as well as acknowledge and reset loop alarms. Commands to perform these functions are invoked from the PLC program. Figure 8-4 illustrates implementation of the loop controller interface module. The loop controllers are normally connected to the module in a multidropped fashion over an RS485 link.

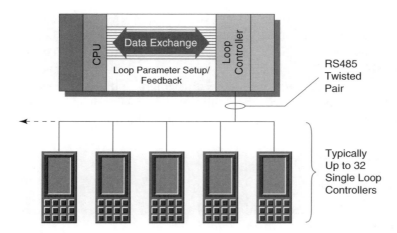

Figure 8-4. Typical configuration of loop controller interface module

Proprietary LAN Module

Most PLC vendors offer one or more proprietary local area networks (LANs) by which their controllers can be linked in a multipoint arrangement to allow data exchange between one controller and any other controller. The term proprietary simply means that the protocols that define the physical parameters of the network, as well as the procedural methods for how data telegrams are packaged and transmitted, are nonpublished or private. This means that products manufactured by the network vendor are likely to be able to exist directly on this network while others are not.

A local area network is normally specified when two or more PLCs need to know what others are doing in order to coordinate control. An example might involve production control PLCs sending product brand information to both the sorter and stacker PLCs in a warehouse. Other applications include connection of multiple PLCs to one or more operator interfaces or to a host computer responsible for supervisory control and data acquisition.

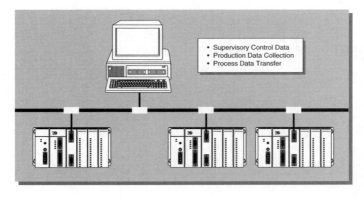

Figure 8-5. Local area network modules allow peer communications among multiple PLCs

As detailed in chapter 10, LANs are characterized by several distinct elements: its *media type*, which is the physical cable type (i.e., fiber, coax, twisted pair); its *topology* or physical arrangement; its *signaling method* or the way that data is driven onto the network cable; its *access method* or the method by which stations gain use of the network; and by its *communications protocols*, which define how messages are assembled and reliably transported from end station to end station. All of these functions are implemented in the network interface module, which is how the PLC is interfaced to the network.

MAP Network Module

Manufacturing Automation Protocol (MAP), is a standard LAN protocol that was intended to address the need in manufacturing operations for a variety of devices to communicate using a single network protocol. Whereas proprietary local area networks were designed to link only PLCs and other products of a single vendor, the MAP network is intended to allow data exchange among a variety of computing devices of different manufacture. This open network architecture supports communication among PLCs, robots, numerical controllers, and any devices adhering to the Manufacturing Automation Protocol.

The MAP network module, when installed, provides connectivity to either an IEEE 802.4 broadband or carrier-band network, conforming to the MAP specification. Since the specification defines two network cable platforms, the module provides two network ports. One port is an IEEE 802.4G interface to an external broadband modem for 10 megabaud transmission; the other is usually driven from an internal modem that supports 5 megabaud carrier-band transmission. Redundant networks are possible simply by using multiple modules.

Contrasted to private protocols of proprietary networks, the MAP protocols are well established open standards. Hence, the physical parameters of the network and the procedural methods for how data telegrams are packaged and transmitted are open standards. This means that products manufactured by different vendors, but conforming to the standards of MAP, will likely function on the network with other conforming devices. An important feature of the MAP network is the layer-7 *manufacturing message specification (MMS)* protocol, a universal command language that makes communication among different devices totally transparent. MAP is introduced in chapter 10.

8-3 Computer Coprocessor Modules

In chapter 3, you learned some of the many cyclical tasks performed by the CPU. These tasks included program processing, I/O processing, communications, and basic housekeeping functions — all of which require time. This section introduces *coprocessors*, the intelligent module group designed to share these tasks. While all intelligent I/O may be called coprocessors, this title truly describes modules that perform tasks that relieve the CPU from certain of its main processing duties. These coprocessors are intended to unburden the CPU of tasks that could be placed outside of its control and at the same time increase performance, program maintainability, and reliability by distributing the computing tasks.

BASIC Language Module

The BASIC module was designed to run user-written programs independent of the CPU. Its main purpose was to provide users with more programming flexibility by augmenting the traditional PLC programming software. The BASIC language offers the ability to perform complex math and algorithms, as well as other data manipulation tasks that are difficult and cumbersome using ladder logic. BASIC modules are particularly useful for formatting and outputting reports and messages to printers, operator terminals and message displays. The BASIC module also simplifies communication with devices such as bar code readers, computers, interactive operator workstations, and modems.

The functions of the BASIC and ASCII modules are typically combined to form a single module, normally called an ASCII/BASIC module. This module contains its own microprocessor, onboard memory for storage of user-developed programs, and serial I/O ports (e.g., RS422, RS232-C, RS485) for connections to peripheral devices. In addition to the normal BASIC instructions, the language includes instructions that allow data transfer between the CPU and the BASIC module over the PLC backplane.

BASIC modules are not all the same. Features to be taken into account when considering a BASIC module are ease of programming, such as added instructions for control, timers, counters, real-time clocks and interrupts to the CPU. Data transfer between the module and the CPU may require programming, but it is easier if key word instructions are available. Some PLCs even perform automatic transfers that occur every scan. Some BASIC modules interpret each instruction while others compile the instructions. Compiled program execution is normally many times faster than interpreted execution.

PC/AT Processor Module

The AT coprocessor module is usually a 80386 or 80486 based computer in the form of a standard PLC I/O module. Like other PLC modules, the AT module is industrially hardened. It is designed to minimize the effects of electronic noise and is tested for electromagnetic and radio frequency interference, as well as for thermal sensitivity, humidity, shock absorbency, and vibration. The AT module incorporates fixed disk and diskette drives, as well as I/O ports for a keyboard, serial and parallel devices and for EGA/VGA video monitor connections.

Placing the AT module on the PLC backplane was a major advancement for the PLC, addressing the need to integrate high-performance computing capability and mass data storage with the real-time control of the PLC. The AT module opens the door for more compact systems, as generic man-machine interface software can now be loaded onto the module. A separate desktop computer is no longer needed. Similarly, third-party operator control and data acquisition software packages have direct access to the PLC's memory at backplane data rates, thereby eliminating the bottlenecks of serial communications. Figure 8-6, illustrates typical applications of the AT module.

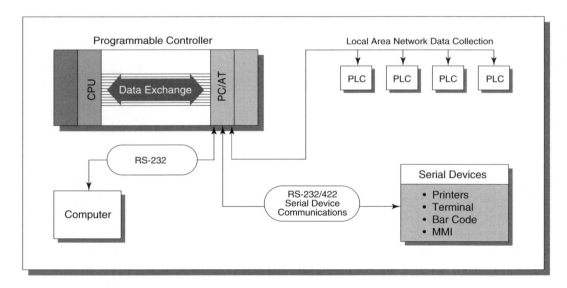

Figure 8-6. Functional block diagram of PC/AT coprocessor module applications

I/O Logic Processor Module

The *I/O logic processor* was designed for high-speed monitoring, logic processing, and control of digital I/O signals independent of the main CPU. Application of this module is intended for those machines and processes that require a constant as well as a guaranteed response time to critical process events. This makes the module highly suitable in high-speed applications such as event tracking, canning, bottling, and material sorting operations.

A key feature of the I/O logic processor module is its programmability. In fact, it is a PLC within the PLC. It has its own memory and program instruction set that consists of basic relay-logic, timing, and counting operations. With these instructions, the control logic for processing high-speed requirements may be completely independent of the main CPU and can continue to operate even if the CPU is halted. The main CPU treats the I/O logic processor like normal I/O; hence, no programming is required to exchange status and diagnostic information between the two.

Input/Output hardware configurations may differ for I/O logic processors depending on the model or controller brand. Typically, the module will support some fixed number of digital inputs and outputs that are either integral to the module (e.g., eight-inputs, four-outputs) or that are external. When the I/O are external to the module, they are usually connected to the logic processor module by a local I/O bus extender connector that allows a fixed number of discrete I/O modules to be accessed.

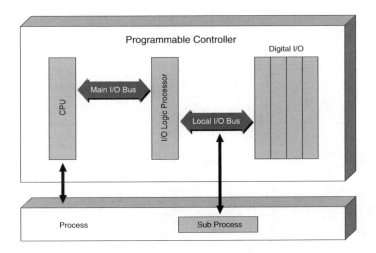

Figure 8-7. Illustration of intelligent I/O logic processor module

183

8-4 Closed-loop Control Modules

Intelligent I/O modules that perform closed-loop control algorithms [i.e., *proportional, integral, derivative (PID)*] are often used for maintaining a desired setpoint for temperatures, flow rates, pressures and tank levels. This function was generally not possible in early PLCs, which were basically logic processors with limited math capabilities. Even CPUs in the mid-eighties, with their faster scan times, would have been bogged down by having to process algorithms for several process loops. Closed-loop modules unburden the CPU scan from having to process loops that require continuous and sometimes fast updates. PID modules allow PLCs to handle control and process parameters for batch and continuous operations.

General Purpose PID Module

This intelligent module is used in those applications where closed-loop analog control based on the *proportional-integral-derivative (PID)* algorithm is required. The basic function of this module is to provide the control action required to maintain a process variable such as temperature, flow, level, or speed at or within set limits of a specified setpoint (see Fig. 8-8). The module monitors the process variable, compares it to the desired setpoint, and calculates the required analog output based on the setting of process parameters. The PID module may be applied to practically any process requiring closed-loop control involving an analog input and an analog output.

In a given process, the process variable in question will normally deviate from the desired setpoint as changes occur within the process (e.g., material changes, load changes, interaction with other process). The closed-loop controller minimizes this deviation. In a PID loop, the analog input normally measures the actual process parameter in question — for example, the temperature inside a steam vessel. This is referred to as the *process variable (PV)*. The analog output signal is called the *manipulated variable(MV)* or the *controlled variable (CV)*; it is being controlled based on the output of the PID calculation. The output corrects the error between the setpoint and the process variable.

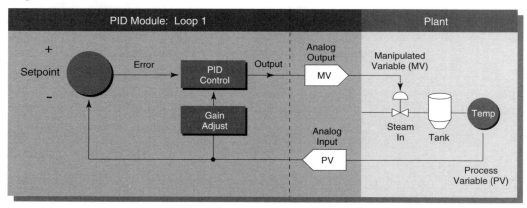

Figure 8-8. Block diagram of PID module

Most PID modules support between four and eight loops. An important specification of the module is the time required to process all of the loops. Like most intelligent I/O, the PID module requires configuration data to perform its control functions. In this case, the data is that which is required for each control loop — items such as loop setpoints, sampling time, upper and lower setpoint limits, alarm limits, and the PID tuning parameters. The configuration data, which is supplied to the module, is either programmed directly into the PID module or may be transferred from the PLC.

Temperature Control Module

The *temperature control module (TCM)* maintains temperature setpoints for several temperature zones, by applying the PID algorithm. Such a module will normally handle eight to sixteen temperature loops that may be configured for two-position (HEAT/OFF), or three-position control (HEAT/OFF/COOL). Normally, the temperature controller receives its setup parameters from the CPU; however, it can continue to run with its last setup values if the CPU fails or is stopped. A typical application of this module is to control the melt, mold, and hydraulic-fluid temperatures in a plastic injection molding machine.

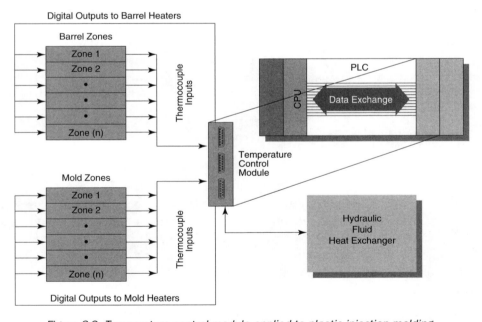

Figure 8-9. Temperature control module applied to plastic injection molding

In operation, the TCM may send the status of all or selected loops to the PLC continually or on demand. This status includes items such as loop variables and alarms. The module is also able to receive new loop setup parameters on each PLC scan. This allows immediate change of setpoints and alarm limits, as well as the gain parameters for any loop. Each loop also has a control word, whose bits allow various operational modes to be selected (e.g., auto/manual, cascade). An associated alarm word reports conditions such as "setpoint too high" and "setpoint too low." The TCM also reports open thermocouples. Some modules even allow a loop to be configured to use an alternate thermocouple input if the primary one fails. Table 8-2 lists features typical of the this module.

Table 8-2. Temperature Control Input Module Features

TYPICAL MODULE FEATURES	PURPOSE
Thermocouple/RTD Inputs	- Allow thermocouple or RTD temperature sensors
Discrete Outputs	- Drive discrete output to HEAT/COOL control zones
2-Position/3-Position Control	- Allows HEAT-OFF & HEAT-OFF-COOL control
Alternate Thermocouple Input	- Allows automatic switchover to alternate T/C
Primary/Standby Setpoint	- Allows reduced setpoint for standby or nighttime
Cascade Control	- Allows output of one loop to be cascaded with another
Automatic Self-Tuning	- Automatic determination of optimum loop settings

8-5 Position and Motion Control

The intelligent modules in this category deal with applications involving high-speed counting requirements, position decoding, and open- and closed-loop control of axis positioning involving linear and rotary motion. In this category, many modules have been developed for position detection using incremental and absolute encoders and positioning with stepper motors, as well as with fixed- and variable-speed drive systems. Intelligent position and motion control modules permit PLCs to control stepper and servo motors involving electro-mechanical, and hydraulic drive systems.

High-speed Counter Module

Often, real-world signals change much more rapidly than what can be read by standard discrete inputs and processed by software counters. The CPU scan is the main limiting factor since many pulses may be missed while the program is being processed. A typical example might involve a high-speed canning operation, where individual cans travel past a proximity sensor such that the sensor sees gaps between cans as a 1 ms pulse.

This duration is far shorter than a typical CPU scan time. Applications that require pulse counting at rates greater than 100/sec, generally need a high-speed counter module.

High-speed counter modules usually provide multiple input channels to accept a variety of inputs in a 5-30 volts range and discrete outputs for high-speed switching. Most modules accept pulse rates in the range of 25KHz to 500KHz; however, some support pulse rates in the megahertz range. The wide count range of the onboard counters also means that cascading of counters is generally not required. The high-speed counter also incorporates several software counter presets that can be used in conjunction with its discrete outputs to allow high-speed switching and emulation of electronic cams and programmable limit switches.

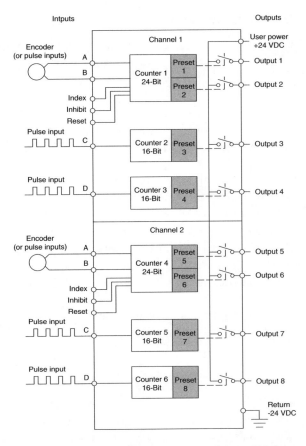

Figure 8-10. Functional diagram of typical high speed counter module

High-speed counter modules are offered with a varying range of capabilities. On the least sophisticated end, the module will provide up or down counting and a digital output for each counter to signal when it reaches its preset. So-called *encoder/counter modules* combine the counter functions with position encoding by allowing quadrature type inputs from incremental encoders. In this case, *home position* and *marker pulse* inputs are added to the normal *count enable, count reset,* and *count direction* inputs. On the more sophisticated end, these modules can be configured for many counting and measurement applications, (e.g., material length, period measurement, or RPM). Some of these features are listed below.

❑ Internal/External Gating and Resetting
❑ Apply Scalar Values to Counters
❑ UP/Down BCD or Binary Counting
❑ Count Leading or Trailing Edge of Pulses
❑ Interrupt CPU on Reaching Preset Count
❑ Counting of Module-generated Clock Pulses

Encoder Input Modules

An encoder is a device that measures position change by counting. Encoders are essential in systems where position must be tracked or where feedback is required to move a tool, workpiece, or product to a destination along an axis. Generally, encoders are classified as an *incremental encoders* or a *absolute encoders*, which define the measuring principle used. Intelligent modules have been developed to accept input from both incremental and absolute encoders. A brief introduction of the operation of these encoders will help you understand encoder input modules.

The incremental measuring method is based on a count taken whenever the tracked element travels in either a forward or reverse direction away from a known *home position*. Operation of the incremental encoder is based on an optical scanning of lines that form vertical tracks on a rotary disc. The evenly spaced tracks form alternating light-reflecting lines and light-transmitting gaps that form the measuring increment of the encoder. This increment, which represents degrees of angular rotation, defines the resolution of the encoder. Computation of the encoder resolution is shown below.

> **Example:**   An incremental encoder has 250 lines per 360 degrees.

> **Solution:** $1 \text{ increment} = \dfrac{360°}{250} = 1.44° = \text{resolution}$

As shaft rotation occurs, the line scanning of the encoder causes output of two pulse trains that are always 90 degrees out of phase. These two pulse trains, called quadrature signals (*quad A, quad B*), provide dual-channel input to the encoder input module. The encoder counter counts forward if the leading edge of quad A occurs before that of quad B. If the reverse occurs, then the encoder counts backwards indicating reverse rotation. Since the pulses are generated as the encoder reads the lines, they actually represent degrees of angular rotation. This angular rotation is used in conjunction with the mechanical gearing ratio to evaluate distance moved from the home position.

As shown in figure 8-11, forward or reverse direction is determined by whichever quad pulse is leading. A *marker* on the disc indicates a complete rotation. The encoder outputs a digital signal at each passing of the marker, which is input to the incremental encoder module for resetting the counter.

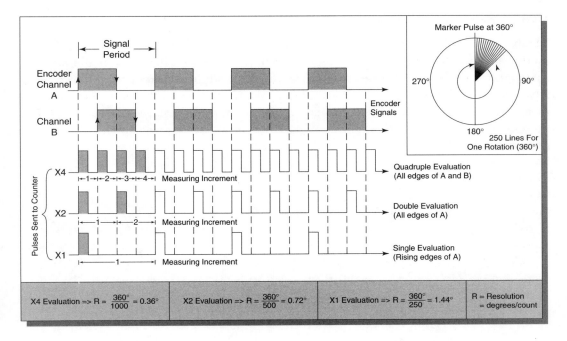

Figure 8-11. Encoder input signals and changing the input pulse resolution

Figure 8-11, illustrates how the resolution of a quadrature encoder can be improved by allowing the encoder to count the leading and trailing edge of the quad-A pulse. This technique doubles the number of pulses counted for one rotation of the encoder. The resolution can be improved still further by letting the module count both the leading and trailing edges of both quad A and quad B. This latter approach results in four times the number of pulses counted for the same degree of rotation.

Absolute encoders are similar to the incremental type, but the encoding process uses several parallel discs that enable them to produce a unique combinations of light-encoded patterns that each represent a different angular increment. The ability to generate unique position patterns for each angular increment means that the position of the axis is immediately available as an absolute value whenever the encoder is activated. Compared to incremental encoders, absolute encoders offer the advantage of knowing the axis position at all times — at startup or even after a power loss. Output from this type of encoder is usually a BCD or Gray code value that is transferred to the I/O module on parallel data lines (usually 12 to 24 bits). Since absolute encoders output parallel data and incremental encoders output a pulse, a separate module is usually required for the respective encoder types.

Stepper-positioning Module

The basic design of the stepper motor is such that a single electrical pulse causes the motor shaft to advance by one increment. This increment, which is called a *step*, is based purely on each motor design and is a distinct and known fraction of a complete rotation of the motor. A given motor, for instance, may make 1,000 steps in each complete rotation. It would therefore make a complete rotation if it were to receive 1000 pulses. In the illustration shown in Figure 8-12, the screw pitch in the slide table causes the table to move one inch with each shaft rotation. Our stepper motor therefore would move the table 10 inches upon receiving 10,000 pulses.

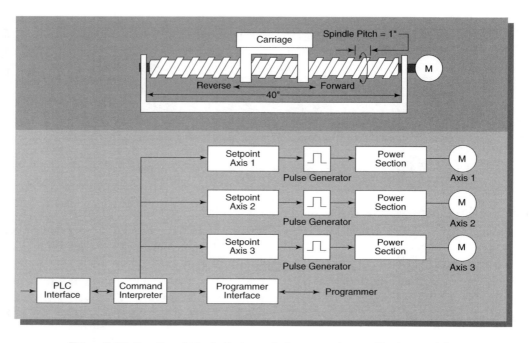

Figure 8-12. Functional block diagram of stepper motor positioning module

The stepper positioning module, which usually allows connection of one or more motors, provides open-loop control of stepper drive systems. Principal operation of the module involves outputting a stream of pulses that are received by the translator section of a stepper motor. The number of pulses output to the motor determines the rotation of the motor and, consequently, how far the axis will travel. The pulse frequency determines how fast the motor should turn (its velocity). Automatic control of stepper-controlled axes, using the stepper motor module, is based on user-programmed *move profiles* designed to achieve different target positions.

To control the stepper axes independent of the CPU, the stepper module usually requires that it be programmed with move profiles and with machine data. Machine data are the essential electrical and mechanical characteristics of the stepper motor and of the drive system. For example, the *step value* allows the module to automatically convert move requests to the correct number of motor pulses. How far the axis moves on one rotation is also considered machine data. So-called move profiles, or *traversing programs*, are canned sequences of move commands to the module. When the module is commanded to move the axis a distance, it uses the preconfigured data to calculate the required number of pulses and then sends those pulses to the motor. Stepper-controlled axes usually may be positioned simultaneously or independently.

A flexible stepper module should allow programming of multiple move profiles that define velocities, target positions, and dwell times for each move. Some systems allow as many as 255 profiles that may be triggered manually from a programming device or automatically by the control program. To allow independent operation, these traversing programs are usually stored on the module although some systems allow the data to be stored in the CPU and transferred to the module. Move profiles should also be independent of an axis to allow the same motion programs to be used by different axes.

In operation, the stepper module generates a symmetrical traversing profile as shown in Figure 8-13. The move consists of an acceleration ramp, a constant velocity range, and a deceleration ramp. A limit-switch digital input to the module allows the travel limits to be monitored. This type of input, which causes motion to be stopped if the travel limits are exceeded, is normally placed such that when the permissible limits are detected, a calculated deceleration is still possible. The module also normally has an emergency stop input to cause immediate interruption of the axis motion.

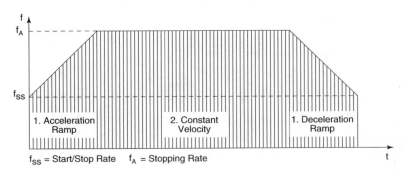

Figure 8-13. Typical traversing profile of a stepper motor control module

Servo-positioning Module

The servo-positioning module provides rapid closed-loop axis positioning of drive control systems involving variable speed AC or DC electric drives or, in some cases, hydraulic drive systems. Servo positioning differs from the previously discussed stepper positioning in that the control loop is closed by providing encoder feedback for actual position of the axis and velocity feedback for the actual speed of the motor. Servo drive control is typical of the application areas listed below.

- ❏ Transfer and Assembly Lines
- ❏ Material Handling and Transport
- ❏ Machine Tool Setting
- ❏ Woodworking Machines
- ❏ Carriage Control
- ❏ Precision Parts Placement
- ❏ Automatic Component Insertion

Servo positioning allows programmed motions that bring a tool or workpiece precisely to the right place at the right speed and at the right time. Figure 8-14, illustrates closed-loop control using a servo-positioning module. The total system consists of mechanical components used in moving the tool or workpiece into place, a positioning drive system, speed and position feedback sensor and position control. Position control

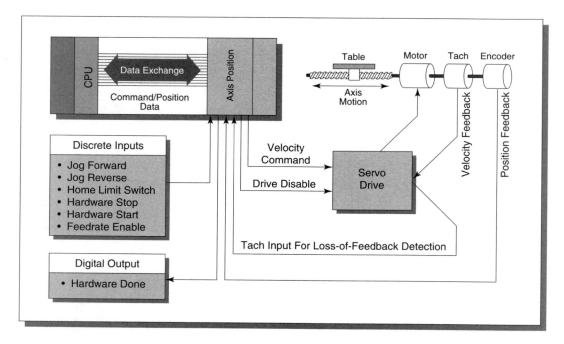

Figure 8-14. Single axis closed loop servo system, using a servo control module

is provided by the servo module.In the servo-position control loop, there is a continuous comparison of the current position setpoint calculated by the module and the actual position of the drive as reported by the position sensor. Depending on the module, position feedback may be provided by an incremental or absolute encoder. Based on the difference between the position setpoint and the actual position, the module calculates the required speed reference to send to the drive. The output to the drive is a bipolar 10V analog signal that determines the drive speed and direction.

Operation and implementation of the servo-positioning module is quite similar to the stepper positioning module. It involves programming the desired move profiles, as well as specifying machine data to adapt the module's control algorithm to the mechanical and electrical characteristics of the servo motor and drive system. In operation, the module translates the positioning commands it receives from the CPU or from stored move profiles into a position versus time profile. It also determines the current position of the axis based on feedback from the encoder and compares it with the position commanded by the profile. This process results in a bipolar 10V analog signal, which is a velocity command output to the drive to move the axis accordingly.

Table 8-3. Typical features of Servo-positioning Modules

TYPICAL FEATURES	FUNCTIONS/BENEFITS
Absolute/Incremental Position Commands	- Allows programming flexibility
Programmable Acceleration/Deceleration	- Optimize machine cycle over varying loads
Programmable In-Position Tolerance Bands	- Allows flexibility in positioning accuracy
Programmable Dwell Times	- Ensures precise and repeatable dwell times
Programmable Jog Rates	- Allows flexible manual positioning
Excess Following-Error Detection	- Automatic drive shutoff if error is exceeded
Loss of Feedback Detection	- Auto-shutoff if speed/position feedback is lost
Software Travel Limits	- Guards against axis over travel
Backlash Take-up	- Compensates for mechanical backlash in axis
Tool-Offset Compensation	- Compensates for tool wear when positioning
On-the-fly Motion Profile Alterations	- Allows modification of profile during execution

8-7 Process-specific Modules

Process-specific modules are intelligent modules that totally or partially perform a specific control function or application. This area of development was a natural place for PLC expansion since in most industries there are many machines that are built by different vendors but have very close, if not the same, functionality. In other words, the same I/O signals are required, similar computations are performed, and similar operations and sequencing takes place. Before these modules were introduced, the functions they performed were often not performed by the PLC, but instead by dedicated or custom computers and software. These control functions typically involved high-speed repetition, precise measurement and control, and complex numerical algorithms.

Parison Control Module

In blow molding, plastic is drawn or dropped, thereby forming a hollow tube of molten plastic, referred to as a *parison*. Controlling the wall thickness of the parison within various zones along its length is known as *profiling*. The record of data to achieve the desired end product is the *parison profile*. Parison control accurately performed allows blow molded parts of irregular shapes to be produced with uniform wall thickness and superior characteristics while using fewer materials.

The basic job of the parison module is to control the wall thickness of a parison by controlling the position of the die head in the injection nozzle. Each parison being controlled is referred to as a profile. The goal is to control the wall thickness within various zones of the profile. Thus, a table of values corresponding to wall thickness is how the desired thickness is determined. Each data point in the table corresponds to the desired wall thickness in a zone along the parison. These values, which are stored on the module, are passed to a closed-loop controller as setpoints. Product weight is controlled by adding an offset to each table value before passing it to the loop controller.

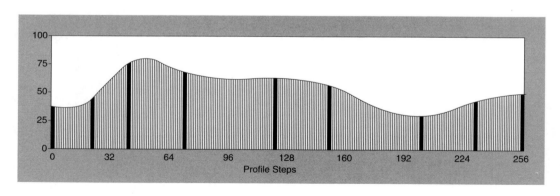

Figure 8-15. Typical 256 step parison profile with curvilinear interpolation

194

The parison module is normally designed to control some number of parisons in one of two selectable modes — time-based mode, which is used in continuous extrusion machines, and position-based operation, used in accumulator and reciprocating screw type machines. In time-based mode, each of the setpoints in the parison profile data is fed to the die head position-controller using a time-base generator as the transition criterion for stepping from one value to the next in the table. In position-based mode, the transition criteria is based on the injection ram position. Figure 8-16, illustrates a typical configuration showing the parison module's I/O points.

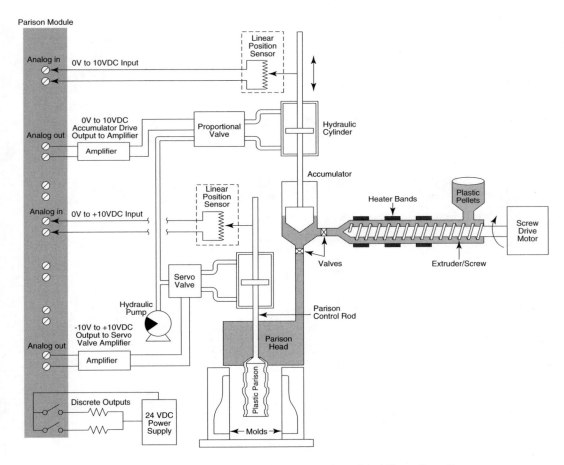

Figure 8-16. Block diagram of parison control module I/O configuration

Injection Molding Module

The *injection molding module* is another example of a process-specific module, designed for the plastic industry. This module uses it own microprocessor, onboard analog, and digital I/O and firmware to provide independent closed-loop control of a plastic injection molding machine. Such a package offers a simpler and more compact system, by preconfiguring the more difficult aspects of injection molding on a single module while still retaining the flexibility of the PLC.

Operation of the injection molding module is based on a fixed algorithm that executes a profile of (n) number of steps for each of the machine's five major functions. These functions are illustrated in Figure 8-17. The actual profile values are taken from recipes stored in the PLC's memory and are transferred to the controlling algorithm of the injection molding module. The PLC also communicates with the module to provide control coordination, start/stop instructions, and to receive status feedback. To accommodate different machine hydraulic arrangements, the module has several switch selectable operational configurations. A typical machine configuration, with I/O connections to the injection molding module, is shown in Figure 8-18.

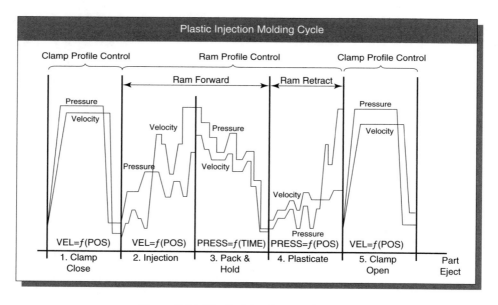

Figure 8-17. Plastic injection molding cycle

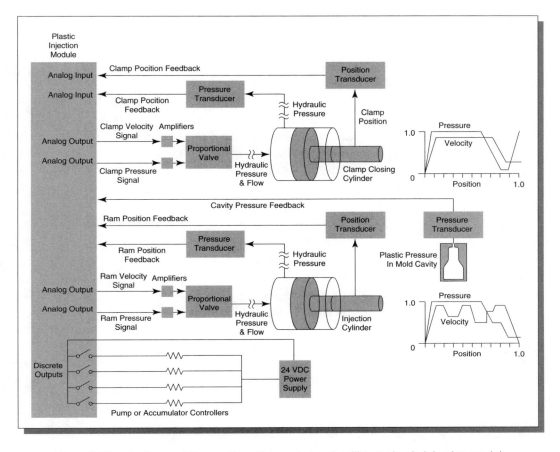

Figure 8-18. Injection molding configuration, using an intelligent plastic injection module

Press Controller Module

The *press controller module*, also called the *clutch/brake module*, provides the prepro-grammed intelligence for controlling mechanical power presses that utilize part revolu-tion clutches. This type of press is generally found in automotive and other metal forming applications. The module contains a standard algorithm for safely and consis-tently directing the operations of mechanical presses. In addition to providing the con-trol logic for the press, the module's algorithm checks for hundreds of possible fault conditions that provide safety levels required by OSHA and ANSI standards.

The complete control system for the mechanical power press is formed by combining the intelligence of the press control module with appropriate discrete I/O modules. Discrete inputs include operator controls, as well as feedback switches from the press. Discrete outputs include solenoid valves, diagnostic indicators, and other press controls. In operation, the press control module continually monitors press inputs for agreement with what predetermined status should be at given steps of the operation. Press motion is prevented or stopped if disagreement is detected before or during operation.

8-6 Artificial Intelligence (AI) Modules

As various areas of artificial intelligence research continue, many of its practical uses will likely be employed in industrial applications. Just as vision and voice techniques were two of the first AI techniques applied to general purpose computing devices, they were also the first applied to PLCs. These were introduced in the vision input module and the voice output module. Although not covered in this discussion, another likely candidate for an intelligent module utilizing AI techniques might be a voice input or voice recognition module. Such a module would allow operators to give spoken commands to initiate certain process events and to query the machine or process machine regarding its operational mode or status.

Voice Output Module

This module outputs synthesized speech that is used for message annunciation. Voice output from the module is based on a stored vocabulary. Each vocabulary word has a corresponding numeric value that, when received by the module, causes the word to be output. Typical applications for the speech module include alarm annunciation, operator instruction, and any situation where an audible message is required to reinforce or substitute for a visual indication. As shown in Figure 8-19, the module normally allows direct speaker or headphone connection, or the line output may be connected to an audio amplifier to provide greater drive capacity.

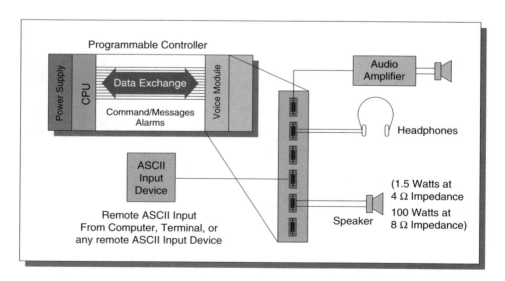

Figure 8-19. Voice module applications

In operation, the speech module acts similarly to a printer, which is also driven by ASCII characters. The module has a serial ASCII port through which it can receive serial transmissions from a computer, another PLC, or any device that can output an ASCII string. Backplane communication with the CPU is also possible. By sending the corresponding ASCII codes, the module can output a single word or a connected series of words forming a message. In addition to the stored vocabulary, the module will usually have suffixes, different tones, and time delays that can be applied to words or phrases.

Vision Input Module

With the increased demand for products of quality, the use of automated inspection involving machine vision techniques has become an important part of manufacturing, even a requirement in others. The vision input module was introduced to address a broad variety of inspection, measurement, and control applications based on machine vision technology. The principal function of the vision module is to perform visual measurements and inspections of parts as they are being manufactured and to make decisions based on results of its image analysis. Decisions can be made independent of or in conjunction with criteria set in the PLC. Typical applications of the vision module are listed below.

- ❑ Dimensional Gauging
- ❑ Hole Detection and Inspection
- ❑ Linear Measurement
- ❑ Assembly Verification
- ❑ Product Flaw Detection
- ❑ Packaging Defect Detection
- ❑ Position Analysis
- ❑ Product Sorting

The vision input module uses machine vision technology to achieve its results. Simply stated, machine vision inspection involves the use of a computer to analyze an image obtained from a video camera. Normally, the module allows anywhere between one and four camera inputs. Once an image is obtained, it is compared with predefined parameters and the results are communicated to the PLC or to an external computer or other device. Output from the vision module may be as simple as a digital output, indicating pass/fail or numeric analyses and measurement data that can be transmitted via its RS232 serial port. A video monitor output also allows the module to display preprogrammed responses based on results of the image analysis.

9 PROGRAMMING AND DOCUMENTATION SYSTEMS

Alternative Programming Systems

Programming System Features and Functions

PLC Documentation Systems

When considering a development tool for PLC systems, one can no longer think simply of providing a programming device. Instead, a complete design and development environment utilizing a systems approach must be considered. An environment that facilitates efficient and accurate program development, documentation, installation, and maintenance will drastically reduce cost and time associated with the development and commissioning cycle. It will also provide an environment for establishing design standards that can be used over and over. Such a system will surely enhance the tasks of providing fast and systematic installations and troubleshooting.

9-1 Alternative Programming Systems

Programming systems allow you to create, modify, and load control programs and data into the PLC. These systems also provide facilities for monitoring operations and troubleshooting malfunctions once the system is installed. Having the right programming equipment and an efficient programming environment is important, since this is the main means by which you will interact with the PLC processor and ultimately the controlled system. Alternative programming systems typically include the following:

❑   Handheld Programming Terminals
❑   Personal Computer Systems
❑   Operator Access Devices

The advancements in programming systems have made it possible for users to select from a variety of programming methods, as well as more sophisticated and easy-to-use systems. In addition to being able to choose between various alternatives, the compatibility of systems makes it possible to select a practical combination of these tools. Finally, with the personal computer being the primary platform for PLC programming, in addition to having access to software developed by PLC vendors, third- party companies offer an array of programming systems that support many brands of PLC hardware.

Handheld Programming Terminals

The *handheld programming terminal*, also referred to as a *miniprogrammer*, is a small, low-cost programming tool designed primarily to support low-end PLCs. Some, however, are compatible with larger PLC family members. As seen in Figure 9-1, the miniprogrammer resembles a handheld calculator, but has a larger display and specialized instruction keys. The displays are typically LCD or LED type with two to eight display lines. While in most cases, miniprogrammers are separate devices, some are detachable units, affixed to the controller's CPU (typical of "brick" style PLCs).

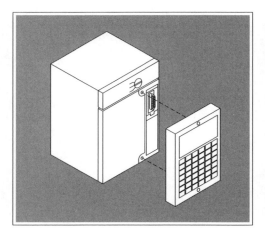

Figure 9-1. Detachable handheld device b) Standard handheld device

The miniprogrammer serves as a means for inputting, monitoring, and editing the control program. In some cases, these units only allow basic instructions (e.g., relay logic, timer/counter) to be programmed. Often, input may only be allowed in Boolean mnemonics or ladder logic. Most miniprogrammers are also restricted to on-line programming operations in which they must be connected to the controller's CPU. These limitations of the handheld device actually reflect design intentions — it is suited more to entry of small programs and perhaps for minor modification of larger programs.

Finally, so-called *intelligent handheld terminals* are designed to support an entire family of PLCs. These smart devices typically incorporate the full-programming capabilities of their industrial terminal and PC counterparts. This, of course, does not include documentation capabilities. A series of prompts and menus combined with soft function keys guide users through the high-level programming functions. These intelligent devices also perform PLC auxiliary functions such as diagnostics, PLC status control, and I/O forcing. They may also serve as operator interface devices that can display messages concerning the controlled machine or process.

Personal Computer Systems

Introduction of personal computer- (PC) based programming systems, like the one shown in Figure 9-2, was a welcome relief for PLC users after many years of using *industrial loader terminals* — the predecessor or the PC programming system. Use of these dedicated proprietary CRT programmers was considered too inflexible and expensive. Most users felt that once an initial program was developed, tested, and installed, further requirements or uses (e.g., minor program changes or troubleshooting) of the industrial loader programmers was too limited to justify its purchase.

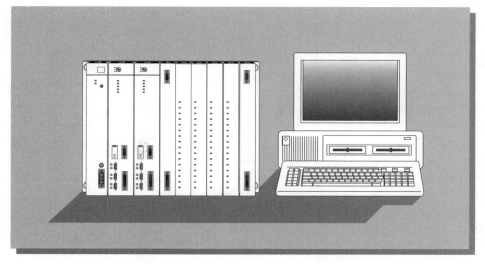

Figure 9-2. PC-based program development system

Most PLC vendors offer PC-based programming software that runs on AT-compatible desktop, portable, and laptop machines. Many third-party software developers also offer PC-based programming systems for the major PLC brands. For the most part, these systems operate under an MS-DOS or Windows environment; however, systems that support other hardware platforms and operating systems are offered. These options allow users to create the development and operating environment that best suit their needs and that support a variety of other manufacturing or business applications.

Typical capabilities of the programming software include on-line and off-line program editing, program storage, on-line program monitoring, basic documentation facilities, and software utilities for diagnosing malfunctions in the PLC and the controlled system. Most packages also offered an optional board that allows PC to be connected as a station on the vendor's local area network (LAN). This ability allows access to any PLC on the network from a central location to monitor or edit programs, and in some cases to upload or download programs over the network.

The use of PC-based programming systems offers many advantages to both users and vendors. A nondedicated system allows a standard device to program a variety of PLC brands. Users will also benefit from more frequent software upgrades and enhancements. Both users and vendors can take advantage of a variety of software packages, such as statistical analysis, documentation, database management, spreadsheets, and operator interface systems, developed by third-party companies. PC-based programming systems also allow vendors to easily adapt programming packages for new intelligent modules, as well as for supporting new programming languages and the development of diagnostic and documentation utilities.

Operator Access Devices

The *operator access device*, sometimes referred to as a timer-counter access monitor (TCAM), is a PLC data entry and display device. This device is an economical and less complicated device for allowing the operator to monitor various program statuses and for making parameter changes. Typically, these are handheld or panel mount devices with a small LCD display and a sealed membrane keypad with alphanumeric and function keys.

Common capabilities of these devices include displaying I/O status, display- entry- and modification of word values, I/O forcing, and display of PLC diagnostic information. Often there are various levels of security with restrictions such as monitoring only, data entry for a specific group of words only, or complete access. More sophisticated devices are also available that provide features such as error/alarm message reporting, timed operator prompting, process display pages with setpoint and actual value displays.

Figure 9-3. Operator access device

9-2 Programming System Features and Functions

A most important feature in programming system software is that of a "systems approach" to PLC system development. A systems approach is one that provides a complete environment with engineering tools for program development, documentation, installation, maintenance, and diagnostics. The system should offer alternative programming languages and methods, portability of software components, allowance for development by several individuals, and appropriate security measures, as well as development tools that will allow for the establishment of standards for program development, documentation, installation, and maintenance of the complete programmable controller system. Several features that should be available in the PLC programming environment are listed in Table 9-1 and are described in the following discussions.

A Common User Interface

The first feature to look for in a programming system is a common appearance and functionality of the software, regardless of the controller within a specific PLC family. These systems are implemented using either icon-based objects or menu-driven operations. Menu-driven means that each operation to be performed is simply selected from a list of choices, typically using pop-up displays and/or windows. Specific function keys, also known as "hot keys", that are tied to specific commands throughout the programming software, also simplify program navigation. Common operations and key strokes minimize retraining and software development time.

Comprehensive help screens should also be a part of the common user interface to the PLC. Help screens are like a user software manual stored in memory. When proceeding through some operation, such as entering a drum sequencer, pressing the "help"

Table 9-1. Typical Programming System Features

- ❏ Typical Programming System Features
- ❏ A common user interface
- ❏ Off-line program editing and storage
- ❏ On-line program create, edit, and monitor
- ❏ On-line/off-line documentation development/display
- ❏ Symbols address editor
- ❏ Upload/download routines
- ❏ Symbolic programming
- ❏ Local area networking
- ❏ Software configuration templates
- ❏ Configurable status displays
- ❏ Program archiving/merging
- ❏ Print operations to serial or parallel printers
- ❏ Program development/documentation in different languages

function key at any point of uncertainty will pull up a help screen that literally guides you through to completing the operation. A so-called *context-sensitive* help system provides assistance on a particular subject based on the specific point in the programming software in which help is needed.

Off-line Programming and Storage

The *off-line programming* capability is a feature supported by industrial loaders and personal computer programming systems. This feature allows development and modification of programs without having to be connected to the PLC processor. Off-line programming systems store programs on a floppy disk, hard disk, or cassette tape. Programs can therefore be developed at one's desk in a more productive and less distracting environment. After the program is developed, it is stored on diskette or loaded to an EPROM or other nonvolatile memory. The program can then be carried to the installation site and downloaded to the controller.

On-line Programming and Monitoring

On-line programming and monitoring involves the ability to create, modify and monitor program sequences and data while the PLC processor is on-line and in the RUN mode. This mode of programming requires that the programming system be connected to the PLC processor. The ability to make on-line program changes originally resulted from user demand and was implemented such that any change would be immediately executed on the next processor scan. This procedure was potentially unsafe, although it enabled users to make needed changes without interrupting the process. An enhanced on-line programming feature available in some programming systems allows on-line changes to be made and tested for correct operation before taking effect on machine operation. (See *Configurable Status Displays.*)

On-line/Off-line Documentation

This feature allows programs to be developed with written comments on program sequences, instructions, memory, and I/O addresses. It also allows the use of symbol names on memory and I/O addresses. Symbolic addresses are user designated names that can be substituted for the absolute addresses assigned to memory and I/O devices. Symbols, or labels as they're called, make referencing the connected devices easier, thereby making programming and troubleshooting faster and easier. In original PLC documentation, many systems could only display the program in documented form while in the off-line mode. Enhanced versions, however, allow complete on-line and off-line display and modification of documentation.

In addition to program documentation, documentation software should allow generation of several standard reports regarding the PLC configuration, operational status, and memory and I/O usage. Typical reports are listed in Table 9-2. Cross-reference reports provide information regarding each occurrence of a particular program element (i.e., I/O address, memory address, timer contacts, etc.) within the entire program. A cross-referenced ladder program listing, for instance, would give a ladder printout showing the contacts of each output coil and all inputs of the program.

Table 9-2. Typical PLC Programming System Documentation Features

❏ Documented program printout
❏ Program title and version information
❏ Comments on each program rung or statement
❏ Symbolic (synonym) addressing
❏ Symbolic address editor
❏ Descriptor on each program element
❏ Free formatted text description
❏ Forced I/O table
❏ CPU Memory and I/O configuration
❏ Timer/Counter/Internal Coil usage report
❏ I/O address usage/cross reference report
❏ Data table usage/cross reference report

Symbols Address Editor

A symbol address editor is a development tool that allows the symbolic names for each memory and I/O address to be entered in table form. Such an editor allows entry of each absolute address along with its symbolic label, and comments to describe the use of the element. Figure 9-4 shows the typical form in which symbol tables are created.

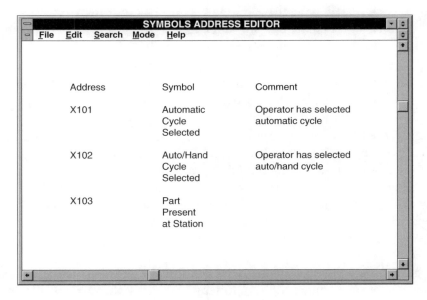

Figure 9-4. Symbolic address (or address labeling) editor

The advantage of this editor is that it allows all of the addresses to be defined, labeled, and commented on prior to any program development. The table can then be used as a programming reference aid. With the table already created, the easy-to-recall labels can be used during program development as opposed to labeling the elements during program creation. Normal symbol table editing features should include things such as copy, cut and paste lines or blocks, as well as inserting blocks from other stored program files. With the ability to import/export the symbol table to standard databases, as offered in some systems, it is possible to customize your own documentation reports.

Upload/Download Functions

Various levels of features are available for the uploading and downloading of programs to and from the controller. The ability to up and download with error checking verifies that the program is free of typing errors such as program construction, invalid addresses, or instructions. Program compare functions allow two different programs or different versions of the same program to be compared for rung-by-rung discrepancies. In the latter case, a master copy is maintained in order to perform the comparisons of the program stored in the PLC to a disk stored program file. Upload/download features should also incorporate security measures to manage access to the controller's software.

Networking Programming Systems

Most PC-based PLC programming systems can be equipped to participate on the vendor's PLC industrial local area network. The software and hardware modules required for these applications may be supplied by the PLC vendor, or by a third-party software company. Typical applications for such a configuration are given below:

❑ Remote data collection/central monitoring
❑ Remote operator interfaces
❑ Remote programming/troubleshooting
❑ Remote uploading/downloading of PLC programs
❑ Network performance analysis/monitoring/troubleshooting
❑ Quasi-Bridge between PLC and office network

As a station on the PLC network, the programming system may act as a workstation that is able to address any PLC on the network and perform remote programming and monitoring (See Fig. 9-6). In this configuration, production data from all of the network stations can be accessed and used in a variety of PC applications (e.g., EXCEL). Most vendors also offer network monitoring software, that allows performance analysis, troubleshooting and capturing of any messages on the network. To be installed on the proprietary LAN, a LAN interface module must be installed in the programming system.

Many programming systems can also be networked on either a proprietary industrial network or on a business network, (e.g., Ethernet, Novell, ARCNET) to allow non-manufacturing related functions. Typical applications of this configuration are listed below.

❑ Access to central data sources
❑ Access to a central services (e.g., printer)
❑ Multiple access to PLC application programs
❑ Access to PC general application programs
❑ File transfers

When several programming systems are networked, typically one is configured as a *server device* and each of the others is configured as a *requester* or *client device*. In this configuration, the requester devices have access to services of the server (e.g., central files, such as PLC programs, or access to central printing other such services). The server will need multitasking operating system software as well as networking software for the specific network — the requester stations also require networking software for the specific network.

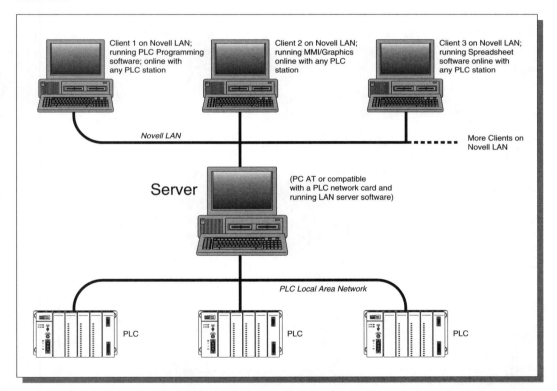

Figure 9-5. Programming systems may be networked to each other and to communicate with PLCs on the network

Software Configuration Templates

In addition to an on-line help system that quickly provides general programming help, a well-equipped programming environment should include software development aids that simplify complex programming problems. One such feature, referred to as *configuration templates,* is a simple, fill-in-the-blank approach to programming certain modules or specific functions. Typically, this method of programming, which involves setting certain parameters such as the module address, setpoints, storage locations, and modes of operation, is used for intelligent I/O modules like the PID control module.

An example configuration template is shown in Figure 9-6. If a controller supports up to 64 PID loops, all loops would be configured using this template. The template allows the user to define loop parameters such as analog address for the process variable and the manipulated output variable, setpoints, high and low limits, deadbands, scale values, alarm deviations, sampling time, gain, rate, and reset tuning parameters. Other examples of using configuration templates include defining alarm setpoints for all analog I/O, I/O address definition, setting positioning profiles for a positioning module, or configuring the setup parameters for a communications module.

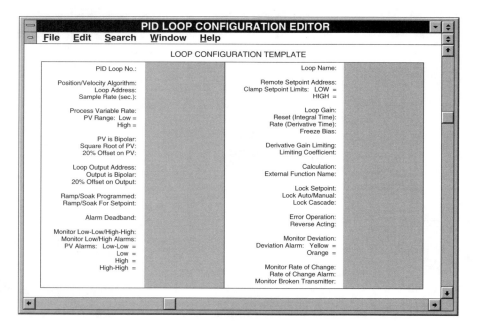

Figure 9-6. PC software provide PID and other fill-in-the—blanks templates

Configurable Status Displays

Configurable status displays are a programming system feature designed to aid in system diagnostics and troubleshooting. This feature allows the program developer to define and save data monitoring screens and program sequence groups tailored to the application. *Configurable maintenance charts,* for instance, allow data screens with data points related to a specific function or device to be grouped on a screen and linked to the corresponding control logic. When a saved chart is recalled by name, the monitoring screen along with the logic are brought into view on split screens or windows, allowing monitoring and manipulation of the data while viewing the actual program status. See Figure 9-7.

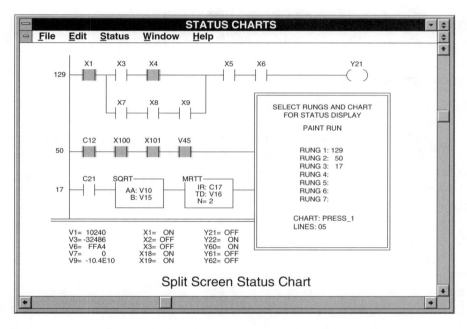

Figure 9-7. Maintenance charts allow programs and process data to be viewed together

In general, the ability to configure status displays tailored to the controlled components of the application allows the development of many reusable aids. With maintenance charts of an entire process, for instance, a maintenance person or operator can be easily guided through the process. The tasks associated with diagnosing problems will be greatly simplified, and downtime situations will be minimized. Typical configurable displays are listed below.

❏   I/O Data Monitoring Displays
❏   I/O Forcing Tables
❏   I/O Timing Charts/Histograms
❏   Program Sequence Status Charts
❏   Maintenance Charts
❏   Process Recipe Data Charts
❏   PID Status/Tuning Charts

Program Archiving/Merging

Archiving is another way of describing the ability to create a library of complete programs or parts of programs that can be used again. To archive implies that the programming system should have sufficient storage capability (e.g., a hard disk drive) to store many useful programs. For instance, an alarm circuit once created can be used repeatedly in the same program or in another program; a complete program created to control a packaging line could perhaps be used in its entirety or with minor changes on a similar line. With the ability to create I/O address symbol tables and link the table with any program, the I/O addresses for the new machine could be easily changed and significantly reduce design time.

Program merging allows users to create separate program modules that can be combined with other modules to form a single new program. The ability to merge programs is useful when combined with the concept of archiving. A library of old programs in many cases may essentially be cut and pasted with program merging to create a completely new program, thereby eliminating the need for complete redevelopment.

9-3 PLC Documentation Systems

Documentation systems are computerized alternatives to producing PLC documentation by hand. The actual documentation components included in these systems may vary widely depending on the suppliers, which include both PLC vendors and third-party companies. The most basic of these systems involve software packages that include both programming and documentation tools that run on an AT-style computer.

More sophisticated systems provide programming, documentation, and design aids for I/O wiring and other drawing documents. These latter systems are often — though not always — supported on microcomputer platforms with multiuser, multitasking operating systems to allow simultaneous program design and development.

Typical Documentation Features

The primary output of a documentation system is the control program, complete with address labeling and rung commentary. As illustrated in Figure 9-9, a ladder program printout from a documentation system also include items such as print date, program name, job number, PLC model, rung numbering, and cross-reference of inputs and outputs. An advantage of such a listing is that it shows on a single document practically all information regarding the control program. This ability eliminates the need for several documents during troubleshooting.

In addition to program listings, the system generates a variety of reports and documents such as those described in chapter 14, under the section *PLC Documentation Requirements*. Address usage reports, for example, list real and internal I/O, and data table registers specifying the use of each location, as well as identifying used and unused addresses. Typical features of documentation systems are listed in Table 9-3.

Table 9-3. Typical Documentation System Features

- ❏ Program development/documentation of PLC families
- ❏ Upload and download PLC programs
- ❏ Off-line program editing
- ❏ Program rung and page numbering
- ❏ Labeling of all program instruction elements
- ❏ Ladder rung commenting
- ❏ I/O and memory address usage reports
- ❏ Cross-reference listings of I/O and memory addresses
- ❏ Fully annotated program listings

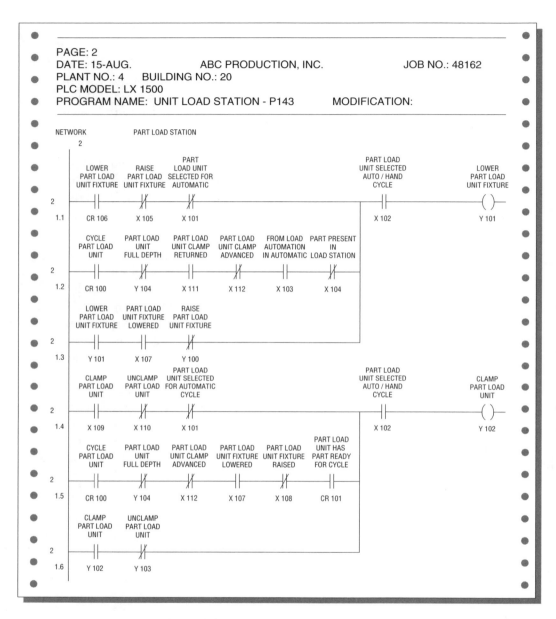

Figure 9-8. Typical ladder program hardcopy

Enhanced Development Systems

The features listed in Table 9-3 outline capabilities of the most basic form of PLC documentation support systems. These systems are designed primarily to provide commenting and cross- referencing of the control program. Of a slightly more sophisticated offering are *design/documentation systems* that serve as word and graphic processors for program development and documentation. The major advantage of such systems is that they facilitate complete design and offer various development tools that aid in reducing the overall design time. Table 9-4 lists some of the major features of PLC design/documentation systems.

Table 9-4. Major Features of Design/Documentation Systems

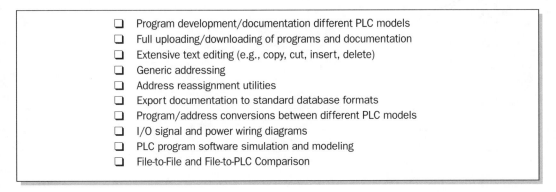

> ❑ Program development/documentation different PLC models
> ❑ Full uploading/downloading of programs and documentation
> ❑ Extensive text editing (e.g., copy, cut, insert, delete)
> ❑ Generic addressing
> ❑ Address reassignment utilities
> ❑ Export documentation to standard database formats
> ❑ Program/address conversions between different PLC models
> ❑ I/O signal and power wiring diagrams
> ❑ PLC program software simulation and modeling
> ❑ File-to-File and File-to-PLC Comparison

Being complete development systems, design/documentation systems typically would provide all of the program development tools discussed in Section 9-2, as well as many others. Generic addressing, for example, eliminates the need for specific PLC addressing, thereby allowing the design to progress without actual or valid addressing. *Address reassignment* allows actual addresses to be automatically substituted later. With the copy feature, if a job uses a similar section of logic several times or if the same or similar circuits are usable on a new job, it can be copied repeatedly with the system automatically reassigning the addresses as well as creating new labels.

Typically, PLC design systems are based on software modules that can be purchased according to needs or budget constraints. For instance, a system configuration package would allow the various system components of a particular PLC model to be configured showing I/O racks, installed modules, and rack interconnections. An I/O drawing package would construct power diagrams and the I/O device connections to the module, showing addresses and wiring numbers. Built-in libraries of I/O modules for different PLC models and of standard JIC device symbols would generate drawings automatically. Finally, a software simulation package could allow the entire program to be tested and validated without the need of the PLC. This feature is required in certain applications and industries.

Figures 9-9 shows a typical document produced by computer-based PLC design/documentation systems.

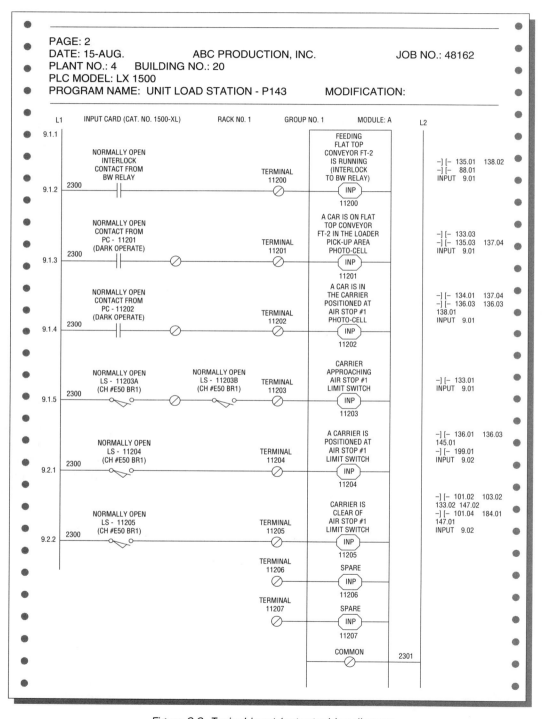

Figure 9-9. Typical input/output wiring diagram

10 INTRODUCTION TO LOCAL AREA NETWORKS

Definition and Application

Network Topologies

Media Access Control

Transmission Signaling Methods and Media

Standards and Protocols

An OSI Protocol Implementation

Internetwork Communications

Network Evaluation and Performance

Until about 1978, local area networks linking production machines or processes on the plant floor were virtually nonexistent. Automated systems, controlled by programmable controllers, were so-called "islands of automation," each functioning autonomously and without knowledge of one another. As in most situations, however, where information is being gathered, there eventually became a need and a desire to share the acquired information. Advantages were also found in gathering information that was distributed among many and making it available at a central point. Sharing information, integrating plant management and production operations, and many other benefits derived from local area networks will account for significant changes in manufacturing operations.

10-1 Definition and Application

Definition

A *local area network (LAN)* is a data communications system that spans a limited geographical area, typically ranging between one and two miles. In a production environment, a single LAN is generally confined to one or more buildings and allows communications among intelligent devices such as PLCs, robots, workstations, and manufacturing computers. Such devices tied to the network are referred to as a *nodes, stations, or end devices*. Unlike *wide area networks (WANs)*, such as those interconnected over public telephone systems, LANs are generally user owned and operated. Figure 10-1 illustrates local area networks in a manufacturing operation.

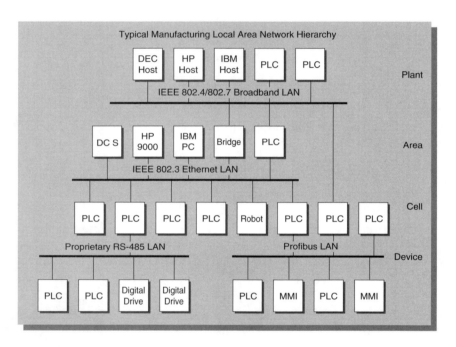

Figure 10-1 Local area networks in a manufacturing plant

Most definitions of a LAN require that it support at least 100 nodes; however, some support as few as 10 or as many as 1,000 nodes. In industrial applications, design philosophies tend toward smaller networks, typically between 10 and 50 stations. Another important LAN characteristic is data transmission speed. Unlike office situations, where speed requirements are not very stringent, control decisions may require that data be delivered within a few milliseconds. Most industrial LANs operate at speeds between 1 and 10 megabits per second, allowing fast response to critical control requirements.

Industrial local area networks must also be adaptable and reliable. A high immunity to electrical and other forms of interference is also essential for networks that have to operate in harsh environments, yet still provide reliable data transmissions. It is also important that a network be flexible enough to allow stations to be placed wherever they are best suited and that adding or removing stations causes little or no disruption in operations. LANs suitable for industrial control applications should at least meet the following criteria:

- ❑ High-speed Data Transmission
- ❑ Suitable for Large Installations
- ❑ High Immunity to Noise
- ❑ High Data Integrity
- ❑ Flexible Architecture
- ❑ Support Real-time Control
- ❑ Support Connection of Various Devices
- ❑ Support Connectivity to other Networks

Networking Applications

In industrial applications, LANs have most often been applied as the communication system for distributed control systems. The distributed approach, illustrated in Figure 10-2, uses individual controllers to control the logical subsystems of a machine or process. This approach contrasts with the centralized approach in which a single controller governs the entire operation. An assembly line for instance, has functions such as drilling, boring, grinding, and a conveying transport system, each of which might be controlled by a separate PLC, while interlocking signals and data are passed over the network among PLCs and other automation systems.

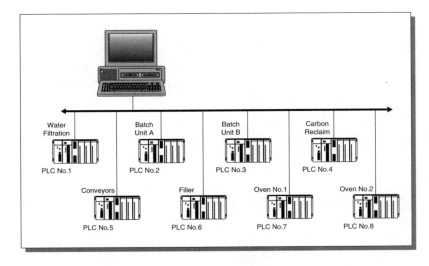

Figure 10-2. Distributed control using a LAN to link control systems

Years of PLC application experience and product enhancements have resulted in design philosophies that prefer distributed control over centralized control for large applications. Distributing the control tasks normally requires that machines share information that is needed to coordinate shared control responsibilities and to alert peer controllers of any local faults. With adequate planning of what information is shared, it is often possible for operations to continue even if one machine is temporarily disabled. While LAN use is not an absolute requirement for distributed control, it is usually more efficient and cost effective.

A second major use of local area networks is that of supervisory control and data acquisition. In many applications, each PLC, in addition to performing its normal control functions, is generally responsible for collecting data, performing necessary processing, and structuring the data for generating reports. This approach places an extra burden on the PLC. Scattered data processing also requires multiple peripherals, such as printers, displays, and storage devices. A LAN allows data collection and processing for a group of controllers to be accomplished using one controller or computer as the central point for collecting data. Listed here are but a small number of possible LAN applications.

- ❑ Production scheduling
- ❑ Recipe downloading
- ❑ Distributed & supervisory machine control (e.g., interlocking)
- ❑ Information sharing among controllers
- ❑ On-line programming across the network
- ❑ Program upload and download across the network
- ❑ Centralized data acquisition and report generation
- ❑ Resource sharing (e.g., programmers, printers, mass storage)

A Networking Hierarchy

Before moving on to our discussion of the elements of local area networks, a look at the so-called manufacturing automation hierarchy and the way LANs may be applied to this model is in order. The hierarchy of manufacturing automation is often broadly described as five levels of functionality as presented in Table 10-1. starting at the bottom with the *device level*. Table 10-1 offers a simplified overview of the automation elements found at each of these levels. This review completes our discussion of the definition and application of local area networks.

The device level involves the various sensor and actuator devices of machines and processes. These devices, typically connect directly to I/O modules and exchange information with the second level automation control systems (e.g., PLCs, NCs, PCs) of the *machine control level*. Third in the hierarchy is the *cell level*, where two or more machines or process units of the machine control level, are coordinated to complete an assembly or process. Each cell is usually coordinated by a high-end PLC or a computer-based device. The *area level* is based on production departments (e.g., assembly, packaging, warehousing), which usually consist of multiple cells. Area control involves process monitoring and scheduling decisions on how production will utilize the available cells. Finally, at the *plant level*, manufacturing operations are tied into the plant management information system (MIS). Plantwide scheduling, monitoring, and collecting of production information are also done at this level.

Table 10-1. Simplified overview of the manufacturing automation hierarchy.

MANUFACTURING AUTOMATION COMPONENT	FUNCTIONAL SYSTEM & DEVICE CATEGORIES	TYPICAL DEVICES AND SYSTEMS
Plant and Production Planning & Management	Plant Information Systems	Mainframe computer, File servers, Printers, Terminal devices
Production Monitoring, Scheduling & Management	Area Controllers	Host Computers, Supervisory systems, MMIs, Data Collections Systems
Process & Machine Monitoring & Coordination	Cell Controllers	High-end PLCs, Host Minicomputers Industrial computers, DCS
Process/Machine Control	Automation Systems and Devices	PLCs, NCs, PCs, Robot Controllers, Drives display devices, loop controllers, MMIs, bar-code readers, line cameras
Sensing/Measuring & Actuator Devices	Discrete and Analog Devices	Discrete Sensors & Actuators, 4-20 ma devices transmitters, valves, flowmeters, photoelectrics, proximity devices

In many companies, the goal is to integrate the various levels of the manufacturing hierarchy through the use of LANs. To do so may involve multiple networks since the data requirements at each level are quite different (See Table 10-2). At the lower levels, the LANs must allow connection of various controllers and computers, as well as intelligent sensors and other field related devices. So-called field level networks address this level. Since communication at this level is for control purposes, data requirements typically involve small messages, fast response, and frequent transmissions.

Table 10-2. Communications requirements in automation hierarchy.

AUTOMATION HIERARCHY	NETWORK LEVEL	TYPICAL MESSAGE SIZE	REQUIRED RESPONSE	DEMAND
Plant Management	Plant	Megabyte	Minutes	Day/Shift
Area Management	Area	Kilobyte	Seconds	Minutes
Cell Control	Cell	Words	100 ms	Seconds
Machine Control	Field	Byte	10 ms	Milliseconds
Devices	Device	Bit	5 ms	Milliseconds

At the cell and area levels, communications primarily involve information transfer (e.g., data collection, recipes, command codes). At this level, there are typically many nodes at greater distances apart, transmitting larger messages, yet messages are less frequent. The requirements of the cell and area can be combined and met by the cell and area level networks. At the plant level, the so-called *backbone network* that runs throughout the plant must extend several miles, support several thousands of nodes, and handle a variety of transmission services. This network may also tie into a corporate-wide area network. Later in our discussion of *internetworking*, you'll learn how communication takes place between multiple networks, allowing complete plant integration.

10-2 Network Topologies

The most obvious characteristic of a LAN is its *topology*. Topology is the physical layout of the network or the geometric configuration formed by the network cables when nodes or stations are attached. Later, in our discussion of the *Open Systems Interconnection (OSI) layered protocol model*, we'll see that network topology is considered under layer 1, which describes physical requirements of the network. Common LAN topologies are the *ring*, *bus*, *star*, and *tree*. The bus topology is the most popular configuration in industrial LANs; however, large networks may involve a combination of these topologies.

As individual network topologies are described, you'll learn that because of its basic configuration, a given topology may be better or less suited depending on the communications requirements of the application. In the following discussions, we'll address how network topology affects the use of a particular cable type and the routing of messages. Further implications of applying a particular topology include information throughput (*volume of data handled*), installation cost, flexibility associated with adding or removing a device, and finally, the overall reliability of the network.

Ring Topology

The ring topology, illustrated in Figure 10-3, involves network nodes connected in a closed circular fashion. A common cable link stations in the ring topology and data transmission usually occurs in one direction around the ring. As data is passed from one station to the next, each station copies any messages addressed to it, then regenerates the message and passes it on to the neighboring node.

Although the ring configuration is not widely used for industrial applications, it is quite prevalent in the office environment. An important advantage of this topology is the way stations transmit messages from one node to the next and in one direction. This aspect means that the ring topology requires no message routing strategy and is suitable for use of fiber optic transmission media. Furthermore, since transmitted messages in a ring eventually return to the sender, message-received verification techniques are easily implemented.

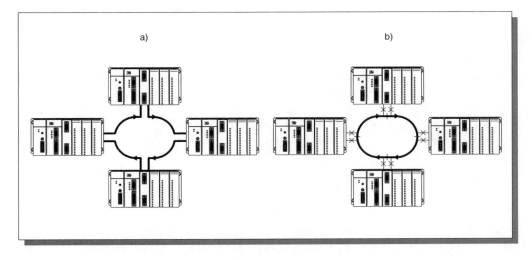

Figure 10-3. a) Standard ring topolgy. b) Ring topolgy with stations connected using bypass relays. The 'X' connections are closed in normal operations.

In order to enhance reliability of the ring topology and take advantage of its adaptability to fiber transmission media, the problem of network disruption caused by a single node failure or a break in the cable must be overcome. This problem is commonly circumvented by installing bypass switches at each node, thereby allowing it to be taken out of the network if it fails. Another method involves running two rings in parallel and connecting the nodes using bypass relays so that a disabled node or cable link may be bypassed. This second alternative would obviously involve the cost of additional hardware and cable.

Bus Topology

The bus topology, illustrated in Figure 10-4, involves a single trunk cable to which individual nodes are attached by a cable drop that taps off of the main cable. For example, each PLC is interfaced to the bus using a network interface module that is attached using a drop cable or connector. Because of the simple linear layout, bus networks require less cable than all other topologies. The broadcasting nature of the bus also allows all transmissions on the cable to be heard by all stations although they may only react to some. This aspect greatly improves information throughput.

In the bus network, no single station controls the network and stations can communicate freely to one another. This freedom of speech is limited, however, by the fact that all stations are tied to a single bus. For stations to transmit messages in an orderly fashion, a method for allowing them to take turns at using the network must first be established. Without such a scheme, stations would always be contending for the bus, and messages would be lost. Several *media access control* methods address the problem of orderly accessing the common bus.

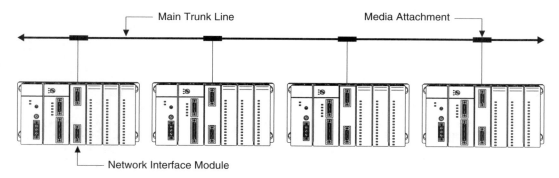

Figure 10-4. Bus network topology

Although the bus topology has its negatives, they are outweighed by the advantages that account for higher network reliability, availability, and performance. The ability to easily add or remove stations and sustain a node failure while continuing to operate makes the bus topology highly suitable for distributed control applications. A single communications cable connecting all stations, makes wiring simpler and less costly. Dependence on a shared cable is the main disadvantage of the bus topology. If the cable is broken at any point, the entire network would be disabled. Finally, bus fault isolation and maintenance may be more difficult than with the star or ring. Diagnostic software tools are important for such networks.

Star Topology

The star configuration, illustrated in Figure 10-5a, was originally used in commercial computer networks where many stations were linked to a central or "master" computer. This same concept was also once used to establish PLC-to-PLC communications. In this configuration, communication between two nodes was only possible via the central node. The sending station would first send the message to the central node, which in turn routed it to the designated receiving station. In computer networks, the centralized star configuration allowed simple message routing, easy network access, easy expansion and only two maintenance checkpoints in case of failures (the central station and the failed station).

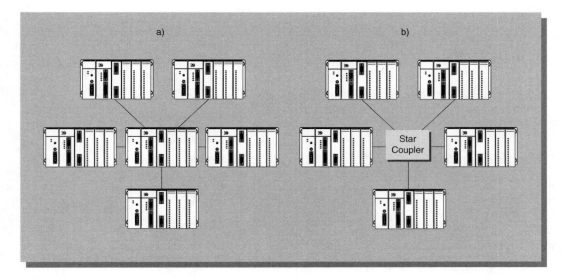

Figure 10-5. a) Star network topology, using a central master. b)Star topology using star coupler

When the star wiring pattern is implemented without the central master as shown in Figure 10-5b, its most obvious drawback of dependence on a single node is eliminated. This single point of failure is not suitable for PLC networks. In this modified configuration, however, many of the star configuration's benefits are obtained. Typically a star-coupler is used as a component of a bus netwok, to allow several stations to be clustered within an area. The point-to- point connections will either be electrical or fiber optic connections. In this hybrid star configuration, stations can be easily added or removed and failures easily detected and corrected.

10-3 Media Access Control

As mentioned in our previous discussion of the bus topology, a network of stations having equal access to a shared communications bus must also have an orderly means to allow stations to gain use of the network. Media access control schemes have been established so that transmitted messages are not lost as a result of two or more stations trying to transmit simultaneously. The following three media access schemes are commonly used in networks having a shared medium. Of these three, *CSMA/CD* and *token passing* are well-established standards upon which many networks are based.

❑ Master-Slave
❑ Token Passing
❑ CSMA/CD

Master-Slave

In industrial LANs, the *master-slave* scheme is typically applied to a linear bus configuration in which one station, designated as the "master" station, governs when so-called "slave" stations transmit on the network. A master-slave bus network is illustrated in Figure 10-6. In some master-slave networks, where all of the stations are more or less equivalent devices, slave stations can talk to one another on a peer-to- peer basis. However, this communication is usually regulated by the master, which is normally a mid-range or high-end controller in a PLC network. In other strategies, slave devices are purely passive devices and only respond when they are polled by the master.

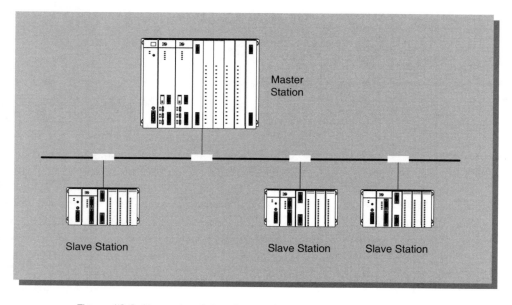

Figure 10-6. Bus network topology, using master-slave access scheme

Typically, in this latter scheme, the master station sends data to each of its slaves, on a cyclical basis, and allows each slave to return any data it wishes to send. This process is called *polling*. The order in which stations are polled is generally predetermined by a so-called *"polling list"* that is stored in the network interface module of the master controller. If a station has no messages to transmit or fails to respond in the allotted time, the master assumes the station is off-line or failed and continues the polling cycle with the next station.

As mentioned in the introduction of this topic, the master-slave access method is an older method and is not widely used as a primary access method. It may be used, however, as a subordinate access method. For example, a token-passing network may allow multiple master and slave nodes, in which only master nodes may receive the token — or the right to transmit. A master station, upon receiving the token, may poll its subordinate slave stations. The master-slave technique may also be used in networks involving a single master device and several slave devices. Typically, in this arrangement, the master device polls each slave device, allowing it to receive data or respond with a data reply. This scenario is typical of a network of coordinated electric drives.

Token Passing

In a *token-passing* scheme, control of the common bus network is distributed among all of the so-called active nodes on the network. Only one station can transmit at a time, and that is the station that has the *token*. A *token* is a unique bit pattern that is passed around the network from one station to the next in a predetermined order. The token-passing scheme has been implemented in two separate standards, the *token ring* (IEEE 802.5) for ring networks and the *token bus (IEEE 802.4)* for bus networks.

When a station holding the token transmits data onto the token network, all other nodes monitor the transmission to detect if the message is addressed to it. If so, it keeps the message, otherwise it discards it. Messages will include source and destination address along with data, or simply the token frame. If a node receiving the token does not wish to transmit, it passes it along to its successor station (i.e., next station in sequence). The next station is not necessarily the next physically adjacent node, but more likely is the next highest address. If the token is presented and the receiving station has nothing to transmit, it passes the token immediately. Otherwise, it places the token back onto the network after it has finished. This process continues until all nodes have received the token, and then repeats in the fashion of a logical ring (See Figure 10-7).

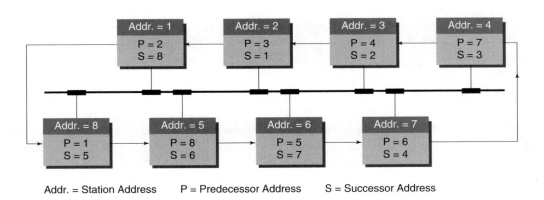

Addr. = Station Address   P = Predecessor Address   S = Successor Address

Figure 10-7. Illustration of token-passing. A logical ring is created as the token is passed.

In the token-passing scheme, each node is allowed to hold the token for a specified amount of time, called the *token holding time*. This feature prevents a single station from "hogging" the network. The time required to pass the token once over the entire network, referred to as the *token rotation time*, can be approximated by multiplying the token holding time by the total number of nodes. The token rotation time represents the time that a node would wait until its next turn to transmit, assuming it had just released the token. The token rotation may also include an overhead time allotted for network housekeeping functions, including things such as checking if new stations have been added to the network.

The fact that it is possible to precisely determine how long a station would wait to transmit its next message makes token passing a *deterministic* system. In addition to this advantage, token-passing also offers the advantages of allowing messages to be given priority, for certain stations to hold the token longer than others, and for the sequence in which stations gain access to the highway to be predetermined. The aspects of token passing, which allows exact system responses to be measured, makes it highly suitable for the time-critical requirements of industrial control LANs.

CSMA/CD

CSMA/CD (*carrier sense, multiple access with collision detection*) is an access method in which stations on a shared media network must contend with one another for use of the network. The term carrier sense means that each station can sense if any other station is transmitting; multiple access means that all stations have equal access to the network as long as no other station is already transmitting; collision detection simply means that each station can detect if its transmission has collided or will collide with that of another station.

On CSMA/CD networks, each station monitors the bus before attempting to transmit, and waits until it detects no other transmission. It is possible, however, for two or more stations to hear no network activity and to begin transmitting at the same time. The result would be a data collision. When a collision occurs, an indication signal is sent over the network, and colliding nodes will back off for a few microseconds before retransmitting. Since the back-off times are random, a second collision is unlikely. If a retry fails, the process is repeated until transmission is successful or until the maximum number of retries are attempted.

An often-cited drawback for CSMA/CD is that the amount of time required to gain access to the network or to complete a successful transmission is variable and cannot be precisely predicted. This aspect makes CSMA/CD a *nondeterministic access method*. Those who argue the point claim that this method is not suitable in industrial applications. In actuality, the time-independent access to the network gives CSMA/CD networks a high response and throughput during periods of low network activity. Stations can gain immediate access to the network if no other station is transmitting.

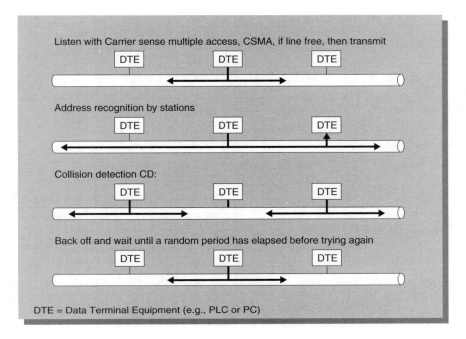

Figure 10-8. Illustration of the CSMA/CD access scheme

With token passing, even though network activity may be low, a station having just released the token cannot transmit again until the token completes the rotation and returns.

Despite the nondeterministic nature of CSMA/CD, which is often cited as a negative, the widely accepted Ethernet is a CSMA/CD system. In 1983, CSMA/CD was approved by the IEEE standards committee and implemented in the IEEE 802.3 standard protocol for medium access control. Since then, many of the most popular and widely installed office computer networks have been based on this standard media access protocol. Many Ethernet networks are also installed on the production floors of manufacturing plants.

10-4 Transmission Signaling Methods and Media

In this section, we examine the physical media used to connect devices to the local area network and how these media types influence characteristics such as noise immunity, achievable network distances, available communications channels, data transmission rates, and network throughput. Before moving on to the discussion of media types, it is important to understand commonly used techniques for actually driving data onto the network medium. These techniques, which are referred to as signaling methods, include *baseband, carrierband, broadband,* and *RS-485.*

Baseband/Carrierband Networks

On baseband networks, information signals are unmodulated. This simply means that the full frequency range (i.e., bandwidth) available on the cable is used without modulating the signals to higher frequencies. Data signals are transmitted along the cable at their original base frequencies, hence the term "baseband." Baseband also implies that only one communications channel exists on the cable and all stations transmit on this single channel (i.e., frequency). Having a single channel capacity also means that a baseband network is a dedicated channel and can serve only one purpose; this contrasts with the multichannel capacity of broadband networks.

Baseband's single channel capacity limits its application such that it is more suitable for use in networks that fall at the cell level of the plant, linking logical groups of controllers and other intelligent devices. As the network hierarchy is implemented within a plant, these networks will generally tie into a broadband network that extends throughout the factory (See Figure 10-9). In the overall scheme, a single channel network is not only highly suitable for linking a group of controllers, but it is also more practical and much less expensive than a broadband network.

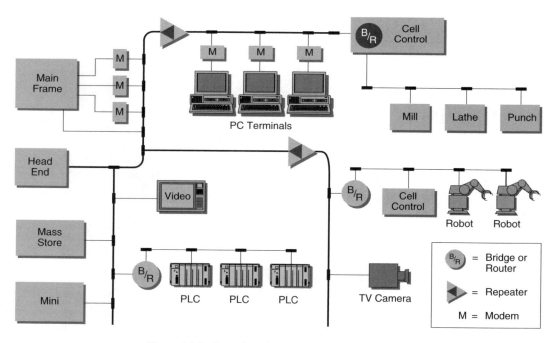

Figure 10-9. Broadband and carrierband networks.

The carrierband network is a type of baseband network. The difference, however, is that the data signals on the carrierband network are superimposed on a carrier signal. This means that instead of transmitting data signals at the base frequency of the cable, the information-bearing signal has been modulated in some fashion, such as in frequency, amplitude, or phase. The changes in the signal represent the information being conveyed. A carrierband network has been defined in the IEEE 802.4 standard and specified by MAP for factory use.

Broadband Networks

The term "broadband" normally refers to use of cable antenna television (CATV) technology to implement a local area network. Broadband networks use the same semi-rigid 75-ohm coaxial cable as used with CATV, which supports bandwidths of up to 450 megahertz. This wide bandwidth, from which the term broadband is derived, allows a single coaxial cable to be subdivided into as many as 100 separate frequency-derived channels. A multichannel capacity means that several sets of noninterfering signals can occur simultaneously on the media. This capacity allows broadband networks to handle different types of data transmission services at the same time.

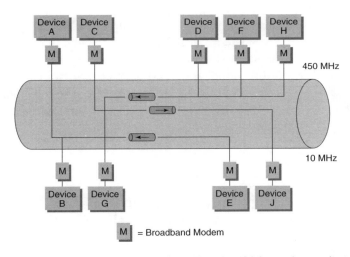

Figure 10-10. Illustration of broadband multichannel capacity

A broadband network can support hundreds of stations and from end to end can extend several miles. Because of the many application advantages and its high performance, broadband networks may serve as the backbone or main plant-level network, connecting plantwide information systems to a hierarchy of cell- and area-level control networks. The multichannel broadband network will allow many different types of devices to be connected — for example, computers communicating to terminals through modems, TV cameras sending to TV monitors, and various control devices.

Such a configuration is illustrated back in Figure 10-9. Note that broadband networks require head-end modems to process the network signals and amplifiers to boost signals as they travel over the cable.

RS-485 Networks

The RS-485 serial communications interface was introduced by the Electronic Industries Association (EIA) in 1983. This serial communication method offered some important enhancements over its earlier predecessors, RS232 and RS-422, which were point-to-point communications schemes.

RS-485 goes beyond allowing simple point-to-point communications by supporting multidrop operation, which allows up to 32 devices to communicate over a single twisted pair of conductors. This method is accomplished by using line driver circuits with tri-state outputs that assume a high-impedance state when they are not driving the communica-tion line. The result is that the connected station is effectively taken out of the circuit.

RS-485 is a balanced transmission design, incorporating differential drivers and receivers. This design gives the network greater noise immunity and allows higher data rates over longer distances. Network distances up to 4,000 feet and baud rates of up to 10 megabits/sec. are achievable with RS-485; however, actual communication distances is a function of the selected transmission speed. As the baud rates increase incrementally beyond 90 Kbits/second, the maximum cable distance is reduced incrementally. Several field bus networks are based on RS-485. These networks use a bus topology with twisted pair cable and allow multiple master or master-slave access schemes. (See *Token-Passing* and *Master-Slave* access schemes).

Twisted Pair Cable

Twisted pair cable is the least expensive and most popular network media. Shown in Figure 10-11, the cable consists of two copper conductors typically insulated with polyvinyl chloride (PVC). The conductor sizes used for LANs are usually 22, 24, or 26 gauge and are twisted about each other so as to equally cancel the crosstalk interference caused by the other. With so-called data grade, or shielded twisted pair, there are about 12 twists per foot. The solid or braided foil shield reduces electrical interference. Twisted pair is very suitable for dedicated links such as those used in the star topology. It is also used, however, in ring and bus networks and in RS-485 multidrop networks. Industrial applications requiring point-to-point links have made extensive use of twisted pair cable.

Figure 10-11. Twisted pair cable.

Coaxial Cable

As shown in Figure 10-12, coaxial cable consists of a copper conductor surrounded by insulation that in turn is surrounded by a tube-shaped outer conductor of copper, aluminum, or braided metal. The outer conductor and the center conductor share the same axis of curvature, hence the term "coaxial." Although the cable cost is slightly higher than for twisted pair, coaxial cable as a networking medium has a much higher immunity to noise, has a far greater bandwidth, allows for greater network distances, and can serve in a greater number of networking applications.

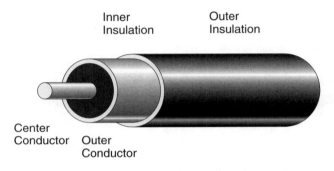

Figure 10-12. Coaxial cable

Coaxial cable has been employed in the cable television industry for many years. Many standard connection devices exist that allow coaxial cable to be used in all of the standard network topologies. Coaxial cable is designed for both baseband and broadband networks. Baseband coax has been approved for CSMA/CD and token bus networks, and for several years has been the popular choice of transmission media for industrial networks. Broadband coax, like baseband coax, has a center conductor surrounded by a dielectric insulator. Instead of an outer conductor of woven copper mesh, extruded aluminum or copper is used, making the cable much more rigid. Broadband cable is a high speed data medium, and end-to-end distances can extend up to 50 kilometers.

Fiber Optic Cables

Fiber optic cable, when compared with coaxial and twisted pair, is a relative new-comer for network transmission media. It does, however, offer several advantages over its predecessors, including higher bandwidth, smaller physical size, larger bending radius, and the ability to support data rates upwards of 400 megabaud. This latter characteristics almost certainly ensures against short-term obsolescence. The most attractive characteristic of fiber cable is its robustness in noisy environments. Although use of fiber in industrial networks has grown, there are still areas of development to be made before its many benefits can be fully exploited.

In fiber optic cable, light beam signals are modulated along thin threads of glass fibers or high-grade plastic that run the length of the cable. Because light beams transmit the data, the cable is virtually immune to outside interference. Also, unlike twisted pair and coax, fiber optic cables do not generate interference and present no resistance to the transmitted signal. These characteristics result in a data medium with virtually no distance limitation and in which extremely fast and practically error-free data transmission is possible.

Past limitations of fiber optic cable have been in the difficulty of constructing interconnection components that allow a network of various topologies. These limitations are gradually being eliminated or circumvented, especially through the use of devices called *star couplers*. Multiple fibers lead into the device, and when light shines into the device from one of the fibers, it is simultaneously reflected out through all of the others. This configuration forms a star, hence the name star coupler. Star couplers allow point-to-point connections in the linking of bus segments and star configurations at various drops of a bus network. Some typical fiber links are shown in Figure 10-13.

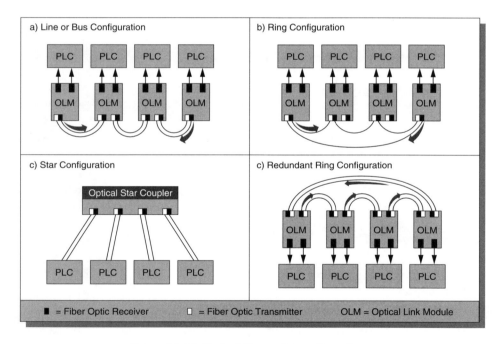

Figure 10-13. Typical fiber optic configurations

10-5 Standards and Protocols

It is standard practice in diplomatic arenas for involved parties to ensure that transactions proceed orderly and correctly by first establishing a set of rules and guidelines. Such guidelines are referred to as *protocols*. In communication systems, it is also important to establish protocols that will ensure that information is delivered timely, correctly, in proper sequence, and in a fashion that is understandable by the recipients.

In local area networks or in any communication involving two or more devices, protocols must be established so that electrical circuits, data format, data flow, information coding, and other functions all cooperate to facilitate understandable communication. Many national and international standards organizations work together with industry to assist in the development of standard protocols for local area networks. A major outcome of this type of effort was the *Open Systems Interconnection (OSI)* model, developed by the International Standards Organization (ISO). This model is widely accepted and used by companies developing network communications equipment.

The OSI Protocol Reference Model

The OSI model was intended to provide a framework for developing standard network protocols that allow open communication between the products of different vendors. The OSI model is just what it says — a standard reference model for development. In itself, it is not a network standard, nor does it promote any particular standard. Instead, its definitions provide a broad guideline for developing standard network protocols. This means that several network protocols could exist that are based on the OSI model. A closer look at this model should help clarify network services and implementations.

The OSI model organizes the various functions of a general communications network into seven layers, as shown in Fig. 10-14 on the following page. Each layer defines the functions that must be performed by the layer. Defining each communication function as a layer is similar to using flowcharted modules to describe the requirements of a software program. Since the functions are modular and independent, each could be handled as a subprogram — even written in different languages. Complex functions are then easier to implement and may be altered or substituted with minimal overall impact. Similarly, the OSI model is a framework upon which network protocols may be built. Each of its seven layers could be satisfied by using one or more already-published standard protocols that perform the functions required by each layer.

OSI LEVEL	LAYER	FUNCTION SERVED
7	Application	Provides appropriate services between communication network and end node's application programs
6	Presentation	Provides data conversion, code conversion to standardize different entities to the standard network format
5	Session	Establishment and termination of sessions, queuing, buffering of data and recovery of terminated sessions
4	Transport	End-to-end communication, error free service, error recovery & data flow control
3	Network	Addressing the entire network or series of networks
2	Data Link	Transfers packets of information for transmission onto the network, error detection and recovery
1	Physical	Transmission & reception of bitstreams onto the network

Figure 10-14. The ISO Open Systems Interconnection layered protocol model.

The Seven Layers

Functionally, the seven layers are interdependent. Each layer has a built-in interface to the adjacent layers. Each layer receives services from the layer below it and provides services to the layer above it. Layer 2, for example, can pass data to layer 3 or layer 1, depending on the direction of data flow, but layer 1 cannot communicate directly with layer 3. If we view the OSI model logically, it provides two sets of services. The combined services of layers 1 through 4 provide reliable data transfer between two stations. Layers 5 through 7 provide various communications services to the network stations. Their main function is to provide data translations and interpretations so that network systems may understand each other.

In an actual network configuration, the cable is the only physical connection between two nodes. The layers above this are generally software running on the end node or firmware implemented on *network interface modules* and provide a logical connection between communicating nodes. As illustrated in Figure 10-15, a station initiates a network service via its control program. The request is received at layer 7 of the network interface, proceeds downward through the layers, is driven across the cable, and proceeds upward through the receiving layers until reaching the destination node's application program, via layer 7.

As we look more closely at the functions of the seven layers, it is important to remember that each layer represents protocol requirements and that a protocol can be described by the services it provides.

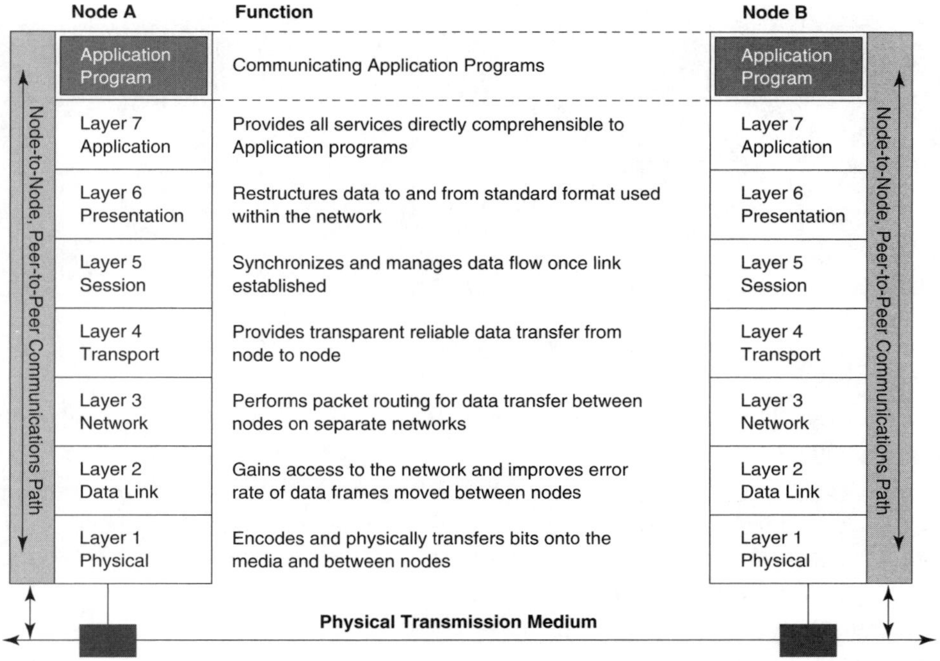

Node A	Function	Node B
Application Program	Communicating Application Programs	Application Program
Layer 7 Application	Provides all services directly comprehensible to Application programs	Layer 7 Application
Layer 6 Presentation	Restructures data to and from standard format used within the network	Layer 6 Presentation
Layer 5 Session	Synchronizes and manages data flow once link established	Layer 5 Session
Layer 4 Transport	Provides transparent reliable data transfer from node to node	Layer 4 Transport
Layer 3 Network	Performs packet routing for data transfer between nodes on separate networks	Layer 3 Network
Layer 2 Data Link	Gains access to the network and improves error rate of data frames moved between nodes	Layer 2 Data Link
Layer 1 Physical	Encodes and physically transfers bits onto the media and between nodes	Layer 1 Physical

Node-to-Node, Peer-to-Peer Communications Path

Physical Transmission Medium

Figure 10-15. Communication between two open systems

Physical Layer. The lowest layer of the OSI model allows for the definition of mechanical and electrical requirements to establish physical connection of stations to the network. This layer establishes transmission media types and topology, as well as connection components such as taps, connectors, modems, splitters, transceivers, and terminators. Since layer 1 is responsible for driving data onto the cable and taking data off of the cable, it also specifies protocols for signaling techniques (e.g., RS-485, broadband, carrierband). Transmission data rates are also defined under this layer since a variety of cable types may be specified.

Data Link Layer. Data link services collectively are to gain access to the network, send data to another node, and subsequently release the network for use by other nodes. The *media access control (MAC)*, sublayer 2a, determines how nodes gain access to the network (e.g., CSMA/CD, token bus, token ring). The *logical link control (LLC)*, sublayer 2b, defines the format for assembling bit information into frames (e.g., HDLC, SDLC). LANs do not send messages as a continuous stream of bits, but instead breaks them up into frames. Each frame normally has a starting control sequence, the data, the address of its source and destination, and a frame check character. This layer also defines whether or not a user station is required to acknowledge receipt of a message at the LLC level. While acknowledgment may not be required at this level, it may be handled at a higher level. Layers 1, 2, and 7 are all that are needed in some networks.

237

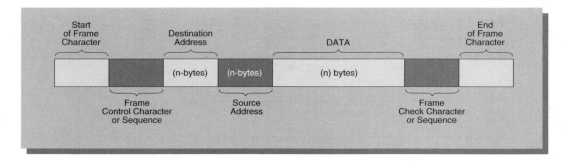

Figure 10-16. Components of a typical data frame.

Network Layer. The network layer provides the protocols for switching and routing to allow exchange of information between two network stations even when the connection involves stations on different *subnetworks*. Subnetworks refer to separate and distinct LANs that have been interconnected using interconnection devices. Layer 3 protocols set up the communication path between nodes and ensure that messages reach their destination by the best route and without any concern by the sending station. In some network protocols, the network layer may not be implemented at all, or may be present but *inactive* since internetwork communication is not required. An inactive network layer is typical of proprietary PLC networks that follow the OSI model.

Transport Layer. The transport layer must provide a reliable and transparent transfer of data between two stations from the time the communications path is set up until the session is over. It does this by first guaranteeing that an error-free, logical (virtual circuit) connection exists between the two stations. End-to-end control of data exchange means that this layer must provide standard functions for ensuring that the transmitting station is ready to transmit, the receiving station is ready to receive, and the connection exists between the two. Using the routes provided by layer 3, the transport layer chooses the best path for information from one station to another.

Session Layer. Layer 5 defines how the communications session between two nodes is established and how it is terminated. In other words, similar to a telephone conversation, which has conventional opening and closing dialogue, the session layer provides functions for opening dialogue, determining the parties at either end, controlling, and closing the dialogue. Another important function of layer 5 is the synchronization of data transfer. By using so-called synchronization points, if a fault occurs during the connection, data transmission can resume from the last synchronization point without loss of data and without starting over.

Presentation Layer. The functions of this layer are data interpretation and conversion. On the sending end, the presentation layer accepts messages from layer 7, and on the receiving end, presents messages to layer 7. To accommodate structural differences that may exist between the data structures and command request codes of two nodes (e.g., different PLCs), the format of the data transferred from one user to another must be translated so that either end can understand the other. The presentation layer performs whatever syntax translations and conversions are required. The presentation layer may not be implemented — or can remain inactive — if all nodes use the same data presentation.

Application Layer. The highest layer of the OSI model must provide network services to the user on the sending or receiving end. Layer 7 defines the application services available via the user-application software for sending or receiving messages or for handling other network transactions. Examples of such services might include upload/download programs or files, data transmission and acquisition, and monitor/control end-device status (e.g., START/STOP PLC). Application layer protocols should provide services such that the user application program has no concerns for how data structures are named and accessed in the remote end station. The other layers exist only to support this layer.

Network Management Functions. Some representations of the OSI model contain an eighth layer to cover network management services. The traditional seven layers are stacked in their hierarchical configuration and layer 8 runs vertically, interfacing to all seven layers. This layer is concerned with the provision of the required resources and tools to allow for configuring, monitoring, managing, testing, maintaining and diagnosing problems of the network. Typical services include access to all nodes; configuration utilities to set up and expand the network or modify communications relationships; a directory service to allow definition and lookup of names and addresses of all network stations; and diagnostic software to view and analyze network data transmissions and problems.

OSI LAYER	BRIEF FUNCTIONAL DESCRIPTION	OSI LAYER
7	Provides standard mechanisms for application programs to gain access to network services such as data access, file transfers, program upload/download.	Application
6	Resolves differences in data representation between the communicating applications of two network stations.	Presentation
5	Establishes, maintains, synchronizes and ends communication between two stations.	Session
4	Provides reliable end-to-end data transfers between two stations.	Transport
3	Translates physical addresses into logical addresses and determines the route for data through the network.	Network
2	Places messages into data frames and manages access to the network media. Performs error checking.	Data Link
1	Defines electrical and physical characteristics of the network. Data transfer over medium occurs here.	Physical

Figure 10-17. Summary of the OSI reference model

Protocol Stacks

A complete set of protocols, selected to fill each of the seven layers and provide the functions required by the OSI model, is called a *protocol stack* or *protocol suite*. Based on this definition, examples of such protocols are *Manufacturing Automation Protocol (MAP)* and *Technical Office Protocol (TOP)*. Each of these protocols is comprised of a set of defined standards that, as a unit, comply with the OSI model. A point to note here is that while these two network protocols happen to be proclaimed standards, it does not follow that a protocol suite is a network standard because it complies with the OSI model. Further, two OSI- compatible network protocols do not necessarily communicate. Close compliance with the OSI model and use of similar established standards do, however, allow easier integration of different networks.

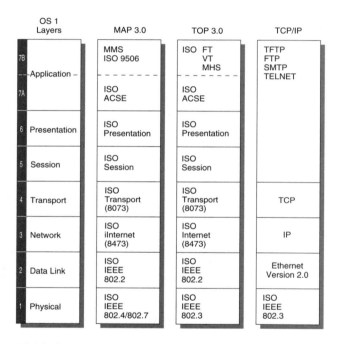

Figure 10-18. Example of network protocol stacks (protocol suites)

10-6 An OSI Protocol Implementation

During the 1980s, MAP was the most widely promoted implementation of the OSI model. It was eventually adopted as a communications standard for the factory floor. MAP was the result of years of cooperative effort, spearheaded by General Motors Corporation. Its specifications were based on established internationally accepted IEEE and ISO standards. Although MAP was a milestone in allowing direct connectivity of communicating devices manufactured by different companies, its has been received with limited industry acceptance — largely a result of its high cost of implementation. Such results are also typical when standardization is attempted for products, like PLCs, that are mature and where proprietary solutions are already well entrenched.

Figure 10-19 shows how MAP was implemented using the OSI model. At the physical level, the choices include a broadband token bus network operated at 10 megabits/sec., or a carrierband token bus network operated at 5 megabits/sec. Both of these hardware platforms are defined by the IEEE 802.4 standard. The broadband specifications were intended to meet the requirements of the backbone network at the plant level, while the carrierband network was intended to serve smaller areas within the plant, such as manufacturing cells.

OSI LAYER	STANDARD PROTOCOLS	FUNCTION
7	ISO 9506 Manufacturing Message Specification ISO 9594 Directory Service ISO 8571 File Transfer Access and Management ISO 8650/2 Association Control Service Element	**Application**
6	ISO Presentation Kernel	**Presentation**
5	ISO 8327 Session Kernel, Full Duplex	**Session**
4	ISO 8073 Class 4 Transport Protocol	**Transport**
3	ISO 8473 Connectionless Network Protocol	**Network**
2b	IEEE 802.2 Class 1 or Class 3 Logical Link Control (LLC)	**Data Link**
2a	IEEE 802.4 Token Passing Media Access Control (MAC)	
1	IEEE 802.4, 10 Mb Broadband IEEE 802.4, 5 Mb Carrierband	**Physical**

Figure 10-19. OSI Implementation of Manufacturing Automation Protocol

At layer 2a, access control is handled by the IEEE 802.4 token passing media access control (MAC) protocol. At layer 2b, the logical linking of two network partners is handled by the IEEE 802.2 logical link control (LLC) protocol. At the network layer, MAP has implemented the ISO Connectionless Network Protocol. This layer defines how communication takes place between networks. The transport layer uses the map provided by the network layer to choose the best path from one station to another. Here, MAP uses the ISO Class 4 Transport Protocol. Layers 5, 6, and 7a combined provide the so-called *transfer syntax* protocol of the MAP stack. Here, the combined services of these layers utilize ISO standards to provide session control and syntax conversion.

Layer 7, the application layer, provides the user interface to the network. Better said, it provides standard network services to user application programs running on the end station. A key element provided to the user at this layer should be network, application, and hardware transparency. In this layer, MAP provides directory and file transfer services and the *manufacturing message specification (MMS),* a universal command specification to support communication to plant floor devices of different types and of different manufacture.

Role of MMS and Layer 7 Protocols

The responsibility of the first six layers of MAP, or of any OSI network, is the delivery of raw data in a standard format between various network stations. With MAP, stations include PLCs, process computers, and other plant floor devices. The completion of useful work, however, by MAP or any layer 7 protocol is only accomplished when the standard data packet is presented to the application programs running on various devices in a way that is completely transparent as to the make, model, or type of device. For example, if data collection software running on a plant computer makes a request for data from all devices on the network, it should not matter if the device is a PLC, another computer, or a robot. The data request looks the same and is interpreted as having the same meaning by all devices.

For such a miracle to occur is the role of the layer 7 protocol. It must define a set of commands that all must implement and adhere to if communication among different types of devices is to occur. MMS provides this standard command set for MAP. It consists of several services that can be requested over the network by or to any device that is MMS compatible. For instance, MMS specifies a generic format for reading and writing data, program uploading and downloading, and for starting and stopping a program on a device. To achieve the MMS functionality or that of any layer 7 protocol would require that it be imbedded in the software of any system that intends to communicate with other MMS-compatible devices. For example, if MMS commands are to be issued from an operator workstation to a PLC, then the application program running on the PLC and on the workstation must have imbedded the ability to invoke and interpret MMS service requests.

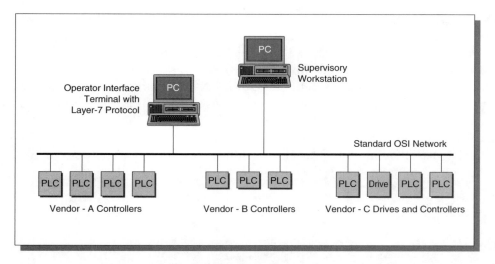

Figure 10-20. Layer 7 provides a standard message/command format, allowing transparent communications among compatible network devices of different manufacturers

The services of the layer 7 protocol provide the interface between the application program running on a particular device and the network protocol stack. Each service request is issued by the application program and is interpreted at layer 7 to have a specific meaning. The request is properly formatted, forwarded down through the layers of the sending side and up through the layers on the receiving side where the request is interpreted at layer 7, and relayed on to the application program of the receiving station, where it causes a specific action in response from the remote device.

Each MMS request generates the same response regardless of the remote device or network hardware (e.g., broadband, carrierband, Ethernet, or token bus). If, for instance, the command is to START or STOP the control program, the response is the same. With MMS or a similar layer 7 protocol, a general application program running on a host computer of the network or on any network device can access each and every other device without knowing the peculiar way in which each device is accessed. Without such an interface, customized software would be required for each new device or each new host.

10-7 Internetwork Communications

In many plant operations, just as in offices that already use or are considering local area networks, various installations involve decisions made by different individuals and often by different departments or groups. Networks are also normally installed well after many isolated systems have been installed and are operational. In many instances where hardware is already installed, decisions made within individual departments have often resulted in entirely different brands of controllers and networks having different communications protocols. This type of bottom-up evolution, as illustrated in Figure 10-21, is typical in plant systems.

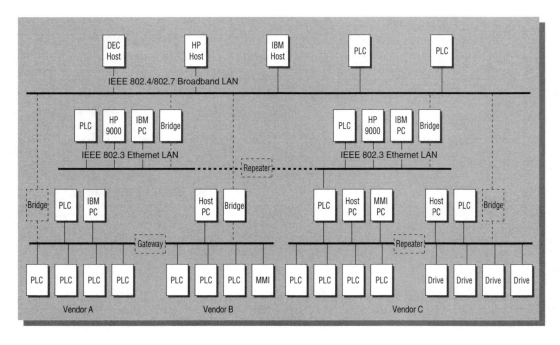

Figure 10-21. Network evolution in plants is often by department and with different PLC brands and models. Dotted lines show potential interconnection

Since bottom-up-developed networks often result in problems in continuity and communications, a method is needed to tie all these links together. While the intent of open standards is to do just this, it is unlikely that installed networks will be thrown out or that all new installations will rely on a single network standard. Although our emerging understanding of networking must result in a commitment to standards, it must allow for a hierarchical approach to networking and must accept the fact that no single solution exists for all problems. The best balance of capacity, performance, and cost will result from a combination of systems achieved through interconnectivity of different networks. The point here is not to suggest a hodge podge of networks, but that networks can evolve over time and take into account systems that are already in place.

Internetting is the process of connecting distinct networks. It permits data to move freely among different levels on networks scattered throughout the plant. The devices used for internetting will depend on the degree of compatibility between the networks. For instance, a bridge is used to link networks that employ identical protocols. Dissimilar networks are connected via gateways. The ability to connect subnetworks will only be possible with careful planning and network selection. Proprietary networks using non-open standards should be avoided at all cost. Those that do utilize open standards and that follow the OSI model, should still be selected based on how well they connect with other networks and with plant-level computers. Where possible and practical, this should always be demonstrated.

Repeater

In local area networks, particularly those with a bus topology, signal levels and waveforms will eventually attenuate depending on the distance traveled from the transmitting station. Signal degeneration is usually avoided by placing restrictions on the maximum end-to-end distances and on maximum distances between stations. When it becomes necessary, however, some LANs use a device called a *repeater* to regenerate and retransmit weakened signals. The device is placed between two bus segments and is responsible for receiving signals from either side and retransmitting the signals onto the opposite segment.

The repeater is also used to join two network segments so that more nodes may be added. As an interconnection device, the repeater provides only a physical linking service. No data link functions such as node addressing, error control, or flow control are performed. While some repeaters, or so-called repeater adapters, allow network segments with different media (e.g., copper and fiber) to be joined, generally, a more complex joining device is needed when segments differ in media, topology, or access method. Since it performs its function on two identical physical network segments, the repeater is also referred to as a *physical relay* or *level-1 relay*. Figure 10-22 conveys this function of the repeater in relation to the OSI layered protocol model.

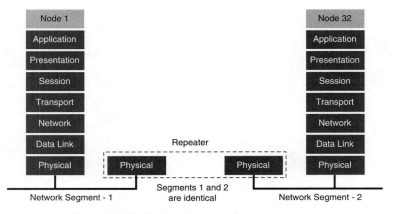

Figure 10-22. Protocols relayed by a repeater

Bridge

A *bridge* is normally used to connect two distinct networks having identical communications protocols and to filter the data traffic between them. The device attaches to the network and functions much like any other network station; however, its presence is not known to other stations, nor does it initiate any message transmission. The functionality of the bridge is best illustrated as shown in Figure 10-23. Since it operates only on the physical and data link layers, it is also referred to as a *data link relay* or a *level-2 relay*. For this same reason, however, the networks must implement the same addressing scheme at layer-2 and the upper layers (i.e., layers 3-7) of both networks must be the same.

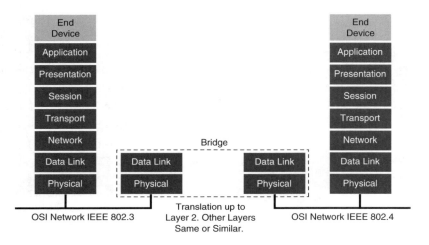

Figure 10-23. Protocols relayed by a bridge

The bridge is similar to the repeater in that it accepts data transmissions from both sides and forwards the data onto another subnetwork. The bridge differs, however, and is more flexible since it is able to read the data frames of the data link. Since a bridge must access the physical links of each network according to its particular access rules and may not be able to gain instant access, it must also be able to store and forward messages. Because the bridge also knows the addresses of the nodes on both subnetworks, it can decide whether a message should remain on the subnetwork where it was generated, be forwarded to the opposite network, or simply discarded. Such decisions are based on a predefined address filtering table or one that is created in bridges that are able to learn the network addresses and filtering requirements.

Bridging networks having related but independent applications (e.g., production management and production control) offers several benefits over a single large network. By separating the data traffic on each subnetwork and only allowing necessary data to pass, a bridge reduces the traffic on both sides and thereby improves the response of both networks. Security is also improved since broadcast data is restricted to the stations local to each subnetwork. Increased reliability and fault isolation can also be gained by using a bridge since faults are isolated to the networks on which they occur. Finally, the ability to read frames and to adjust to different media access schemes allows a bridge to connect networks having identical higher-level protocols but different modes of transmission (i.e., media and access methods, Layer-1, Layer-2). For example, a bridge could link a carrierband network with a broadband network if the higher-level protocols are identical.

Router

A router is a network station placed between networks in order to route messages through two or more local and/or remote networks. The router is also referred to as an *intermediate system*, *network relay*, or a *level-3 relay*. As illustrated in Figure 10-24, in relationship to the OSI model, the router implements the functionality of layers 1, 2, and 3 of the networks it is configured to interconnect.

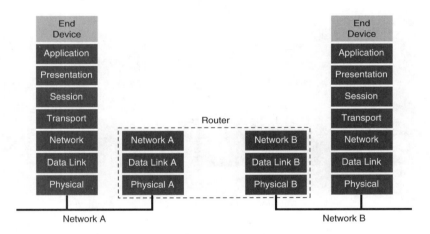

Figure 10-24. Protocols relayed by a router

Whereas the bridge acted upon the data frames transferred between the data link layers of two stations, the router acts upon the packets transferred between the network layers of two stations. Further, unlike the bridge, routers have network addresses that are known to other network stations. This characteristic allows the other stations to address the router to request routing services. Since the router maintains a list of stations on local and remote networks, a station wishing to send a message may need to relay the message through the router if the station is on a remote network. Although it is not typical, one or more stations on an industrial LAN may require the services of a router. At the higher levels of the plant, a router might be used, for instance, to connect a station on the factory level network to a wide area network.

Gateway

To connect two networks having very different protocols, an intelligent device called a *gateway* is required. A gateway is typically a dedicated computer or an optional board designed specifically to perform a complete translation between the protocols of two completely dissimilar networks. Figure 10-25 illustrates gateway use. The gateway handles bidirectional data transmission from both networks and recreates the messages to the format used by the opposite network. A common use of gateways is to interconnect vendor-proprietary networks to one another or to an open-systems network.

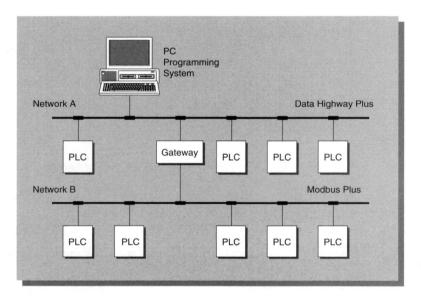

Figure 10-25. A gateway connects two dissimilar networks, by translating hardware signals and each layer's protocols

In relation to the OSI layered model, the gateway performs translation at every level, as illustrated in Figure 10-26. For this reason, it is also referred to as an *inter-working unit* or *level-7 relay*. Translation normally requires repackaging the message, adjusting to different access schemes and routing schemes, as well as retransmitting the message to account for any differences in network speeds.

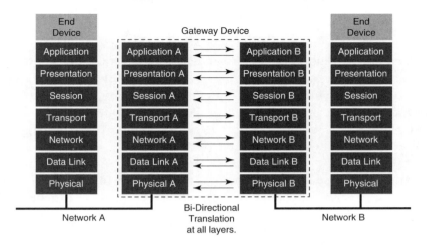

Figure 10-26. Protocols relayed by a gateway

Because of its complete translation capability, gateway devices must play a major role in initially allowing proprietary-to-proprietary and proprietary-to-standard network communications. Since there is no universal gateway, each proprietary network will require a unique gateway to other network protocols. With the eventual widespread use of open systems, use of the gateway will eventually decline.

10-8 Network Evaluation and Performance

The previous sections presented a broad introduction to the essential elements of LANs and a review of the OSI model. Hopefully, you have gained a basic understanding of LAN design and a good feel for what design aspects are desirable or most suitable for manufacturing operations. Although more complex issues exists for the topics introduced, the main goal was to lay the groundwork for more enlightened discussions and decision making. Probably the most important points to be taken from these discussions are a) the importance of using networks where possible, b) that no single network solution exists for all requirements, and finally, c) the insistence on open networks that employ well-established standard protocols. This latter point is essential for networking strategies that will ensure future expansion and interconnectivity.

In this final section is a brief review of some of the key subjects that may help in your final network evaluation and selection. With each application, it is important to start with a detailed list of the immediate application requirements for the network and then review this with the plantwide plan for networking. The application details should consider what devices must be connected, how they will communicate with each other, and how they will tie in to other networks.

Network Media

The network transmission media affects the gross network speed, allowable distances, topology, and cost. Susceptibility to interference is purely cable dependent. In large installations, the overall cost is greatly influenced by the choice of cable. Twisted pair cable, common in many industrial networks, is the least expensive of the network transmission media, but compared with coaxial and fiber cable, it offers relatively low gross transmission rates. Where high-speed and high-volume data transmissions are required, coax and fiber should be considered.

In networks that allow use of fiber, configurations usually can involve all fiber cables or a combination of both copper (electrical) and optical media. Fiber networks may also offer a greater flexibility of topologies (e.g., linear, ring, star, tree). Fiber cables should also be considered if the layout requires lengths that must travel through noisy parts of the plant or when interconnecting nonadjacent buildings. Although the per-foot cost of fiber is higher than twisted pair, the cost of copper systems may require conduit, hangers, fittings, and associated labor for bending conduit and terminating many wires.

Devices Supported

The devices supported by a given local area network are important network selection considerations. This performance factor, referred to as device connectivity, is a key factor to successful integrated manufacturing. While it is certainly important to ascertain what devices can be physically connected to a particular network (e.g., PLCs, computers, field devices, etc.), it is equally important to know what software is already available to support the connectivity of these devices. For instance, with computers, you need to know what operating system environments are possible.

Remember as mentioned earlier that no single network will satisfy performance requirements of all levels of the networking hierarchy (i.e., device and field, cell and area, and factory). Networking within the factory will undoubtedly involve multiple networks with graded performance levels. At the device levels, for instance, more than a single network will probably be required to handle discrete bit-oriented devices, analog process devices, and intelligent sensors. At the field level, a wide variety of automation systems must be supported (PLCs, PCs, MMIs, operator stations, drive systems, etc.). For each network you should seek open systems and verify device connectivity, device interoperability, software requirements, and how this network will interconnect to other networks.

Access Method

As we discussed earlier, the access method is the scheme used by a network to allow stations on a shared media to access the network in an orderly fashion. Most commercial or industrial networks will use either CSMA/CD (IEEE 802.3, Ethernet) or token passing (IEEE 802.4). While both of these methods have strengths and weaknesses, the differences in network performance resulting from the choice of access scheme will be insignificant in most applications and it would be unwise to base a selection entirely on this factor.

In performance, CSMA/CD has a slight edge during bursty traffic conditions. That is, a lot of short messages. This is true since stations may gain immediate access to the network if it is clear. As traffic conditions become heavy, however, more collisions will occur, network overhead will increase, and efficiency will decrease. Given a token-passing network under the same low traffic conditions, the network stations would spend a significant part of the time waiting to receive the token. On the other hand, a token network is more efficient when network traffic is high. Its main advantage, however, is that it is deterministic. If a known network response time is an absolute prerequisite, then a token-passing network may be the only choice.

Finally, compatibility and support are important evaluation criteria with regard to the access scheme. If a particular access scheme is already being used, then staying with this scheme will certainly be simpler and less expensive. This choice still must not be made in a vacuum. CSMA/CD or Ethernet has a heavily installed base, compared with token-passing, and consequently more hardware such as bridges, routers, and gateways is available. This latter fact and its non-deterministic nature would make CSMA/CD networks more feasible at the higher levels of the network hierarchy. At the higher levels, larger volumes of data are required, and response requirements are less stringent.

Network Response and Throughput

Network performance is often related in terms of *throughput* and *response time*. Both of these performance measurements are a function of the gross transmission speed of the network, which is usually given in raw bits per second (e.g., 1 million bits per second, 1Mb/s). Although throughput and response time are related to network speed, they are quite different.

Throughput, simply stated, is the volume of actual data that can be moved in a fixed period — typically some number of bytes or words per second or minute. Factors that affect throughput are the number of nodes on the network and how much and how often these nodes are transmitting messages. With a token-passing network, for instance, each station is given access to the network in a round-robin fashion whether it has data to transfer or not. With a greater number of nodes, however, a token-passing network is slightly more efficient since the network gets greater usage and all nodes are guaranteed access to the network. In a similarly loaded CSMA/CD network, more nodes and more traffic would result in more collisions. The result would be lower throughput.

Network response time is the worst-case time required for a sending station to prepare and send a message, and for the receiving station to become prepared to receive the message and receive the message. A more practical example is the time it takes for a given station to recognize a signal to request a data transfer and process the instructions that sends the data, for the message to travel the cable, for the receiving station to receive the message and to make program decisions based on the new message.

$$RT = IT + 2(STI) + PTI + AT + TT + 2(ST2) + OT$$

where:

IT	=	Input transition time at sending station (if applicable)
PT1	=	Processing time of sending station (network interface)
ST1	=	Scan time of sending station
AT	=	Network access (bus) time for sending network interface module
TT	=	Transmission time for data to travel across network
ST2	=	Scan time of receiving station
PT2	=	Processing time of receiving station (network interface)
OT	=	Output transition time at receiving station (if applicable)

Often it may be necessary to know prior to selecting a given network whether or not it will provide the control response required by a given aspect of the application. The response is a summation, that can be roughly estimated as shown in the following equation.

The given equation considers the I/O delay times in case the message is triggered from an external signal. I/O delay times are readily available from I/O specifications. Since the input signal that triggers the transmission may have gone high just after the point in the program where this is evaluated (worst-case condition), the scan time is doubled since the signal is not recognized until the next program scan. The opposite may occur on the receiving end so its scan time is also doubled. The new data may be received by the CPU from the network interface module just after the point in the program where the data is to be used.

With a token bus network, the manufacturer should be able to provide you with exact network parameters and a formula for calculating the response time. You will be able to supply variables to the equation, based on your expected network configuration and the amount of data you expect to be transferred by each node. Given a CSMA/CD network, an estimated response will have to be determined on assumed conditions of network loading. A guaranteed response time, however, could never be determined.

11

THE LADDER PROGRAMMING LANGUAGE

The Ladder Program Format

Relay-logic Instructions

Timer-Counter Instructions

Scan Control Instructions

Data Manipulation Instructions

Data Transfer Instructions

Special Function Instructions

Networking Instructions

Ladder logic was the first and is the most widely used language for even the most sophisticated of PLCs. Original design criteria of the first PLC called for a computer-like device that would replace the inflexible electromechanical control systems with programmable control. A simple language was developed to perform logic control, sequencing, timing, and counting. This original language was elegantly implemented using relay-schematic coil and contact symbols as programming instructions — it met all of the original design criteria. Besides performing basic relay-equivalent functions, this language needed to be simple to use and easily implemented and maintained by the very people who had installed and diagnosed the failures of the old systems.

This chapter will present a generic set of the most commonly used ladder instructions, including relay-logic, timer and counter, scan control, arithmetic, data manipulation, and data transfer operations. These instructions are implemented in practically all PLCs.

11-1 The Ladder Program Format

The main function of a ladder program is to determine the control sequence of operation for a given machine or process. A typical ladder program is illustrated in Figure 11-1. The complete program consists of several *ladder rungs*. It is the logic of a ladder rung that will command a device to turn ON or OFF, or an arithmetic or data transfer operation to be performed. The complete ladder program, when entered into the PLC's memory, is the basis upon which the processor determines what it needs to do and exactly when it should be done.

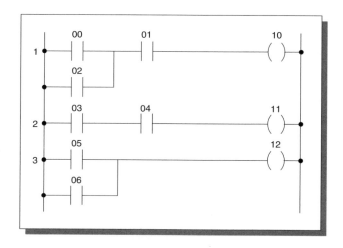

Figure 11-1. A typical Ladder logic program

The Basic Rung

A ladder rung, as shown in Figure 11-2, consists of a set of *input condition instructions*, represented by contact symbols, and an *output instruction*, represented by a coil symbol. The program symbols referenced here are introduced later in this section. Condition instructions are programmed on the left side of the rung in series, parallel, or some combination to determine the desired control logic for driving the output. The output instruction is placed in the right-most position of the rung.

On the left side of the rung is an imaginary "hot" power rail, and on the right side is its corresponding "neutral" power rail. By convention, an output will be activated if any left-to-right path of input conditions of the logic side of the rung is closed or "made." In such a case, the rung is said to be "TRUE", meaning that it has a completed circuit. The rung is also said to have *logic continuity*.

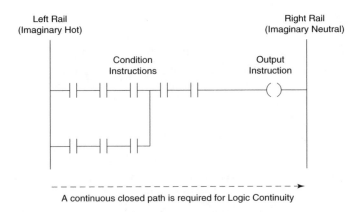

Figure 11-2. The basic Ladder rung

Function Block Rung

To perform more computer-like instructions, the ladder language incorporates what are referred to as *function block* instructions. In some controllers, timing and counting, arithmetic, data transfer, and other enhanced operations are represented in a block type of format. Since function blocks are operations to be performed based on certain input conditions, they can be considered output instructions although in some cases they will simply perform an operation and will not necessarily be placed at the end of the ladder rung.

A ladder rung with a function block is shown in Figure 11-3. Notice that there are outputs from the function block and that input conditions are programmed to determine when the instruction should be executed. Like the basic rung format, a rung with a block instruction must have logic continuity before the operation is performed. A difference, however, is that a block instruction may have more than one coil symbol at its output and multiple input lines affecting its operation.

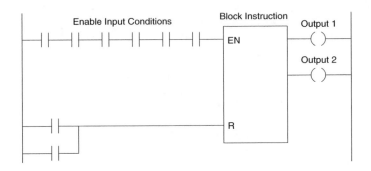

Figure 11-3. A Ladder rung with a Function Block output instruction

Typically, there is an *enable line* (or control line) that determines if the instruction should be executed. Depending on the instruction, a *reset line* may also be used to reset the function and clear specific data words or storage bits associated with the instruction. Output coils associated with the block instruction are generally used from the available internal output table and indicate conditions such as instruction executing or done, or error during execution.

Basic Program Symbols

The basic program symbols for the ladder instruction set are described in Table 11-1. They include *contact* and *coil symbols*, similar to those of electromechanical relay diagrams, as well as what is referred to as the *function block symbol*. Function blocks typically perform operations that are beyond basic relay-like control. The symbols in this table are not the only instruction symbols; however, they represent the fundamental programming elements of the ladder language, from which other instruction symbols are derived.

Table 11-1. Basic Ladder Program Symbols

LADDER SYMBOL	DESCRIPTION
Examine-ON Contact —] [—	This program element is used to examine or test the state of ON/OFF signals, for an ON state. Elements that may be examined include discrete inputs and outputs, internal storage bits, or any bit address in memory.
Examine-OFF Contact —]/[—	This program element is used to examine or test the state of ON/OFF signals, for an OFF state. Elements that may be examined include discrete inputs and outputs, internal storage bits or any bit address in memory.
Energize Output Coil —( )—	This output instruction represents any discrete output that is driven by some combination of input logic composed of input condition instructions. This symbol may reference an external or an internal output signal.
Function block —[ ]—( )—	The function block symbol represents several instructions typically used to perform non-relay logic operations. Typical block instructions include TIMER, ADD, COUNTER, COMPARE, MOVE WORD, BCD-IN, BCD-OUT.

The contact symbol instructions programmed in a ladder rung provide the ability to evaluate the conditions that determine the control of the outputs. Outputs are command instructions that cause the processor to perform an operation. Outputs are represented in the ladder rung by coil symbols or by function blocks.

Arrangement of the rung contacts is dependent on the desired control logic. Contact symbols are placed in series, parallel, or series/parallel combinations in order to achieve desired control actions, whether it be switching an output device or executing a function block. Typically, only one output instruction is allowed in a rung. However, some controllers allow parallel outputs. In most PLCs, several function blocks may be programmed in series on a single ladder rung.

The Power Flow Concept

A key aspect of PLC ladder logic operation is the concept of *power flow*. Power flow is the imaginary flow of electrons through the programmed contacts of a ladder rung. Referring back to Figure 11-2, the left power rail can be envisioned as "hot," connected to the high side of a voltage source, and the right power rail as "neutral," connected to the low side of the power source. The programmed output will energize (ON) if any path is completely closed, allowing power flow. If there is no power flow, then the output will not be activated or will de-energize.

It should be noted that by convention, power flows from left to right through contacts, and vertically either up or down in circuits with parallel branches. Power cannot flow from right to left or through horizontal contacts as with some electromechanical relay circuits. This restriction on the direction of power flow prevents the occurrence of undesired "sneak paths." Note in Figure 11-4 the possible paths for power flow. When a logic rung has complete power flow through at least one path, the rung conditions are said to be TRUE or to have logic continuity, in which case the output will be activated.

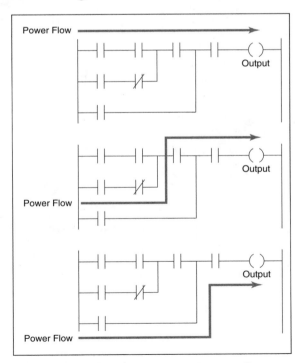

Figure 11-4. Illustration of logic power flow (or logic continuity)

Address Reference Numbers

When programmed, each condition instruction and output instruction is given a reference number that identifies what is being examined in the case of logic input conditions and what is being controlled in the case of logic output conditions. Recall that these reference numbers are actually memory locations of the data table where the status of connected I/O and internal outputs is stored. Unlike contact-type devices, which have a fixed number of normally-open and normally-closed contacts, the status of real I/O or internal outputs may be referenced throughout the control program as many times as needed.

In Figure 11-5, each device from the machine or process has been given a reference address in the ladder program. Although output coils are generally only referenced once in a program, input conditions, examine-ON (normally-open) and examine-OFF (normally-closed) contacts of internal or external outputs, can be referenced as many times as required.

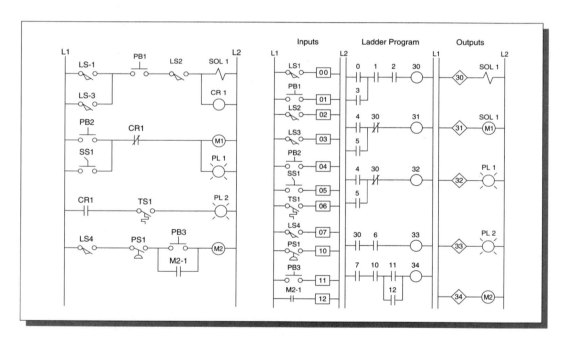

Figure 11-5. a) Hardwired relay logic b) Hardwired logic translated to Ladder logic

The Rung Matrix

This final discussion of the ladder program format relates to the maximum arrangement of program elements (symbols) allowed in a single ladder rung. Each ladder rung is limited to a maximum number of contact symbols that can be programmed in series (on one line) and a maximum number of contacts that can be programmed in parallel. Typically, the limitation of series contacts ranges between eight and ten, while the number of parallel branches ranges between six and eight.

When the series and parallel contact limitation is fully expanded, an arrangement as shown Figure 11-6 is obtained. This maximum format of columns and rows is referred to as the *rung matrix*. Generally, this format restriction is only a limitation of the display area of the programming device. In fact, many systems will allow an unlimited rung matrix. Where there are limitations, circuits that exceed the maximum number of series or parallel contacts can be rearranged to provide the same logic. The discussion of *Using Internal Outputs* in Chapter 14 addresses this situation.

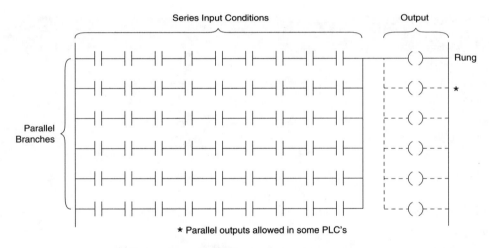

Figure 11-6. Illustration of the fully expanded ladder rung (the rung matrix)

11-2 Relay-logic Instructions

Relay-logic instructions are labeled as such because the basic program symbols used for creating the ladder diagram program are the same as those used for representing hardwired relay control circuits; the normally-open contact, normally-closed contact, and the coil symbol. In programmed logic, however, all mechanical switch contacts are represented by a software contact symbol and all mechanical coils are represented by a software coil.

Table 11-2 lists a generic set of relay-logic instructions. Since this is the most fundamental subset of ladder instructions, each of these with, the possible exception of the "transitional contacts," is found in any PLC processor that incorporates ladder programming. Although the programming symbols may differ slightly depending on the controller, the functions are generally the same.

Table 11-2. Relay-Logic Instruction Summary

INSTRUCTION	PROGRAM SYMBOL	PROGRAM FUNCTION
Examine-ON	-] [-	Test referenced signal for ON state
Examine-OFF	-]/[-	Test referenced signal for OFF state
Energize Output	-( )-	Switch output ON if logic is TRUE
Latch Output	-(L)-	Latch output ON if logic is TRUE
Unlatch Output	-(U)-	Reset latched output if logic is TRUE
One Shot Output	-(OS)-	Energize for one scan if logic goes TRUE
Positive Transitional	-]^[-	Close contact for one scan on each OFF/ON transition of referenced signal
Negative Transitional	-]v[-	Close contact for one scan on each ON/OFF transition of referenced signal
Branch Start	!-] [-	Start a parallel logic path
Branch End	-] [-!	End a parallel logic path

Note: *The transitional contact instructions have no hardwired relay equivalent, yet perform a useful function and are found in many PLCs.*

Relay-logic Application

In programmable controllers, relay-logic instructions provide the means by which the status of discrete input signals are examined and discrete output signals are controlled. In other words, these instructions allow the user to program logic circuits for processing ON/OFF signals and controlling ON/OFF type devices as opposed to examining or controlling analog or other numerical I/O devices.

In addition to providing the facility for processing ON/OFF control signals, relay-logic instructions also allow the programmer to create internal decision logic used to make the controller perform other operations that are not necessarily ON/OFF switching. Initiating an analog or positioning control function, performing an arithmetic calculation, or sending a message to an alphanumeric display all could be caused by relay logic. As long as the decision can be based on internal or external conditions that are TRUE or FALSE, these basic instructions perform the job.

Relay-logic Operations

As mentioned earlier, relay-logic instructions form the most basic subset of any ladder programming instruction set. By providing the ability to examine or control the ON/OFF status of any I/O image table bit or data table bit location, these instructions allow the programmer to create ladder logic circuits for controlling externally connected discrete devices or internal outputs used to interlock or control other portions of logic within the control program. The following discussion describes the operation of the set of instructions listed in Table 11-2.

Examine-ON   **Symbol: -] [-**

The *examine-ON* is programmed when an ON(1) status or the presence of a signal is required to allow logic continuity through the programmed circuit. Statuses that may be examined include connected digital inputs and outputs and the status of internal storage bits. When evaluated, the processor examines the referenced bit address for an ON(1) state. If the referenced address is ON(1), this normally-opened contact closes allowing power flow through the contact; if the status is OFF (0), the contact will assume its normally-open state and not allow logic continuity through the contact.

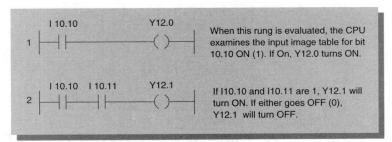

Figure 11-7. Illustration of examine-ON contact instruction

Examine-OFF   **Symbol: -]/[-**

The *examine-OFF* is programmed when an OFF(0) status or the absence of a signal is required to allow logic continuity through the programmed circuit. Statuses that may be examined include connected digital inputs or outputs and the status of internal storage bits. When evaluated, the processor examines the referenced bit address for an OFF(0) state. If the referenced address is OFF(0), this normally-closed contact remains closed, allowing power flow through the contact; if the status is ON(1), the contact opens and disables logic continuity through the contact.

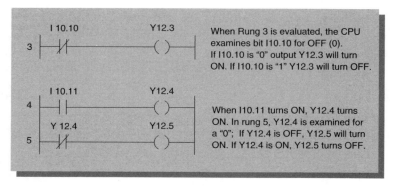

Figure 11-8. Illustration of the examine-OFF contact instruction

Energize Output   **Symbol: -( )-**

The *energize output* instruction is programmed to control the ON/OFF state of a connected digital output or an internal output. When evaluated, if any left-to-right path of series or parallel input conditions driving the output is TRUE (a closed path), the circuit will have logic continuity and the bit address referenced by the output symbol will be turned ON. The output is turned OFF if no path of input conditions is TRUE or if logic continuity is lost. When the output is turned ON, all examine-ON (N.O.) contacts of the same address will close throughout the program; all examine-OFF (N.C.) contacts with the same address will open throughout the program.

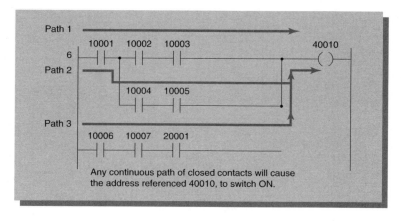

Figure 11-9. Illustration of energize output instruction

Latch Output   Symbol: -(L)-

The *latch output* instruction is a *retentive output*. It is programmed when it is desired to maintain a connected digital output or internal output in its ON state once turned ON, even though logic continuity for the circuit is lost. When evaluated, if any left-to-right path of series/parallel input conditions driving the output is TRUE, the circuit will have logic continuity and the bit address referenced by the latch symbol will be turned ON. The referenced output will remain latched ON until reset or unlatched by an *unlatch output* instruction programmed with the same bit address.

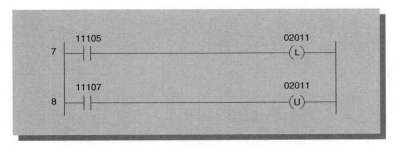

Figure 11-10. Illustration of latch output and unlatch using coil symbols

Unlatch Output   Symbol: -(U)-

The *unlatch output* instruction is programmed to reset or unlatch a latched output of the same address. When evaluated, if any left-to-right path of series/parallel input conditions driving the output is TRUE, the latched output reference by the same bit address is reset or turned OFF. The unlatch output instruction is the only automatic means of unlatching a latched output.

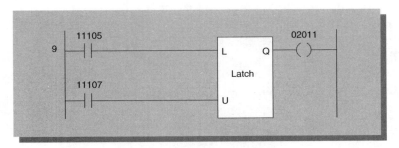

Figure 11-11. Illustration of latch/unlatch function block

One-Shot Output   Symbol: -(OS)-

A *one-shot output* is programmed to provide a pulse signal for one scan. If the rung condition goes from FALSE to TRUE, the one-shot output will energize and remain ON until the end of the current scan, at which time the output is turned OFF. The logic driving the one-shot output must go OFF and ON again to retrigger the one-scan pulse. Normal uses of the one-shot output are for setting or resetting latched outputs and initiating data movement and other operations needing to be active for only one scan. As with other output coils, contact symbols that reference the one-shot coil may be used throughout the program.

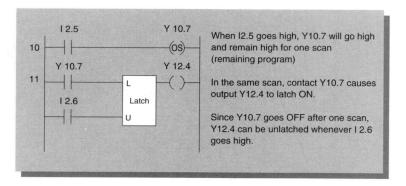

Figure 11-12. Illustration of the one-shot output instruction

Positive Transitional Contact   Symbol: -]^[-

The *positive transitional contact* is programmed to provide a one-shot pulse whenever the referenced trigger signal makes a positive or OFF to ON transition. The reference address of the transitional contact may be that of any external discrete output or an internal output. When the trigger signal referenced by the address of the positive transitional contact goes from OFF to ON (0 to 1), the contact will close and allow logic continuity for one program scan — even though the triggering signal may remain ON. The trigger signal must go OFF and ON again for the contact to close again. This instruction is used like the positive transition output coil of some PLCs.

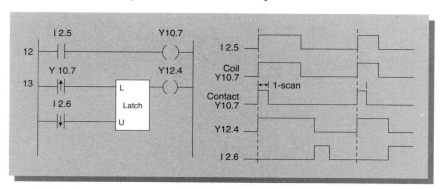

Figure 11-13. Illustration of the positive transitional contact instruction

264

Negative Transitional Contact　　　　**Symbol: -]v[-**

The *negative transitional contact* is programmed to provide a one-shot pulse whenever the referenced trigger signal makes a negative or ON-to-OFF transition. The reference address of the transitional contact may be that of any external discrete output or an internal output. When the trigger signal referenced by the address of the positive transitional contact goes from ON to OFF (1 to 0), the contact will close and allow logic continuity for one program scan — even though the triggering signal may remain ON. The trigger signal must go ON and OFF again for the contact to close again.

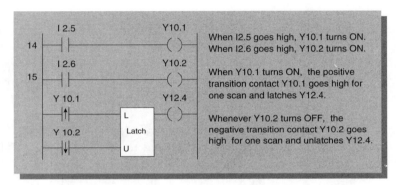

Figure 11-14. Illustration of the negative transitional contact instruction

Branch Start/Branch End　　　　**Symbol (s) !—] [- / —!**

The *branch start* instruction simply opens up a parallel branch to allow more than one logic path of input conditions to drive the output coil or input to a function block. In essence, it allows the creation of an *OR gate*. Once the branch is opened, one or more examine-ON or an examine-OFF contact element can be programmed in series. The *branch end* instruction closes the parallel branch.

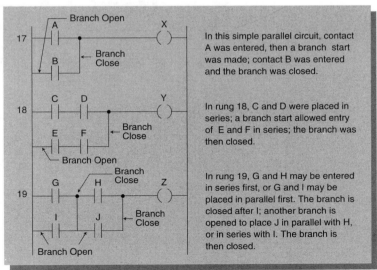

Figure 11-15. Illustration of the branch start/branch end instruction

11-3 Timer and Counter Instructions

Timer and counter instructions, like relay-logic type, are fundamental to the PLC instruction set. They provide the same functions of their electromechanical and solid-state counterparts — but are much more flexible and reliable. Table 11-3 lists a typical set of timer and counter instructions. Although the representation and details of operation may differ slightly depending on the PLC, these functions are generally implemented using coil symbols or function blocks.

Timer and Counter Application

Software timers and counters provide the ability to time intervals and count events, thereby enabling the control of various devices or internal operations based on elapsed time or based on the number of occurrences of certain events. Combined with the relay-logic instructions, timers and counters allow complete implementation of combination and sequential logic operations.

Definite advantages of software timers and counters over electro- mechanical or solid-state relay type devices, include but are not limited to the following: 1) The fact that they are internal to the processor and more or less free eliminates the purchase of hardware timers and counters that could cost as much as one $100 each; 2) The fact that they are software means there is no wiring, an unlimited number of normally-open and normally-closed contacts, the ability to easily change presets either manually or automatically, and, finally, no mechanical wear and tear.

Timer and Counter Operations

Software timers and counters are internal output instructions since they replace electromechanical devices that involved coil elements. The operation of software timers and counters is quite similar since they are in fact both counters. A counter counts the number of occurrences of some event — a timer on the other hand counts each time that a fixed time period elapses. Each PLC system has internal clock pulses, known as *time bases*. Time bases are generally .01 second, .1 second, and 1.0 second periods. To time an interval of 5 seconds, a software timer, depending on the required resolution, might count five 1.0- second intervals or maybe 500 intervals of .01-seconds.

Table 11-3. Timer and Counter Instruction Summary

INSTRUCTION	PROGRAM SYMBOL	PROGRAM FUNCTION
Timer ON-Delay Energize	TON_DE PW: AW: TB:	Energize after ON-delay time out
Timer ON-Delay De-Energize	TON_DD PW: AW: TB:	De-Energize after ON-delay time out
Timer OFF-Delay De-Energize	TOF_DD PW: AW: TB:	De-Energize after OFF-delay time out
Retentive ON-Delay Timer	RTO_DE PW: AW: TB:	Retain elapsed ON-time until reset
UP/DOWN Counter	CNTR UP PW: DN AW: R	Increment count by one on each OFF-ON transition of UP input line Decrement count by one on each OFF-ON transition of DOWN input line

In performing their operation, both timers and counters generally require two sixteen-bit word locations; a *preset word(PW)* to hold the preset time or count, and an *accumulator word(AW)* to keep track of the accumulated time or count. The preset word, which is entered by the programmer, tells the processor how many time-base intervals to count (timer instruction) or how many occurrences of an event to count (counter instruction) before energizing the time-reached or count-reached output. The maximum value that can be held by the preset and accumulator words is dependent on the data format used by the controller, but is typically 999 for three-digit BCD or +32767 for signed decimal.

ON-delay Energize

The *ON-delay energize* instruction is programmed to provide time-delayed action or to measure the duration for which some condition is enabled or an event is active. When evaluated, if any path of conditions driving the timer goes TRUE, the timer begins counting intervals of the programmed time base. The elapsed time is stored in the timer accumulator word (AW) and is continually compared to the timer preset word (PW). When the accumulated time equals the preset time, the timer output is energized (See Figure 11-16) . All examine-ON (N.O.) contacts of the timer will close; all examine-OFF (N.C.) contacts of the timer will open. If logic continuity is lost before the timer times out, the accumulated time is reset to zero.

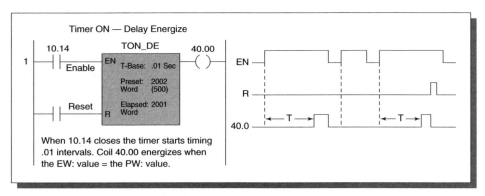

Figure 11-16. ON-delay energize timer instruction

ON-delay De-energize

The *ON-delay de-energize* instruction operates similarly to the ON-delay energize, except that when the timer is enabled, the timer output coil will energize immediately. The output remains ON until the programmed delay has elapsed or until the signal that triggered the timer goes OFF. When the contents of the accumulated word (AW) equals that of the preset word (PW), the timer output coil will de-energize. A timing diagram of the ON-delay de-energize is illustrated in Figure 11-17.

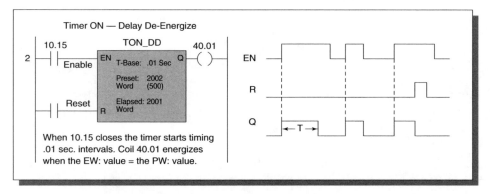

Figure 11-17. ON-delay de-energize timer instruction

OFF-Delay De-energize

The *OFF-delay de-energize* instruction is programmed to provide time-delayed action or to measure the duration for which some condition has been disabled or some event inactivated. When the logic driving the OFF-delay de-energize instruction makes a FALSE- to-TRUE transition, the timer output immediately goes TRUE. If logic continuity goes FALSE, the timer starts timing. The elapsed time is stored in the timer accumulator word and is continually compared to the timer preset word. When the accumulated time equals the preset time, the timer output is de-energized. All examine-ON (N.O.) contacts of the timer will open; all examine-OFF (N.C.) contacts of the timer will close. If logic continuity is restored before the timer times out, the accumulated time is reset to zero and the output is re-energized.

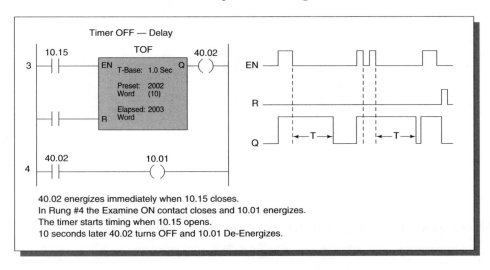

Figure 11-18. OFF-delay de-energize timer instruction

Retentive ON-delay Timer

The *retentive ON-delay timer* instruction is programmed if it is necessary for the accumulated time to be retained even if logic continuity or system power is lost. When evaluated, if any path of conditions driving the timer goes TRUE, the timer begins timing and stores the elapsed time in the timer accumulator word. If logic continuity is ever lost before the timer times out, the accumulator word retains the elapsed time and will resume timing at the same value when the rung goes TRUE again. When the accumulated value equals the preset value, the timer output is energized and the timer stops timing. If any rung path driving the reset line goes TRUE at any time or while the timer is timing, the accumulated value and the status bits of the retentive timer are reset to zero.

Up/Down Counter

The *up/down counter* instruction will count up by one for each OFF-to-ON transition on the UP line and counts down by one for each OFF-to-ON transition on the DOWN line. A count up or count down pulse may be generated by any discrete I/O or an internal signal that makes a periodic OFF-to-ON transition. When the accumulated count equals the preset value, the counter output coil will energize. Depending on the controller, the down count will stop when it reaches zero or at the maximum negative value. Since counters are retentive, unless reset, the accumulator word will retain its contents and continue to count for each OFF-to-ON transition of the counted events. If the reset line goes TRUE, the accumulator word of the referenced counter is reset to zero and all status bits associated with the counter are reset.

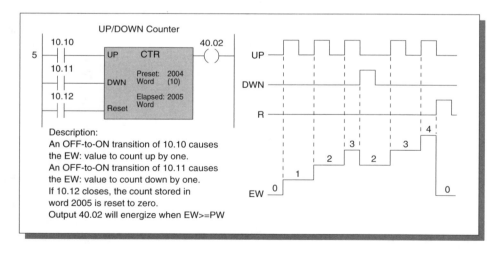

Figure 11-19. UP/Down counter instruction.

11-4 Scan Control Instructions

Before *scan control instructions* were available, the user had no control over the order of program evaluation by the processor. Program sequences would be executed in the exact sequential order in which they were entered into memory. This inflexible nature of ladder program execution had two major drawbacks.

The first drawback was the inability to reduce the program scan even if it was required — this was true since each sequence was executed sequentially from start to finish, regardless of whether or not changes had taken place in I/O status or if there was no need to scan a segment of program code. A second consequence of an inflexible scan was the inability to read critical changes in input status or to immediately change the state of an output based on this critical change in input status. This inability resulted from the fact that program execution had to complete before the I/O could be updated.

Table 11-4. Typical Scan Control Instruction Summary

INSTRUCTION	SYMBOL	PROGRAM FUNCTION
Jump	-(JMP)-	- Causes a jump to the designated label.
Jump to Subroutine	-(JSR)-	- Causes a jump to the designated subroutine.
Label	-]LBL[-	- Labels target jump to rung for JMP.
Subroutine	-(SUB)-	- Labels the start of a ladder subroutine.
Return	-(RET)-	- Identifies end of subroutine program.
Master Control Relay	-(MCR)-	- Enable/disable a partitioned program zone.
Zone Control Last State	-(ZCL)-	- Enable/disable a partitioned program zone.
End	-(END)-	- Identifies end of partitioned program zone.
Immediate Input	-]II[-	- Immediate (direct) input status read.
Immediate Output	-(IO)-	- Immediate (direct) output status write.

Scan Control Operations

Scan control instructions, otherwise referred to as *program flow control instructions*, will differ widely with different PLCs — both in terms of what functions are provided, as well as in how they are implemented. In general, these instructions provide the user with the ability to determine when certain control sequences should or shouldn't be evaluated and the ability to read input status or update output status on demand and prior to the normal I/O update. Overall, these instructions allow processing needs to be serviced on an as-needed basis.

Jump-to-Label   Symbol: -(JMP)-

The *jump-to-label* instruction redirects the normal order of program execution if its rung conditions are TRUE. If the rung is TRUE, program execution jumps to the network referenced by the JMP coil address and resumes execution. Typically, the rung to which execution is redirected is identified by a label instruction (e.g., -]LBL[-) having the same address referenced by the JMP coil. The label instruction is normally programmed as the first contact in the target sequence. (See Figure 11-20). In some processors, the JMP coil address references the coil address of the rung to which it is jumping. Other instruction sets use a SKIP instruction that allows a designated number of rungs to be skipped.

Label Contact   Symbol: -]LBL[-

The *label contact* instruction identifies the target rung to which program execution is passed, by a JMP instruction. The LBL instruction is typically programmed in the first position in the rung and its reference address must match that of the JMP coil instruction with which it is used. Each LBL instruction then is programmed only once with a unique address and is paired with a JMP instruction. (See Figure 11-20.) The LBL contact simply acts as a pointer and marks the first rung of a section of program or subprogram.

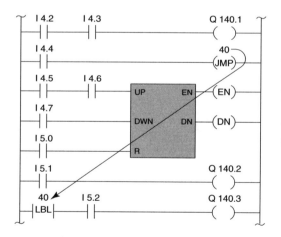

When input I4.4 is set, the processor passes control or jumps to label 40 and continues program execution from there.

The rungs between these two points are not executed.

Figure 11-20. Illustration of jump-to-label instructions

Start Subroutine   Symbol: -(SUB)-

The *subroutine* instruction is used to mark the beginning of a ladder subroutine. A subroutine is a set of ladder program rungs that perform a specific function. When called by a jump to subroutine output instruction having the same reference number, the rungs within the subroutine are executed until reaching the RET coil instruction, which causes program execution to return to the ladder rung immediately following the rung that called the subroutine. The start subroutine rung simply marks the first rung of the subroutine and therefore is programmed without any conditional inputs.

Jump-to-Subroutine   Symbol: -(JSR)-

The *jump-to-subroutine* instruction redirects the normal order of program execution if its rung conditions are TRUE. When executed, program execution jumps to the rung having a subroutine output coil of the same address referenced by the jump-to-subroutine coil instruction. Program execution continues from the first rung of the subroutine until a *return-from-subroutine* instruction is encountered. Each subroutine program segment must be partitioned with a labeled rung identifying the subroutine start (e.g., -(SUB)-) and end (e.g., -(RET)-). A subroutine call is illustrated in Figure 11-21.

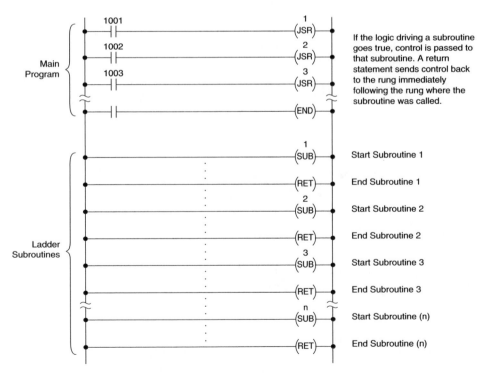

Figure 11-21. Illustration subroutine instruction

Return Coil   Symbol: -(RET)-

The *return coil* instruction is used to terminate each programmed subroutine. It is programmed without any conditional inputs and as the last rung of each subroutine. Because it has no conditional inputs, it is unconditionally executed whenever encountered. When executed, it causes program execution to return to the sequence immediately following the JSB instruction that called the subroutine. The RET instruction is illustrated in Figure 11-21.

Master Control Relay   Symbol: -(MCR)-

The *master control relay* instruction is used to control the enabling or disabling of a partitioned group of ladder rungs. Its operation is similar to the electromechanical master control relay which, if not energized, disables power from a section of a control circuit. As illustrated in Figure 11-22, each MCR output rung marks the beginning of the partitioned zone and is used in conjunction with an END output coil, which marks the end of the partitioned zone. When the conditions driving the MCR are TRUE, the referenced output is energized, enabling logic rungs within the zone to be executed. If the MCR output is switched OFF, all non-retentive outputs inside the zone are reset.

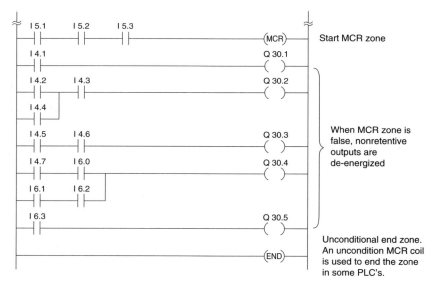

Figure 11-22. Illustration of the MCR instruction

Zone Control Last State   Symbol: -(ZCL)-

The *zone control last state* instruction is used to control the enabling or disabling execution of a partitioned group of ladder rungs. Its operation is similar to that of the MCR output instruction. Each ZCL output rung that marks the beginning of a partitioned group of ladder rungs and is used in conjunction with the END output coil, which marks the end of the partition. When the conditions driving the ZCL output are TRUE, the referenced output is energized, enabling logic rungs within the zone to be executed. If the ZCL output is switched OFF, execution of the zone is disabled and all outputs inside the zone are held in their last state.

End Zone   Symbol: -(END)-

The *end zone output* instruction is used to mark the last rung of a partitioned group of logic rungs inside a MCR or ZCL zone. This output instruction simply marks the end of a zone and therefore has no conditional inputs. The END output instruction is generally referenced with an address to match a programmed MCR or ZCL output, thereby allowing a partitioned zone to be nested inside another partitioned zone. A partitioned zone is illustrated in Figure 11-22.

Immediate Input   Symbol: -]II[-

The *immediate input* instruction is used when the status of a digital input is required immediately — that is, prior to the normal I/O update at the end of the program scan. When evaluated, the processor bypasses the I/O image table and reads the status of the referenced input directly from the I/O bus. Processing of the immediate input instruction may vary depending on the controller. Some controllers update the input image table with the status of the referenced input only; others may read the entire module. The symbol shown here, is used to examine the ON state; a separate immediate input instruction (e.g., -]I/[-) for examining for an OFF state is also usually available. (See Figure 11-23 on next page.)

Immediate Output   Symbol: -(IO)-

The *immediate output* instruction is used when the status of a digital output must be updated immediately as opposed to waiting until the normal I/O update at the end of the program scan. When the logic conditions driving the immediate output coil are evaluated as TRUE or FALSE, the processor immediately writes the new ON/OFF status directly to the module of the referenced output address. (See Figure 11-23.)

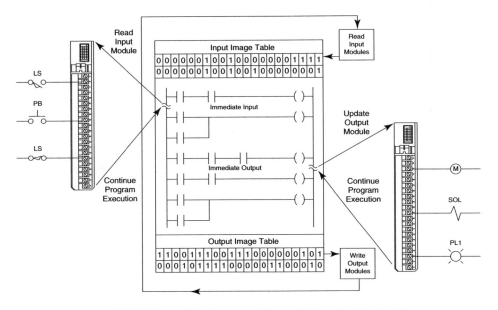

Figure 11-23. Immediate input and immediate output instructions

11-5 Data Manipulation Instructions

In simple terms, data manipulation instructions allow numerical data stored in the controller's memory to be handled and operated on within the control program. This category of instructions, called *word operations*, provide the software elements through which the user may begin to truly exploit the computer capabilities of the PLC.

In essence, data manipulation instructions extend a controller's capability from that of simple ON/OFF control based on binary logic, to quantitative decision making involving arithmetic, data comparisons and conversions — which in turn can be applied to analog, positioning, and other forms of numerical control. Moreover, these instruction subsets allow data to be gathered, tracked, manipulated, and formatted to produce meaningful diagnostic and production reports. Data manipulation instructions can be categorized into five subsets, which are described in subsequent subtitles of this section.

- ❑ Arithmetic Operations
- ❑ Comparison Operations
- ❑ Conversion Operations
- ❑ Logic File Operations
- ❑ Shift Operations

Arithmetic Operations

Most PLCs provide the four basic arithmetic functions of addition, subtraction, multiplication and division. These instructions allow the control program to perform basic production accounting and event tracking, as well as providing the ability to solve simple algorithms for control and diagnostic purposes. Mid-range processors and those at the higher end of the product spectrum offer enhanced instruction sets that may include greater functionality such as floating-point arithmetic, square root extraction, and logarithmic and trigonometric functions.

Table 11-5 illustrates typical formats of basic arithmetic operations. Programming for these operations generally involves specifying three word addresses. Two source addresses, Word A and Word B, reference the locations of two numbers upon which the operation is to be performed. Word C references the sixteen-bit location where the result of the operation is stored. When the logic driving the rung is TRUE, the source data is retrieved, the operation is performed, and the result is stored in the location designated as the destination word. Coil outputs report conditions such as execution enabled (EN), overflow (OV), done (DN), results, or other conditions.

Table 11-5. Typical Arithmetic Instruction Implementation

OPERATION	TYPICAL FORMATS	PROGRAM FUNCTION
Add Block	ADD EN ( ) WA: WB: WC: DN ( )	Perform sixteen-bit Addition/Store Result
Subtraction Block	SUB EN ( ) WA: WB: WC: DN ( )	Perform sixteen-bit Subtraction/Store Result
Multiplication Block	MUL EN ( ) WA: WB: WC: DN ( )	Perform sixteen-bit Multiplication/Store Result
Division Block	DIV EN ( ) WA: WB: WC: DN ( )	Perform sixteen-bit Division/Store Result

The *double-precision* arithmetic blocks (ADD_D, SUB_D, MUL_D, DIV_D), shown in Figure 11-24, are used for integer numbers greater than 32,767. Such numbers are stored in two consecutive words (32-bits). In this case, the source and destination addresses designate the starting addresses of the source data and the destination data.

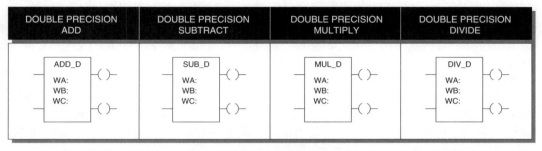

Figure 11-24. Double precision arithmetic instructions for 32-bit integers

Some controllers also provide what is referred to as *arithmetic file operations*, as shown in Figure 11-25. This simply means that the operation is performed on two blocks of words. In this case, the parameter "L" allows the length or number of words in each block to be specified. Figure 11-26 illustrates a file addition. Each word of file A is added to the corresponding word in file B, and the individual results from each addition are stored in the corresponding word in file C. With such operations, it is usually possible to specify the number of processor scans allowed to complete the entire operation.

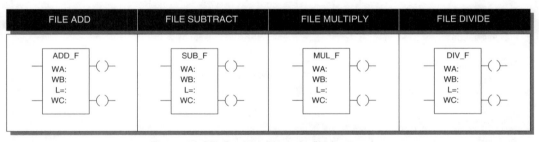

Figure 11-25. Basic arithmetic file instructions

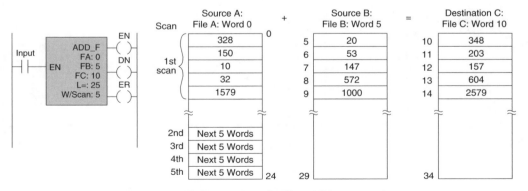

Figure 11-26. Illustration of a file addition operation

Comparison Operations

Comparison instructions allow program decisions to be made based on the outcome of comparisons made between the values stored in word locations. These instructions include comparisons such as, *greater than*, *less than*, *equal to* and *not equal to*. Typical applications involve range checking, setpoint control, limit checks on calculations, and other such comparison checking. A typical use of the *compare for equality*, for instance, is to determine whether or not a timer has reached a certain intermediate value.

Ladder diagram comparison instructions are normally represented using either contact symbology or the block format, as shown in Table 11-7. While some controllers may provide a separate block instruction for each type of comparison, others may use a single block that includes a mode parameter that allows the comparison type to be specified.

Table 11-7. Typical Data Comparison Instructions

OPERATION	TYPICAL SYMBOL	PROGRAM FUNCTION
Less Than Comparison	A B -]<[-	Test if word A is less than word B
Greater Than Comparison	A B -]>[-	Test if word A is greater than word B
Equality Comparison	A B -]=[-	Test if word A is equal to word B
Not Equal Comparison	A B -]><[-	Test if word A is not equal to word B
Less Than or Equal to	A B -]<=[-	Test if word A is less than or equal to word B
Greater Than or Equal to	A B -]>=[-	Test if word A is greater than or equal to word
Compare Block CMP	CMP EN -( )- A: B: MODE:<= DN -( )-	Perform specified comparison and set result bits

Conversion Operations

Conversion operations, like comparisons, are performed on PLC words. They are used when it is necessary to change the format of the data stored in one location to some other format before the data can be used in a particular operation. Typical conversions are listed in Table 11-8.

A typical conversion, is from binary-coded decimal (BCD) to binary (decimal) format. Such a conversion would be necessary if a BCD number input from thumbwheel switches, is to be used in an arithmetic operation, but the CPU performs its arithmetic operations in decimal. Before the operation can be performed, the BCD value must first be converted to binary. Conversely, binary data output to a seven-segment display or other BCD device, would require binary-to-BCD conversion.

Table 11-8. Typical Ladder Conversion Instructions

OPERATION	TYPICAL SYMBOL	PROGRAM FUNCTION
BCD-to-Binary	BCD_BIN EN —( )— WA: WB: L=: DN —( )—	Convert word A from BCD to Binary store in word B
Binary-to-BCD	BIN_BCD EN —( )— WA: WB: L=: DN —( )—	Convert word A from Binary to BCD store in word B
Fixed-to-Floating Point	FIX_FLT EN —( )— WA: WB: L=: DN —( )—	Convert word A from Fixed to Floating store in word B
Floating-to-Fixed Point	FLT_FIX EN —( )— WA: WB: L=: DN —( )—	Convert word A from Floating to Fixed store in word B

Generally, if a word operation such as arithmetic or comparison is to be performed on the data stored in two words, the data stored in the two locations must be of the same format. In other words, two BCD values may be added or two decimal values may be compared. If one of the numbers was not first converted to the format of the other, the result would be erroneous. Data input to or output from the PLC may also require conversion, depending on the input or output device and the operation performed on the data. The parameter "L" here allows file conversion operations; L specifies how many locations are converted.

Logic File Operations

Logic file operations, also called *logic matrix operations,* perform logical operations on groups of sixteen-bit or 32-bit words, referred to in this case as a file. A file may consist of one or more words.

The number of words in a file is called the *file length,* which may vary in terms of maximum length depending on the controller. Generally, any word locations may be used in logic operations, including I/O table words, timer and counter words or any general purpose word locations. The basic logic file instructions are listed in Table 11-9.

The AND, OR, and XOR instructions perform the specified operation between two files (A and B) and store the result in a third file Y. When either of these instructions is executed, the operation is performed on the corresponding bits of each word of file A and B, and the result is stored in the corresponding bits of each word in file Y. The NOT file instruction performs the operation on one file A and stores the result in a second file B. When executed, each bit of each word in file A is inverted (1=0, 0=1) and the result is stored in the corresponding word of file B.

Logic file operations are generally implemented in a block format that specifies the starting word address of the source files and destination file and the length of the files. A *control line* causes execution of the operation when the rung is TRUE. Some blocks have two or three outputs to signify block enabled, execution done, and error. These instructions are very useful once mastered and properly applied. Through the execution of one of these instructions it is possible to simultaneously set the desired states of sixteen-bits of a single word or of several words. Let's examine the operation of these instructions.

Table 11-9. Typical Logic File Instructions

OPERATION	TYPICAL SYMBOL	PROGRAM FUNCTION
AND File	AND_F EN — EN —( )— WA: WB: — DN —( )— L=: WY:	Perform logical AND on two or more words
OR File	OR_F EN — EN —( )— WA: WB: — DN —( )— L=: WY:	Perform logical OR on two or more words
XOR File	XOR_F EN — EN —( )— WA: WB: — DN —( )— L=: WY:	Perform logical XOR on two or more words
NOT File	NOT_F EN — EN —( )— WA: —( )— L=: WY: — DN	Perform logical NOT on two or more words Note: Also called Complement

AND File. The AND instruction performs the logical "AND" function on the contents of file A with the contents of file B and transfers the result to file Y. Operation of the AND is illustrated in the truth table in Figure 11-27. If the logic driving the block is TRUE, the AND is performed on the number of words defined by the file length, as illustrated in Figure 11-27. The contents of files A and B are unchanged by the operation.

AND TRUTH TABLE	AND FILES A AND B	
A B Y 0 0 = 0 0 1 = 0 1 0 = 0 1 1 = 1	1100 0011 0000 1111 1100 1010 1111 0101 1100 0010 0000 0101	File A File B File Y is Result

Figure 11-27. Example AND File operation, length = 1

OR File. The OR instruction performs the logical "OR" function on the contents of file A with the contents of file B and transfers the result to file Y. Operation of the OR function is illustrated in the truth table in Figure 11-28. If the logic driving the block is TRUE, the operation is performed on the total number of words defined by the file length, as illustrated in Figure 11-28. The contents of files A and B are unchanged by the operation.

OR TRUTH TABLE	OR FILES A AND B	
A B Y 0 0 = 0 0 1 = 1 1 0 = 1 1 1 = 1	1010 0101 1111 1100 1111 0000 0000 0011 1111 0101 1111 1111	File A File B File Y is Result

Figure 11-28. Example OR File operation, length = 1

Exclusive-OR (XOR) File. The XOR instruction performs the logical "XOR" function on the contents of file A with the contents of file B and transfers the result to file Y. Operation of the XOR function is illustrated in the truth table in Figure 11-29. If the logic driving the block is TRUE, the operation is performed, as illustrated in Figure 11-29, on the total number of words defined by the file length. The contents of files A and B are unchanged by the operation.

XOR TRUTH TABLE	XOR FILES A AND B	
A B Y 0 0 = 0 0 1 = 1 1 0 = 1 1 1 = 0	1100 0011 0000 1111 1100 1111 1111 1111 0000 1100 1111 0000	File A File B File Y is Result

Figure 11-29. Example XOR File operation, length = 1

NOT File. The NOT instruction, sometimes called "complement," performs the logical "NOT" operation on the contents of file A and transfers the result to file B. If the logic driving the block is TRUE, the operation is performed, changing each 1 to 0 and each 0 to 1 in each word in file A. The results of each inverted word is transferred to the corresponding word in file B, as illustrated in Figure 11-30.

NOT TRUTH TABLE	NOT FILES A	
A Y 0 > 1 1 > 0	0000 1111 0101 1100 1111 0000 1010 0011	File A File Y is Result

Figure 11-30. Example NOT File operation, length = 1

Negate File. The Negate instruction is used to change the sign of the numbers within a file A. When the operation is performed, each positive number is changed to a negative number and each negative number is changed to a positive number. Depending on the controller, negative numbers may be represented using one's complement or two's complement. Figure 11-31 illustrates the results of file A after negation using the one's complement method. (See chapter 2.)

NEGATE OPERATION	FILE A	FILE A NEGATED
+5 > -5	0000 0000 0000 0101	1111 1111 1111 1010
-7 > +7	1111 1111 1111 1000	0000 0000 0000 0111
-10 > +10	1111 1111 1111 0101	0000 0000 0000 1010

Figure 11-31. Example Negate File operation, length = 3

Shift Operations

Shift operations are used to move bit data to the left or right within a given word location, or to move word data within a stack of words. These instructions are often used in materials conveying applications where information on discrete parts must be tracked for some distance, prior to performing some other function. For example, as different parts moving along a single conveyer enter a paint area, they are tracked according to part number, which later down the line determines what color paint is used. A more common usage is to track good parts and rejects for a given distance, then later using this information to perform a sort. Typical shift and rotate instructions are listed in Table 11-10.

Table 11-10. Typical Shift/Rotate Instructions

OPERATION	TYPICAL SYMBOL	PROGRAM FUNCTION
Shift Left	SHW_L EN EN —( )— WA: L=: SH DN —( )— RESET	Shift word to the left by the specified number of bits
Shift Right	SHW_R EN EN —( )— WA: L=: SH DN —( )— RESET	Shift word to the right by the specified number of bits
Shift Register	SHIFT_R SH EN —( )— WA: L=: DATA DN —( )— RESET	Shift the bit (1 or 0) generated on the DATA input line. Shift one position to the right whenever the SHIFT line goes TRUE.

Shift Word Left/Right. The shift word instructions allow the bits within a word to be shifted to the left or to the right by some number of positions. The number of positions is determined by the position parameter. As illustrated in Figure 11-32, in the shift right operation, as the data is shifted the least-significant bit is lost with each shift by one position.

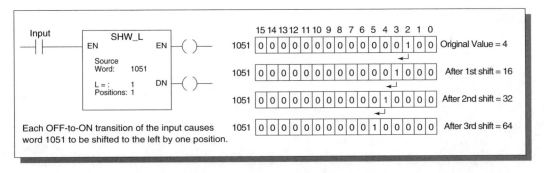

Figure 11-32. Illustration of shift left operation (shift right is in opposite direction)

Depending on the instruction set, the shift instructions will require that a word address be specified, the number of positions to be shifted on each shift, and the length which determines the number of words to be used. For example, a length of two would mean that two 16-bit words or 32 bits would be shifted. The LEFT/RIGHT lines determine the direction of the shift, while each ON/OFF transition of the control line determines when the shift is performed.

While application of the shift word instruction is not readily apparent, two common uses are to perform fast multiplication or division by multiples of two (i.e., 2,4,8,16, etc.). The value in a word location is multiplied by 2 simply by shifting to the left by one position. Shifting four positions to the left multiplies the value by 16. Conversely, shifting four positions to the right results in a division by 16.

Shift Register. The classical PLC shift register is shown in Figure 11-33. In operation, whenever the SHIFT line makes an OFF-to-ON transition, the current value of 1 or 0 on the DATA line is what gets shifted through the specified word location. As each new data value enters the shift register, the previous values are shifted to the right through the register. The input driving the DATA line is typically an external discrete I/O point or an internal output. The length parameter specifies the width of the shift register or the total number of 16-bit words that make up the shift register. The RESET line, when activated, clears the shift register data to all zeros.

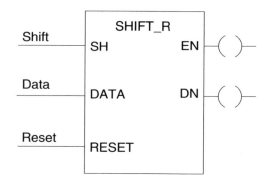

Figure 11-33. Illustration of the shift register instruction

A shift register is generally used in material handling applications where some form of binary information must be linked or synchronized with a moving part on a conveyer. The term binary information as used here applies to any two conditions that can be assigned to the moving product — for example, a good part or bad part, size A or size B, pass or reject. As the part moves along the conveyer, some form of sensing element will decide which of the two categories the passing product falls into. If, for example, a photoeye that drives the DATA line on the shift register is fixed such that the beam is blocked if a case is tall enough and is not blocked otherwise, then a 1 will indicate a tall case and a 0 indicates a short case.

11-7 Data Transfer Instructions

Data transfer instructions involve taking the numerical data from one or more storage locations and copying it to one or more new storage locations. The place from which data is moved is called the *source location* and the place to which it is moved is called *destination location*. When the data transfer involves more than one word, the specified source and destination addresses give the starting address. The memory locations from which data can be accessed or moved to, generally include the entire application memory. However, certain areas utilized by the processor may be off limits for user application.

In general, data transfer operations serve two basic requirements that you will have in your control programming:

1)   Internal Transfers: Moving data from one place to another prior to performing an operation, or moving the data to a new location after an operation has been performed.

2)   I/O Data Transfers: Reading or controlling an externally connected numerical I/O device, such as analog, BCD, or other devices requiring word manipulation.

An internal data transfer may involve automatically changing the preset value for a timer or counter or setting a new high or low pressure limit. Such a transfer may be based on certain true or false conditions. The process of reading the BCD value generated by a thumbwheel switch or controlling the value sent to a seven-segment BCD display, are both examples of I/O data transfer operations. A list of commonly used data transfer instructions are provided in Table 11-11. Let's proceed to a description of these instructions.

Move Word

The *move word* instruction essentially performs a copy function. The parameters of a typical move instruction are shown in Table 11-11. When the control line driving the block is TRUE, the contents of the word location specified as the source word (WA) are copied into the word location specified as the destination location (WB). The contents of the source word are left unchanged. The internal output is energized when the instruction is completed.

Table 11-11. Typical Data Transfer Instructions

OPERATION	TYPICAL SYMBOL	PROGRAM FUNCTION
Move Word	MOVE_W EN EN —( )— WA: WB: DN —( )—	Move contents of word A to word B
Move Block	MOVE_B EN EN —( )— WA: WB: DN —( )— L=:	Move words from block A to block B
Move Word to Table	MOVW_T EN EN —( )— WA: WB: DN —( )— L=: PTR: ER —( )—	Move specified word A to table of word B
Move Table to Word	MOVT_W EN EN —( )— WA: WB: DN —( )— L=: PTR: ER —( )—	Move word from table A to word B

Depending on the controller's instruction set, the move word instruction may also be used to read input data from a word input module, such as a BCD input, or to write data to a word output module, such as a BCD output. In this case the source word or destination word need only reference the specific word location to which the I/O module has been mapped. In Figure 11-34 a four-decade thumbwheel (TWS) is connected to a sixteen-point input module that was mapped to input word address IW10. The *move word* instruction reads the module input from word ten of the *input image table* and copies it to word location 30.

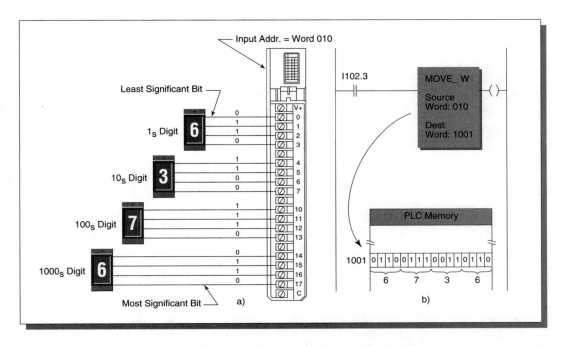

Figure 11-34. Illustration of the move word operation

Move Block

The move block instruction performs the same operation as the move word instruction; however, it serves to copy a group of words from one location to another. In addition to being used to move the data from any block of words, this instruction is also how some PLCs handle reading or controlling word I/O modules, such as analog, encoders, BCD, or intelligent I/O. Figure 11-35 shows that the move block instruction requires a starting source location and starting destination location to be specified, along with a length (L), designating the number of words in the block.

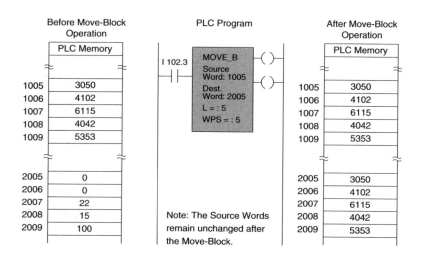

Figure 11-35. Illustration of the move block operation

A control line determines when the block is executed and an internal output signals when the block move is done. When logic continuity is TRUE on the control line, the data contents of the block starting at word A are copied to the new locations starting at word B. Typically, the instruction will also specify the maximum number of words to be moved on one scan. This parameter minimizes the effect on overall scan time.

Table Move Instructions

In the PLC's application memory, a contiguous grouping of sixteen-bit words are referred to as a *block, table* or *file*. In previous discussions of instructions, the concept of a block of words has already been introduced. A table is generally used to group a set of data values that are related in some way — for example, a recipe or a set of PID parameters for a known response. There are two basic table instructions, *move word to table*, and *move table to word*. Table instructions transfer the contents of a sixteen-bit word to a table or extract it from a table.

In each of these instructions, a word address is specified for the first word of the table. A length parameter specifies the number of words in the table and a pointer word determines where data is placed into or extracted from the table. A word location is also specified for the source of data moved to the table, or for the destination of data extracted from the table. A pointer is merely a number whose value represents an address location. It is therefore said to point to a location. The pointer can be manipulated by the program to determine the location of the value to be loaded into or taken from the table.

Move Word to Table

The *move word-to-table* instruction is shown in Figure 11-36. When the *control line* is enabled or has continuity, the value stored in word A is transferred to the location in the table specified by the value currently in the pointer word. The initial pointer value is generally set to equal the starting word location of the table or is preloaded to point at a location other than the first word. When the control line is TRUE, the pointer can be incremented to point to the next table location. The reset line when TRUE, resets the pointer to the top of the table.

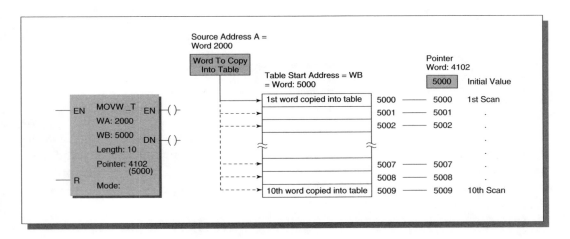

Figure 11-36. Illustration of a move word-to-table operation

Although the *move word-to-table* instruction allows data stored in a single sixteen-bit word location to be transferred to a table of words, it is generally used to take data stored in scattered locations and transfer it to the table. The data in these words would first have to be moved, one at a time, to the location that is subsequently moved to the table. In other words, data is multiplexed through a specified location. Common reasons for doing this might be to prepare data to be transferred over a network to an operator display station, or simply to log recipe data that was used on the last machine cycle.

Move Table to Word

The *move table-to-word* instruction is shown in Figure 11-37. It functions just the opposite of the *move word-to-table*. When enabled, the values stored in the table are transferred to the destination location specified by word B, starting with the location specified by the current value in the pointer word. The pointer value is generally set to equal the starting word location of the table or is preloaded to point to a location other than the starting word, if required. When the control line is TRUE, the pointer is incremented automatically after each word is moved from the table. The reset line when TRUE, resets the pointer to the top of the table.

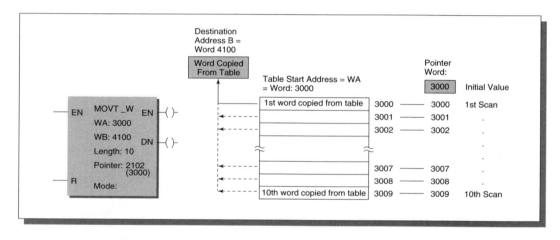

Figure 11-37. Illustration of a move table-to-word operation

A common application of this instruction is to access and use data from a table in which each value in the table is a setpoint for the same function, but for different machine or process cycles. In this case, the pointer is incremented once on each machine cycle, thereby transferring the appropriate word from the table to the word used in the process.

11-8 Special Function Instructions

This discussion of ladder language operations will cover PID control, drum sequencer, and diagnostic instructions. Although the instructions covered here may be implemented in a variety of ways depending on the controller, as with the other instructions covered already, the basic functionality of the operations is quite generic. Therefore, an understanding of our example instructions will provide the basis for how these operations will be carried out in any controller.

PID Block

Proportional-integral-derivative control, typically referred to as *PID control*, is a type of closed-loop control that seeks to maintain a process variable, such as temperature, at a given setpoint by maintaining a zero difference between the desired setpoint and the actual value of the process variable. PID control is generally implemented in the form of an algorithm incorporated in the firmware of some PLCs or in an intelligent PID module in others. A PID function block is shown in Figure 11-38.

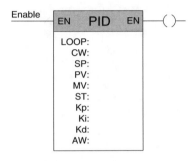

Figure 11-38. A typical PID Function Block

The PID block must be supplied with word storage locations for each loop parameter, as well as initial values for each parameter. Typical parameters include the loop number, the loop tuning parameters, *proportional gain* (P), *reset* (I), *rate* (D), loop *setpoint* (SP), *process variable* (PV, analog input), *manipulated variable* (MV, analog output), the *manual manipulated variable* (MMV, manual output), and loop sampling time (ST). Other parameter settings may include alarm limits for the setpoint and process variable, dead bands, remote setpoint word locations, and ramp rate if setpoint ramping is possible. A control word (CW) in the function block allows the various operating modes of the loop to be controlled. An alarm word reports various loop alarm statuses.

While the PID function is shown implemented in the ladder format, some PLCs provide a loop programming template for easy setup of the loop parameters. The parameters are passed to the algorithm and specified word locations provide output from the algorithm to allow access to the loop from the control program. Word storage locations for the various parameters and data input will still have to be provided; however, this is all supplied in a fill-in-the-blank approach.

Drum Sequencer Block

The sequencer block is illustrated in Figure 11-39. This block instruction is applied to sequential machine or process operations in which a complete cycle consists of several steps. Each step involves the simultaneous activation or deactivation of several devices. Sequencing from one step to the next is either caused by a unique event or is time driven. Operation of the sequencer is analogous to the mechanical cam, which as it rotates, engages other mechanical elements. A more graphic illustration might be the mechanical music box, in which a pegged cylinder rotates in steps, striking multiple resonators at each step, thereby producing music.

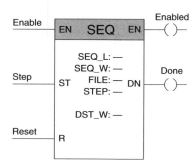

Figure 11-39. Drum sequencer function block instruction

Operation of the sequence block is based on a table of words or a file, as shown in Figure 11-40. The values contained in the words are output to one or more digital output modules at each step. As shown in the block format, the *sequencer length* specifies the number of steps in the sequence while the *sequencer width* specifies the number of sixteen-bit words output at each step. The bit values in each word are preset to 1 or 0, determining whether a device will be turned ON or OFF. The starting word address of the file is specified by the FILE parameter, while the destination word (DST_W) sets the starting word address of the digital output modules that drive the output devices.

STEP	OUTPUT WORD 1	OUTPUT WORD 2
001	0011010111000101	0111010000011101
002	0001010110100000	0001011100110011
003	0101000001011111	0101110101011111
004	0101010101010101	1011110000110011

Figure 11-40. Illustration of a drum sequencer table file

In operation, the sequencer block is activated when the ENABLE line goes TRUE and remains ON. An OFF-to-ON transition on the STEP line causes the word values of the table to be transferred to the output modules one step at a time, starting with step 1. Transition from one step to the next is either event driven or time driven. With each step transition, the corresponding word locations from the table are output until reaching the final step. A transition while on the final step returns the sequencer to the initial step. The sequencer may also be returned to step 1 by an OFF-to-ON transition on the RESET line.

Diagnostic Block

The diagnostic block instruction, found in some controllers, allows the known or expected conditions of a machine or process to be compared with actual conditions. Such a comparison allows machine or process faults to be quickly diagnosed or, in some cases to be avoided.

A typical diagnostic block is illustrated in Figure 11-41. The instruction requires that the starting word address of two word files be specified with a given length that designates the number of sixteen-bit words in each file. One of the word files contains *reference states* or the expected states of the I/O at each step. The other word file contains *actual states* of the I/O at each step. When the block is enabled, a bit-by-bit comparison is performed to determine if the files are identical. If a miscompare occurs, a block output is energized and the discrepancy is stored. Another internal output is used to signal when the comparison is done.

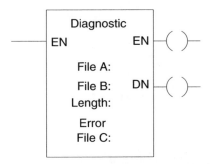

Figure 11-41. Illustration of the diagnostic block instruction

Operation of the diagnostic block is much like that of the drum sequencer. Typical use of the diagnostic function involves an application that has a fixed number of steps. At each step of the application, a number of bit status conditions determines how certain outputs are activated. The diagnostic block is used at each step to compare the latest statuses of actual process conditions to a set of reference input conditions. If the actual conditions are not what they should be at a given step according to the reference and the known behavior of the process, then it is possible to not activate the outputs of this step until the discrepancy is cleared.

11-9 Networking Instructions

Networking capabilities and configurations may vary with different products. However, a few basic operations help to understand the transactions that take place among controllers on the network.

Fetch Operation

The fetch operation allows one PLC to directly access another PLC's memory over the network and to read a block of words without any involvement by the controller from which the data is being taken. The controller fetching the data is considered the *active partner* in this data link, since it initiates the transaction. The controller from which the data is taken is referred to as the *passive partner*. The fetch is often used instead of the send instruction, when it is desirable to get data from another controller whenever necessary. Otherwise, for the station needing the data to have it whenever required, the node having the data would have to send it constantly to the station needing it.

In the fetch operation, the node from which the data is taken is completely uninvolved. As shown in Figure 11-42, the node requesting the data specifies its own address, the address of the node from which data is requested, and the starting word address of the requested data, as well as the destination of its storage upon return. When the fetch request packet is put onto the network, the network module in the node to which the request is being made recognizes its own address and responds by getting the data from the CPU in its rack and putting it back onto the network forwarded to the requesting partner.

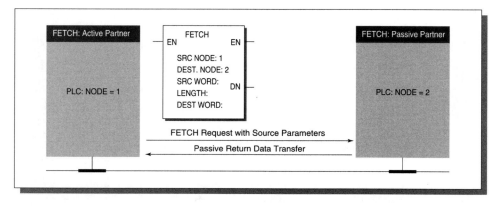

Figure 11-42. Illustration of a fetch data link relationship

Send and Receive

The *send instruction*, is used by one network station to send data to a specific network station. In this particular data link, the receiving node must have a corresponding *receive instruction* to be prepared to receive the data from the specific partner from which the data is being sent. Since the node sending will always initiate the transaction, it is considered to be the active partner in the data link. The send instruction is typically used when the node sending the data determines when the data is required at the receiving partner.

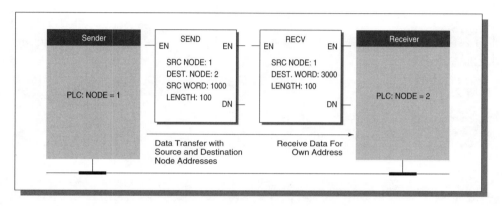

Figure 11-43. Illustration of a send/receive data link relationship

A typical send and receive data link is shown in Figure 11-43. The sending node specifies its address, the start address of the source data and the number of words, and the address of the receiving (destination) node. The receive block in the receiving node must specify the sending (source) node, the starting address at which to store the data, and the number of words. To accomplish bidirectional communication between any two nodes, using this type of link, each node would require a pair of send and receive blocks that specify the data link partner.

Broadcast

The *broadcast* function gives a controller the ability to transmit data to the entire network, using one instruction. The term broadcast means that data is simply put onto the network and any nodes having a the appropriate receive instruction can take the data off of the network. As illustrated in Figure 11-44, the node initiating the broadcast simply specifies a block of words that it is writing to the network.

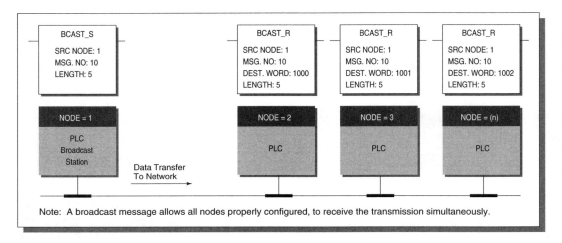

Figure 11-44. Illustration of a broadcast operation

The broadcast is used when several network stations need the same information simultaneously, such as with some transfer line operations. This method is much more efficient than having a send block for every node requiring the information. It also guarantees that the data is current and not several scans old.

Broadcast Receive

The *broadcast receive* instruction, allows a controller to take *broadcast* data off of the network. As shown in Figure 11-44, the node broadcasting data simply specifies a block of words that it is writing to the network. Any station needing the data can simply read it while those that do not may simply ignore it. All that is required is that the broadcast receive instruction specify where the data should be stored. In most implementations, it is unknown by the receiving node, as to when new data will arrive, hence the broadcast receive must be processed cyclically.

Global I/O

Global I/O is a broadcast communications capability found in some controllers, as a method of allowing network stations to share interlocking data over the network. Usually, each controller has a separate area of memory allocated to global data — for example, each station may allow 256 global I/O words addressed as GW1 through GW256. Each controller is able to read or write to this area in order to automatically exchange interlocking data with other controllers on a cyclical basis.

While the implementation of this service varies in different controllers, global data is normally processed on each scan, much like the discrete I/O image table. Unlike other network services, that require programming, global I/O is generally transferred automatically by the network interface module in each PLC. On each scan, it transfers to the CPU global inputs received from the network and it reads global outputs from the CPU and sends them out over the network. For a station to receive global data, the network interface in that controller must be configured to receive the specific *global input* word addresses. *Global output* addresses designate global data to be sent out over the network. A typical global I/O configuration is illustrated in Figure 11-45.

GLOBAL I/O CONFIGURATION		NETWORK ADDR: 4
GLOBAL WORD INPUTS	NETWORK SOURCE	GLOBAL WORD OUTPUTS
GW10	PLC- Addr. = 1	GW40
GW11	PLC- Addr. = 1	GW41
GW12	PLC- Addr. = 1	GW42
GW21	PLC- Addr. = 2	GW43
GW22	PLC- Addr. = 2	GW44
GW23	PLC- Addr. = 2	GW45
GW31	PLC- Addr. = 3	GW46
GW32	PLC- Addr. = 3	GW47

Figure 11-45. Example of global I/O configuration on a network station

Global I/O is used when several network stations must know the operational and general health status of one or more other stations. This requirement is typical where different PLCs share control functions of a complete process. For an assembly line, global I/O might include machine operational modes STOP, RUN, AUTO, and IDLE; health status might include STATION OK, and STATION FAULT TYPE xx. As illustrated in Figure 11-46, for a node to utilize a global input it has received, it simply specifies the bit or word address in the program. Global outputs are written to using word transfers, or coil symbols for writing to bit addresses.

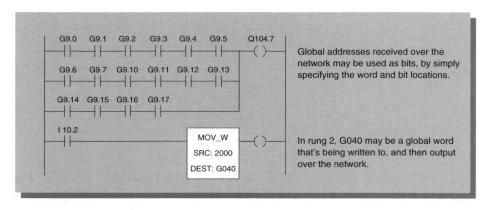

Figure 11-46. Using global I/O in the control program.

Because global I/O is truly "global" in some implementations, the global words are considered *global objects* and the global addresses are shared by all network stations. For this reason, words written to (i.e., global outputs) by one station may not be written to by another. Words designated as an output in one station may only be designated as a global input in all other stations. As illustrated in Figure 11-45, each station would define words that it intends to write to, as global outputs. Any words to be read in from other stations must be specified as global inputs. In other global I/O implementations, source addresses are transmitted along with the global data. This approach allows all stations to broadcast their entire global database.

12 ALTERNATIVE PROGRAMMING LANGUAGES

In the early 1980s, the Ladder language came under scrutiny from users who felt that more versatile languages were needed. Although there was no doubt that Ladder would continue to be an important PLC language because of its ease of use, it had become obvious that the advantages of maintaining a familiar presentation was offset by the fact that Ladder diagrams were not always best suited for creating the control code.

For certain applications, Ladder is not only not the most suitable language, but also is inadequate for solving the problem. Ladder is cumbersome for performing complex calculations, intensive data processing, communications, and, in general, for solving complex control algorithms. The method in which the Ladder program was processed was also cited for shortcomings in sequential control applications. This chapter will introduce various PLC programming languages and examine the areas in which each is most suited. Finally, a summary of the languages is presented, showing advantages and disadvantages of their application.

12-1 Introduction

Offering multiple PLC programming languages provides a way of matching the appropriate tool to the task and suiting the needs of the program developer and the end-user. The ideal objective is to create a programming environment that uses the best suited language or languages to create a single program. Three needs must be met by this objective.

First, number of useable languages are needed to allow the user to choose the best-suited language for each task. Second, the environment must allow for simultaneous development by several individuals. This requirement calls for the ability to create modular blocks of code that may be combined to produce a whole program. Finally, the combination of languages must allow programs to be written and maintained by people having different skill levels. This last objective, while allowing the more sophisticated developers to use the language of choice, must also provide a way of masking the complexity of such languages from the users of the simpler languages. In addition to Ladder, other languages used to program PLCs include the following:

❑ Boolean Statement List
❑ Boolean Gate Flowchart
❑ Function Block Diagrams
❑ High-level Languages
❑ Sequential Function Chart

12-2 Boolean Statement List

Boolean Statement List, also referred to as *Instruction List* or simply *Statement List (STL)*, is one of the oldest text languages used to program PLCs. The name of course comes from the fact that the instructions are based on the classical Boolean operators of AND, OR, and NOT, however the instructions are programmed in list format similar to BASIC and other text languages. STL instruction sets implement the same relay-logic, timing and counting, comparison, arithmetic and data manipulation instructions as in Ladder (See chapter 11).

Statement List programming is more likely found in products of European and Asian origin and is usually offered in conjunction with one or more language options (e.g., Ladder). On the other hand, STL is not usually found in products of American manufacture. When it is used, however, it is generally in low-end PLCs with limited I/O and primarily discrete logic functionality. In communities abroad, users are more acquainted with instruction list languages and use them in mid-range and high-end PLC products as well.

Logic Function	Statement List (STL)	Ladder Diagram Equivalent
Simple AND (series logic)	A I 1.1 A I 1.2 = Q1.0	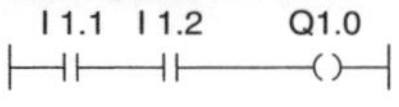 I 1.1 I 1.2 Q1.0
Simple OR (parallel logic)	O I 1.3 O I 1.4 = Q1.1	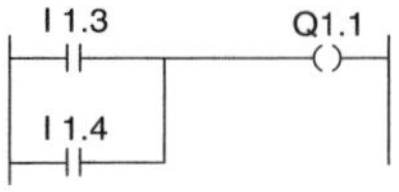 I 1.3 Q1.1 I 1.4
NOT w / AND	AN I 1.5 A I 1.6 = Q1.2	I 1.5 I 1.6 Q1.2
NOT w / OR	ON I 1.7 ON I 1.8 = Q1.3	I 1.7 Q1.3 I 1.8
AND-before-OR (parallel-series logic)	A I 5.0 A I 5.1 O A I 5.2 A I 5.3 = Q2.0	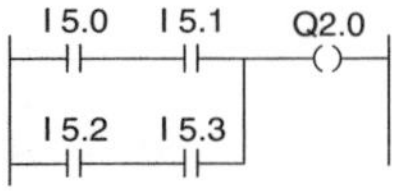 I 5.0 I 5.1 Q2.0 I 5.2 I 5.3
OR-before-AND (series-parallel logic)	A(O I 7.0 O I 7.1) A(O I 7.2 O I 7.3) = Q2.2	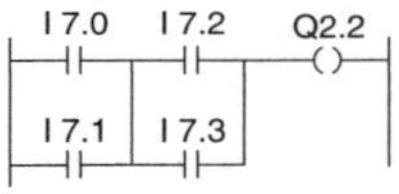 I 7.0 I 7.2 Q2.2 I 7.1 I 7.3

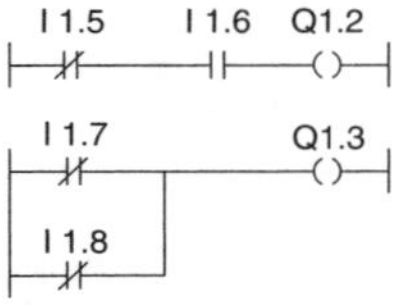

Figure 12-1. Statement List (Instruction List) logic with Ladder equivalent code

The closeness of Statement Lists to the actual machine code makes it quite efficient, and processing of binary operations is especially fast. For simple applications, the control algorithm may actually resemble its English description. Complex applications, on the other hand, may require more effort to translate from functional specifications of the system design to the actual code. Although the linear nature of STL lends itself to extensive line-by-line commenting, large programs can be more difficult to debug, to follow program flow, and to troubleshoot. This is especially true for personnel generally not familiar with developing and analyzing high-level language programs. Statement Lists, because it is a high-level language, is more suited to program flow control and for modular code development.

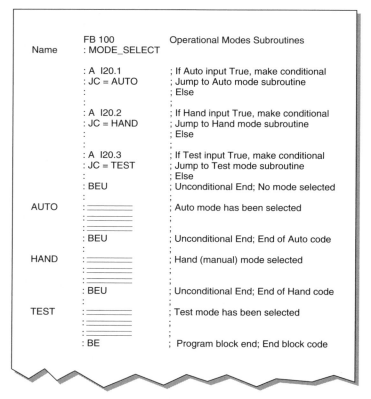

Figure 12-2. Statement List program, with local jumps to labels.
External jumps to other code blocks is also possible

12-3 Boolean Gate Flowchart

The *Boolean Gate Flowchart*, or *Control System Flowchart*, language is a graphic programming language that uses a set of block symbols to define the control logic of a machine or process. Programs developed in Boolean Gate Flowcharts, as shown in Figure 12-3, show the interconnection of dynamic variables and I/O signals within a process. This language representation, whose main elements include the AND and OR gates, closely resembles the logic gate diagrams often used by process design and circuit design engineers for system design.

Like Instruction Lists and Ladder, Boolean Gate Flowcharts offers instruction sets with the major categories of relay-logic, timers and counters, basic arithmetic, and data comparisons. Again, the same basic operations are provided but are presented in a graphical format that many are already familiar with. Many European-designed systems, for instance, are programmed in this language — perhaps as a matter of preference.

Like Ladder, the Boolean Gate presentation offers the main advantages of simplicity and the familiarity of Boolean logic design. Its disadvantages, on the other hand, are also similar to those of Ladder — mainly, a lack of complex data handling capability. Data operations such as conversions, bit and word searches, word and table data transfers, indirect addressing, indexed loop operations, and other complex operations are not usually available unless standard function blocks are included for these functions. Generally speaking, this language is intended for discrete logic operations and is not very suitable for analog operations. The language is also not supported in many PLCs.

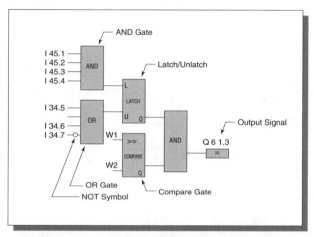

Figure 12-3. Control logic program, using Boolean Gate Flowchart language

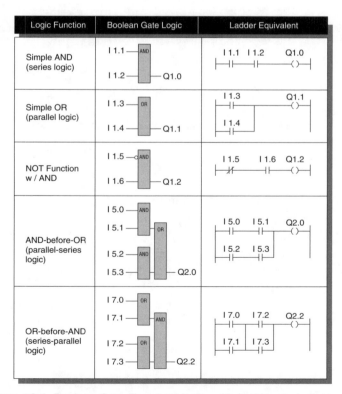

Figure 12-4. Boolean Gate Flowchart logic, with Ladder equivalent code

12-4 Function Block Diagram

The *Function Block Diagram* language is a high-level graphic design language primarily intended for implementing continuous or regulatory control strategies (i.e., analog control, PID loops). The language is based on a symbol set defined by the *Scientific Apparatus Manufacturing Association (SAMA)*, an industry standards organization. Function Block diagrams use a variety of configurable symbols for logic, control, data, device, and arithmetic functions that can be graphically arranged to convey both batch and continuous control strategies. Figure 12-5 illustrates a portion of a Function Block program.

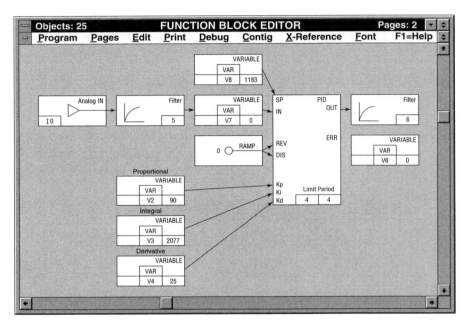

Figure 12-5. Control logic using Function Blocks

Developing control logic with the Function Block language typically involves grid-like configuration forms similar to spreadsheets, upon which one or more function blocks are placed. Each box represents a predefined function that is configured to produce a desired control response. The developer interconnects the boxes using lines to define input/output relationships, including data passing, to drive the final elements. Typical function blocks include analog I/O functions, PID functions, mathmematical functions, device functions, and control functions, for example, filters, lead/lag and feed forward functions. Users are also allowed to create their own blocks.

This Function Block method of programming, which is typical of distributed control systems (DCS), allows the developer to define the required functions, but without concern for actual coding details. Figure 12-6 shows some of the typical function diagram symbols.

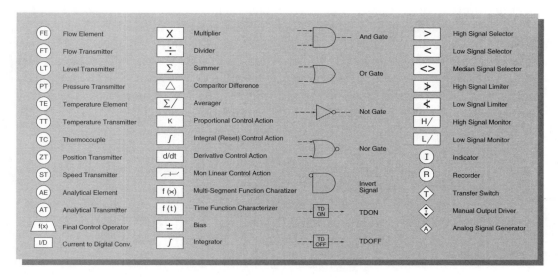

Figure 12-6. Typical SAMA function block symbols

12-5 High-level Programming Languages

The availability of personal computers having significantly improved horsepower and lower costs has allowed control engineers to exploit the use of both the PC and its high-level languages. Languages such as BASIC, C++, Pascal, and Visual Basic are finding a place on the plant floor in traditional PC applications, as well as in PLC control programs. These languages are filling the gap where Ladder falls short — in tasks involving complex calculations, control algorithms, data processing, diagnostic indication, and communications.

Most vendors offer one or more high-level language options to supplement the Ladder programming tool. BASIC is the most popular of the high-level languages because of its ease of use and wide-spread awareness among engineers. C, which is ideal for tasks ranging from PID algorithms to communications protocols, opens the PLC to the most sophisticated of programmers. Pascal, like BASIC, is widely known and easy to learn. These language options are usually offered on a separate coprocessor module that is independent of the main CPU. The module is able to share data with the CPU through backplane communications. Serial ports for external communications, and video ports for connecting monitors are also provided.

Another high-level language approach allows the user to create Function Blocks using one or more supported languages. The blocks are compiled and downloaded to the CPU, and may then be used as canned instructions in the Ladder program. This technique allows difficult functions to be masked from the user. With this method, a subroutine can be written in any supported language, for example, Ladder, BASIC, or C. The subroutine developer gives the block a library name and number, for example SUB100, and documents it for others to use. End-users of the function block need only to understand its documentation, not the subroutine itself. In Ladder, the subroutine is called by either a conditional or unconditional call to SUB100. During execution, the operating system knows where to find SUB100. It calls SUB100, passes the inputs from the Ladder, and then passes the outputs from SUB100 back to the Ladder program.

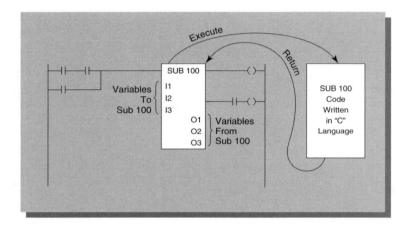

Figure 12-7. A user-created function block called from a Ladder program

High-level Language Advantages

Although high-level languages are wanted to a great extent because engineers accept them, they offer several advantages. They aid in structuring and organizing programs, which makes programming easier to plan, develop, and document. They also make it easier for programs to be divided and developed by several individuals. Team members with expertise in different areas, for example, in communications, controls, operator interface development — are also able to write portions of the program in their best language. PC languages also affect system design efficiency; once a problem has been solved and an algorithm or subroutine designed and programmed, the code can be stored and reused later with little or no modification. With the convenience of the PC, the utilities it offers, and the portability of software, new developments may be tested and implemented quickly.

12-6 Sequential Function Charts

The *Sequential Function Chart (SFC)* language is a graphics-based language that allows the developer to represent a machine or process and its application program as a series of sequential steps and transitions. The language was developed specifically for defining systems whose operations occur in a sequential fashion, with the execution of each step being time-driven or event-driven. Typical applications include transfer lines, container filling, rotary machinery, drilling, and press operations.

As a process overview design language, SFC allows the user to graphically build the basic structure of a process as a combination of sequences. A complete SFC program may consist of several sequences. Sequences consists of steps and transitions. Each box represents a process step, which may involve one or more logic operations. As illustrated in Figure 12-8, the control logic of each step is written with a subordinate language such as Ladder or Instruction List. The SFC user is allowed to view the details of the step by "zooming in" on the step. SFC is considered a *primary language* since it is only used to describe the process overview.

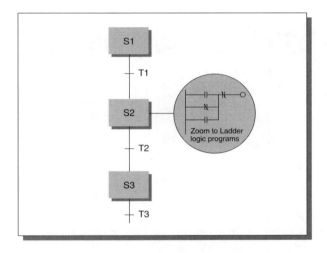

Figure 12-8. Sequential Function Chart (SFC) programming structure

An Overview

In Figure 12-8, SFC is shown in its most basic form — the linear sequence, comprised of *steps* and *transitions*. Steps, depicted as boxes, are event- or time-dependent actions that represent each phase of operation in which predefined operations take place. A transition is a logic condition that determines when one step should be deactivated and the next step activated. Lines, or so-called *directed links*, connect the boxes to define the program flow from one step to another. The way in which links are drawn allows parts of the program to be executed selectively or concurrently.

Development of SFC programs involves the use of a few basic symbols. These symbols shown in Figure 12-9, are the *initial step*, *step*, *transition*, and *directed links*. The initial step is the first step of the program. Execution always returns to this step after the last step unless otherwise directed by the program logic. Each step contains programmed logic for the tasks associated with that step. The sequence step is the function chart's most basic element and contains the control logic for each stage of operation for the machine or process. The transition consists of one conditional statement that when TRUE disables the current step and enables the next step.

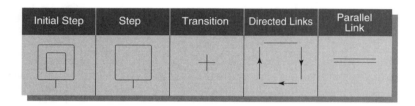

Figure 12-9. Basic symbols of the SFC language

An Illustration

In order to allow the machine or process to take alternative courses of action, the SFC language allows parallel branching that makes it possible to process two or more sequence paths simultaneously and the ability to select one of several alternate paths based on specific circumstances. These two SFC structures are shown in Figure 12-10a and b. A basic description of the SFC symbols is given in the following paragraphs.

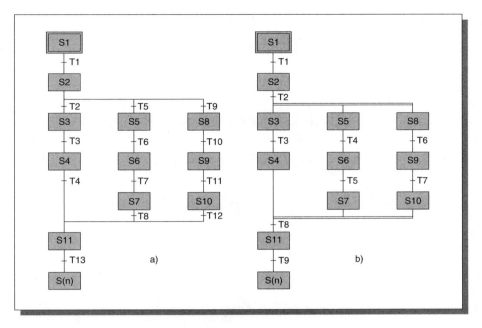

*Figure 12-10. a) SFC with selective branching and
b) SFC with concurrent or simultaneous branching*

Initial Step. The initial step, as shown in Figure 12-11, is represented by a rectangle drawn inside another rectangle. There is only one initial step. Like all the other steps, the initial step is usually followed by a transition. When the process is started, the logic of the initial step is executed until the following transition is activated. Control is also usually returned to this step after completion of the last step unless directed otherwise. Control may also be directed to this step from another step.

Figure 12-11. The SFC initial step symbol

Step-Transition Sequence. In an SFC program, steps are assigned from S1 to S(n) where (n) is the last step. After each step is a transition, and each transition follows a step. The sequence, as shown in Figure 12-12, is one step and transition pair, followed by another step (S1 - T1 - S2). Transitions define the conditions that must be satisfied before the control sequence can continue to the next step or steps. Generally, the transition logic is a simple logic rung that, when activated, disables the current step and enables the next step. The IEC 1131-3 standard specifies that in the SFC diagram there must always be a transition between every two steps and a step between every two transitions.

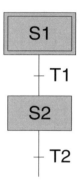

Figure 12-12. Illustration of the SFC step-transition sequence pair

Selective (Link) Branching. Figure 12-13 illustrates the selective or alternative branch. Here, one of a number of alternate sequences is selected and processed. The transitions here are S3, S5, and S8. Notice, how with the selective link, a unique transition is placed in front of each path, immediately following the prior step (i.e., T2, T5, T9). This structure indicates that each of the paths has equal priority. The transition that occurs first deactivates the previous step and activates the subsequent step of the selected sequence. Generally, the left-most sequence is taken if two or more transitions occur simultaneously.

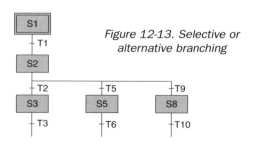

Figure 12-13. Selective or alternative branching

When selective branching is used, the alternate paths are completed by bringing all of the alternate paths back to a single line of execution. As illustrated in Figure 12-14, each of the paths concludes with its own transition, all of which converge at a common step (S11). When the final step of the selected sequence path is completed, the final transition disables the previous step and enables the common step at which the selected paths converge. Selective branches are necessary when a definite result, e.g., shutdown of plant for safety reasons, has to be implemented on the basis of different conditions.

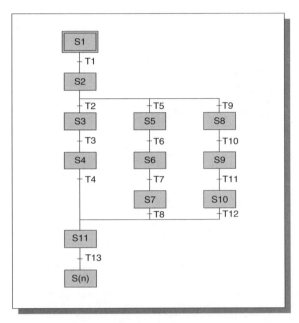

Figure 12-14. Illustration of Selective branch close

Concurrent (Link) Branching. *Concurrent* or *simultaneous branching,* indicated by a double line, as shown in Figure 12-15, involves passing control to multiple branches. This type of link is used where two or more processes must proceed simultaneously. Notice how the transition (T2) is inserted immediately following S2 and before the parallel branches. This is to show that when the single transition preceding the branches is satisfied, the controller processes all of the branches simultaneously. In this example, control is passed to the sequences starting with S 3, S5, and S8.

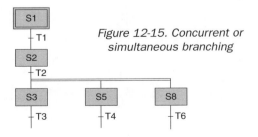

Figure 12-15. Concurrent or simultaneous branching

When all of the parallel branches have reached their last step, the independent steps converge by means of a common transition (e.g., T8). When the transition is satisfied, the parallel branches are simultaneously deactivated and a common step (S11) is activated, as in Figure 12- 16.

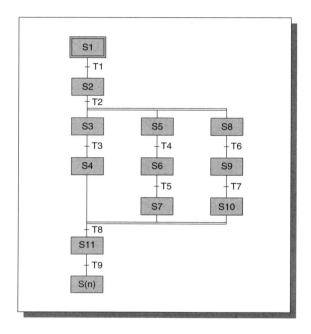

Figure 12-16. Illustration of Simultaneous branch close

Reference (Jump) Link. A *reference link*, also referred to as a *jump link*, is placed after a transition to complete a cycle or to jump to another step within the SFC logic. This element usually completes a nested or subordinate sequence and passes control back to the main sequence. An illustration of the reference link is shown in Figure 12-17.

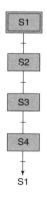

Figure 12-17. The SFC reference link references a step number to which control is passed

SFC Advantages

The SFC method of programming offers many advantages in all areas of the control system, from design and implementation to documentation and troubleshooting. First and foremost, SFC provides a graphic display of the operational steps of the machine or process. Because the SFC diagrams mirror the process and it is graphically evident when states are active and inactive, the process can be easily monitored and diagnosed for faults. Since the language uses a small number of symbols and rules, it can be quickly learned.

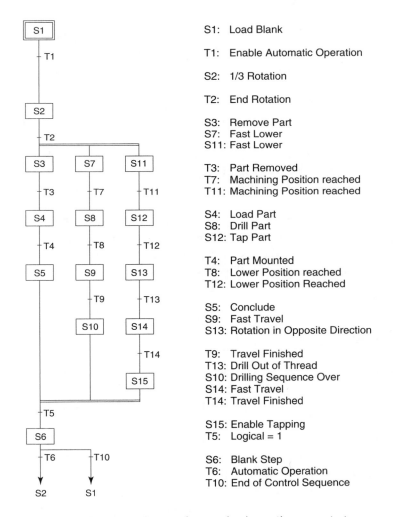

S1:	Load Blank
T1:	Enable Automatic Operation
S2:	1/3 Rotation
T2:	End Rotation
S3:	Remove Part
S7:	Fast Lower
S11:	Fast Lower
T3:	Part Removed
T7:	Machining Position reached
T11:	Machining Position reached
S4:	Load Part
S8:	Drill Part
S12:	Tap Part
T4:	Part Mounted
T8:	Lower Position reached
T12:	Lower Position Reached
S5:	Conclude
S9:	Fast Travel
S13:	Rotation in Opposite Direction
T9:	Travel Finished
T13:	Drill Out of Thread
S10:	Drilling Sequence Over
S14:	Fast Travel
T14:	Travel Finished
S15:	Enable Tapping
T5:	Logical = 1
S6:	Blank Step
T6:	Automatic Operation
T10:	End of Control Sequence

Figure 12-18. SFC program in overview mode shows the current step

317

From a design standpoint, an SFC program is modular in nature, which produces a logically structured design that can be interpreted and used by both control and process engineers. This modularity also means individual function charts can be written or modified without affecting the design structure or causing operational problems elsewhere. SFC also allows the developer to create the control design for a complete process, using both a top-down and a bottom-up approach. Since a number of charts may be created, it is possible to create a main sequence that describes the major steps of the process and subordinate sequence flow charts that control individual parts of the process.

In operation, SFC allows both selective and concurrent processing, which is a major advantage over Ladder programming processing. The result is to streamline the application flow, which improves scan time and reduces computing time to dramatically improve overall application efficiency, Performance may improve because cyclic scanning of all logic is eliminated; multiple conditions are evaluated only when multiple logic paths are allowable. Unlike with Ladder, once an SFC step is ended or inactive, no logic has to be written to ensure that operations of that step no longer occur.

The very nature of Sequential Function Charts is self-documenting, such that a program may be used and understood by all, from plant and design engineers to maintenance to management personnel. As shown in Figure 12-18, program comments are possible while in the overview and detailed representations. The sequence comments are typically viewed on a split screen to one side of the diagram while the current status of steps and transition conditions are being displayed in a status bar. Sequence charts simplify maintenance and troubleshooting by pinpointing faults and malfunctions in the control system immediately.

12-7 PLC Language Standardization

Language standardization for PLCs has long been an issue for users, especially those in the automotive industry. This issue, like many other standardization issues, has been largely neglected in North America but has been addressed at a steady pace in Europe. In 1995, standardization efforts resulted in the creation of the IEC 1131-3 standard for PLC programming languages. This standard specifies the syntax and semantics of a unified suite of programming languages for PLCs. The standard encompasses five languages, including *Sequential Function Chart*, *Ladder Diagram*, *Function Blocks*, *Instruction List*, and *Structured Text*. The first three are graphic languages, while the latter two are text based. Structured Text, is a simplified Pascal-like language, comprised of instructions that are intuitive to the automation engineer.

In the standard languages scheme, Sequential Function Chart is considered the primary design language used to represent the application program as a series of sequential steps and transitions. The other four languages are considered secondary, or languages in which the various steps of the application code are written. The IEC 1131-3 standard simply defines a core set of instructions for each language. Suppliers, however, may augment the standard set with their own specific instructions and/or functions.

The goals of the IEC 1131-3 standard are similar to those already suggested at the outset of this chapter for an optimum PLC programming environment. The first was to support multiple languages that may be combined to create a single program, and that suits the needs of the task, the program developer, and the end-user. Another goal was to provide the ability to create modular blocks of code that can be written with any of the secondary languages. Ladder, for example, would allow programs to be written and maintained by plant floor electricians and technicians. More sophisticated programmers may use the high-level language of their choice to generate industry- or plant-specific function blocks that hide or mask the complex logic from the users of the simpler languages.

A secondary goal of the standard was to make coding more uniform among suppliers and to increase the existence of reusable blocks of code in the form of universal libraries. These libraries might include categories such as machine specific, industry specific, device control, control algorithms, and many others might be created. With such universality of languages and standard function blocks, end-users will eventually be able to learn the basics of programming and utilize the newly learned principles across various products, reducing their costs and time to continuously learn new PLC software.

Table 12-1. Common PLC languages—Summary of advantages and disadvantages

Language	Advantages	Disadvantages
LADDER	- Widely used and accepted - Easily understood by field electricians - Applicable to many applications/industries - Widely Supported - Graphic symbols easily learned - Discrete logic continuity easy to show - Programs easily altered - Good for discrete logic tasks	- Longer design time for complex programs - Standard instruction set not yet widely used - Limited data processing functionality - Limited analog functionality - Becomes confusing with complex logic - Often scan dependent - No historical sense in sequential application. - Overall limited software functionality
INSTRUCTION LIST	- Familiar to many high-level programmers - Uses efficient assembly-like instructions.	- Little familiarity among PLC users - Requires more training - Somewhat complicated for maintenance - May be difficult to follow program flow
BOOLEAN FLOWCHARTS	- Familiar to electrical and process engineers - Simple graphic symbols - Requires little training - Easy to learn for Ladder users	-Limited to binary/Boolean logic operations - Standard instruction set not yet widely used - No data processing functionality - No analog functionality
FUNCTION BLOCKS	- Easily Implemented - Graphic symbols eliminates tedious code - Shortens development time - Allows problem focus instead of details - Ideal for PID loops - Suitable for batch & continuous processes	- Limited instruction (symbol) set - No widely accepted standard - Not very flexible where changes are frequent - Not very suitable for relay logic operations - Overall limited functionality
SEQUENTIAL FUNCTION CHARTS	- Allows top down design - Releases mind from details early in design - Shows overview of whole process - Shows process flow and current step - Good for sequential applications - Easily documented and understood - Provides segmentation for large programs - Offers selective and concurrent processing	See Note:
HIGH-LEVEL LANGUAGES (ANSI C & STRUCTURED TEXT)	- Allows team programming - Allows modular, structured and code - Allows more complex functions - Opens PLC to high-level programmers - Greater portability and flexibility of software - Allows user written function blocks	- Not Easily maintained by field personnel - Compiled code not field serviceable - More complex to develop - Code often must be re-compiled and loaded - Compiled code requires external debug tools

Note: Sequential Function Charts is the core language of the IEC 1131-3 standard. It is a design-overview language, where steps are able to encapsulate any of the supported subordinate languages. For this reason, it does not have the inherent disadvantages of the other languages listed in the table.

13

CONTROL SYSTEM CONFIGURATION AND HARDWARE SELECTION

The Conceptual Design

Input/Output Requirements

The Control System Configuration

CPU Requirements

Program Development and Operator Access Devices

Understanding PLC Product Ranges

Evaluating The Intangible Factors

PLC Product Selection Summary

Programmable controller products cover a wide spectrum of capabilities that serve an equally diverse range of applications. At the low-end are microcontrollers and small PLCs with limited I/O, memory, and software capabilities. At the high-end, large supervisory controllers perform sophisticated control, data acquisition, and communications needed to integrate production processes with plant information systems. In between these two extremes lie mid-range controllers with extended instruction sets and expanded I/O and communications capabilities. The mid-range controller bridges the expanse between the low- and high-end by providing the ability to expand as application requirements change.

This chapter, presents an expanded analysis of the PLC product ranges first introduced in chapter 1, and an analysis of control system requirements that will impact product selection. Finally, a set of intangible factors that should influence PLC selection are presented along with a selection criteria summary.

13-1 The Conceptual Design

The conceptual design is an engineering phase in which preliminary expectations of the control system, as well as others items, are defined. This process which involves outlining the intended operation of the machine or process, is vital to the ultimate selection of a particular controller and control system configuration. It is important that this phase of the project include someone familiar with PLC technology, as well as the project and plant goals with respect to its application.

Defining the control system usually occurs at many levels. Individuals within each department involved must be consulted to determine what information is required or has to be provided, so that all participants understand what tasks are being performed and who will be performing them. For example, in a project involving the automation of a packaging area and the warehouse, personnel from both areas must collaborate with the engineering group during the conceptual design. The management information system department should be involved if the system is to be eventually tied into a network that will allow upward reporting or downward scheduling.

Once the control system requirements are defined, selecting a suitable PLC is possible. Selecting the right controller involves consideration for both present and future system needs. It involves evaluating capacity constraints such as the amount of I/O and memory and functional constraints, such as speed of response, variety of I/O interfaces and sophistication of software and networking capabilities. It also involves addressing the need for system resources that can be adapted for expansion and change.

This initial process will not necessarily lead to a particular controller. It will, however, reveal broad physical and functional requirements that meet present as well as foreseeable needs for additions, modifications, or integration with other systems.. The following items need to be evaluated and defined for each application, for determining the control system requirements and for reaching a decision on physical and functional requirements of the PLC.

> ❑ Input/Output Requirements
> ❑ Control System Configuration
> ❑ CPU Requirements
> ❑ Programming and Operator Access Devices
> ❑ Physical and Environmental Constraints

13-2 Input/Output Requirements

Most PLCs offer a wide variety of standard digital and analog I/O modules capable of accepting a variety of currents and voltages. There are also many different types of special signal processing and intelligent I/O that are generally available with mid-range and high-end controllers. Since the range of compatible I/O modules is generally determined by the class of controller, it is not until interfacing requirements for a particular system are known that the level of controller can be determined.

System Size

Determining the total number of I/O is typically the first step in the PLC selection process. This determination will identify the minimum size constraints (i.e., low-end, mid-range, high-end) of the PLC's central processing unit. Allowing for future I/O expansion, if required, should also be considered at this point to ensure that the right CPU size is selected. Once minimum size is determined, further evaluation of the types of I/O modules required, specific interfacing requirements, and placement of I/O modules in the field (i.e., local or remote) will lead toward the decision of the PLC product range.

Remote I/O Considerations

Remote I/O should always be considered in large systems. Advancements in this area have made remote I/O not only more reliable but also less expensive. Effective use of distributed I/O can reduce I/O installation cost by as much as 50 percent. Defining opportunities for use of remote I/O involves identifying groups of sensors and actuators that are in close proximity to each other and can be grouped together as a *remote drop*. The more remote drops, the less expensive the cost for installing them. Since the I/O modules will be closer to the sensors and actuators, cabling, conduit and terminations are reduced.

I/O Module Considerations

While this phase of the selection process is to determine if the PLC has the I/O modules to match the signals required by the application, a more critical need is to ensure that any special signal characteristics can be handled. Items to note include the module response times (delays associated with recognizing an input or energizing an output), sinking/sourcing current, input pulse durations, and continuous and surge current ratings on outputs. Features to look for include power and logic status indicators, circuit protection, and module fault diagnostics, especially in the case of remote I/O.

Finally, where possible, take advantage of intelligent I/O modules. Properly used, these modules can greatly reduce the processing required by the CPU, thereby improving system response and reducing the program complexity. Intelligent modules almost always are sure to reduce engineering development time and cost by eliminating the need for generating complex programs or designing for complex or special interfacing requirements. Some of these modules are also stand-alone and can continue to operate even if the CPU is stopped. Table 13-1 lists a set of I/O system checkpoints.

Table 13-1. Input/Output System Checklist

Maximum I/O Count	**Analog I/O Checkpoints**
- Maximum Digital I/O	*General*
- Maximum Analog I/O	- Resolution and Accuracy
- Local/Remote I/O	- Calibration Method
- Maximum Remote I/O Distance	- Circuits/Module
- Total Remote Drops	- Isolated I/O Modules
- I/O Points/Remote Drop (min., max.)	- Galvanic Isolation
- Remote Cable (coax, fiber optic, twisted pair)	- I/O Current/Voltage Ranges (Selectability)
- Remote I/O Communication Data Rate	- Sampling Rate
- Worst-Case Remote I/O Update Time	
- I/O Communication Error Checking	*Thermocouple and RTD Inputs*
- Rack Communication Failure Diagnostics	- Thermocouple Types (J,K,S,T,B,E,R)
- Remote Intelligent I/O Supported	- Cold Junction Compensation (ext., int.)
- Quick Disconnect Terminal Assembly	- Linearization (onboard, software coding)
- Removal Under Power	- Isothermal Barrier
- Open Wire Detection	- RTD Types (10,100,120,1000 ohms)
	- Alternate Channel (Switchover on Failure)
Digital I/O Checkpoints	
- Circuits/Module	**Special Function and Intelligent I/O**
- Isolated I/O Modules	- Fast Response Input
- Galvanic Isolation	- Voltage (Setpoint) Comparator Input
- Input/Output Voltage Ranges	- High Speed Counter Input
- Sourcing/Sinking I/O	- Position Encoder Input
- I/O Status Indicators (power, logic)	- Closed Loop Positioning Module
- Blown Fuse Indicator (individual, shared)	- Multiplexed BCD I/O
- Output Current/Circuit	- High-Speed Analog I/O
- Inrush Current Capacity	- ASCII/BASIC Module (s)
- Output Circuit Protection (fuse, electronic)	- PID Control Module
- Output Circuit Protection (individual, grouped)	- Temperature Control Module
- Application Specific I/O	- Vision System Module
- AT-Computer Module	- Serial Communication Modules
	- LAN Interface Modules

13-3 The Control System Configuration

Deciding on the control system configuration or strategy is a natural next step after determining the amount and locations of the I/O devices of the machine or process. This decision deals with how the various elements of the system will be placed and interconnected in the field. This configuration will directly affect the requirements for the PLC processor. The three basic configurations are *individual control*, *centralized control*, and *distributed control*.

Individual Control

Individual Control, illustrated in Figure 13-1, is an informal term describing systems in which a single PLC controls a single machine or process with little or no need for communication with other controllers or computers. The segregated nature of this configuration is typical of low-end controllers controlling equipment not requiring present or future integration with other systems. Typical examples include OEM and end-user equipment such as punch presses, palletizers, compressors, or any small single-function or independent system. Application of this kind of control system is generally to simply replace other outdated or less effective controls.

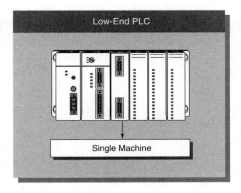

Figure 13-1. Illustration of individual or isolated control configuration

Centralized Control

Centralized control, illustrated in Figure 13-2, involves a single controller governing the functions of an entire machine or process. Typical of large continuous or batch processes, centralized control places the CPU in a central location and remote I/O drops nearby various sections of the field equipment. A major disadvantage of centralized control is that a single failure can potentially disable the entire system; its use however is necessary in some cases due to the complexity of partitioning a single large task into several smaller ones. In critical applications, this problem of single-point failure may be circumvented by using a *redundant (hot backup) system.* (See chapter 3.)

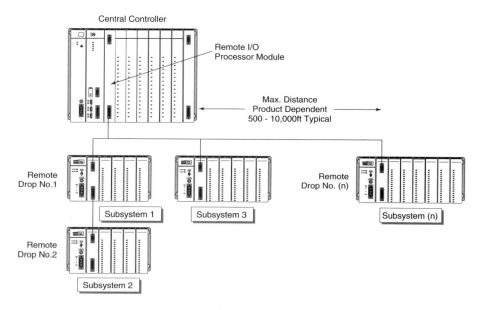

Figure 13-2. Illustration of centralized control configuration

Distributed Control

Distributed control, illustrated in Figure 13-3, involves two or more PLCs that share portions of a complete control task. Each PLC performs its own functions and communicates pertinent information to other controllers over some form of communications network — typically a local area network. A typical application is the assembly or transfer line in which many machines perform separate operations to complete a finished part. Each section of the machine might be controlled by a separate PLC. To participate in this type of configuration, the selected processors would require networking ability, generally a feature of enhanced low-end, mid-range, and high-end controllers.

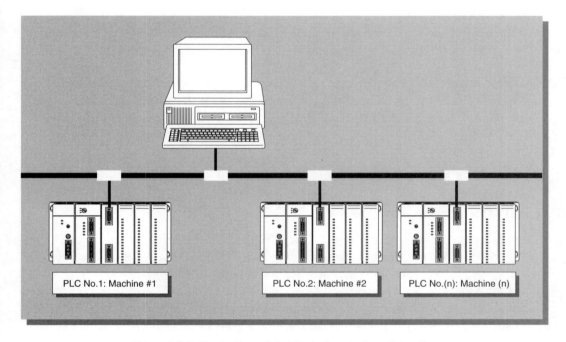

Figure 13-3. Illustration of distributed control configuration

13-4 CPU Requirements

The capabilities of the PLC stem from the central processing unit. To evaluate and determine CPU requirements requires detailed knowledge of the machine or process to be controlled, knowledge of any peculiar requirements of the application, as well as any plant goals for integration with other systems. This step of the selection process requires that the previous steps of defining the I/O requirements and the overall system strategy be adequately defined.

As previously discussed, the CPU determines hardware capabilities and physical limitations of I/O devices and memory, as well as the various system configurations. Items such as CPU and I/O redundancy, multiple CPUs, intelligent I/O, remote I/O, and local area networks capabilities are all determined by the CPU. To select or determine the need for these physical elements will require an understanding of the physical elements and the desired configuration of the application components.

Software components of the PLC are also determined by the CPU. These components will include the overall programming environment which stem from the operating system of the CPU. Features such as integrated PID, system interrupt capability, floating point arithmetic, multiple programming languages and fault handling routines are items to be considered. The following discussions of memory and software, cover the final major considerations for determining the CPU selection.

Memory Considerations

Determining memory requirements involves deciding on the type and amount of memory and whether or not future expansion is required. Since low-end PLCs are generally limited, memory is not usually expandable, but instead is available in a few fixed sizes, for instance 2K, 4K, or 8K words. This amount is generally more than adequate for typical small PLC applications. Mid-range and high-end controllers, on the other hand, are generally expandable up to some maximum in units of 8K, 16K, or 32K words.

As for memory type, all applications will require a read/write memory such as battery-supported CMOS RAM for program development. The nature of the application will dictate whether or not the finished program will be executed from the RAM or from a nonvolatile memory, such as EPROM or EEPROM. If infrequent program and data changes are expected, then EPROM or EEPROM will add an extra measure of reliability. On the other hand, if frequent manual changes are expected or if program or recipe downloading is required, then a read/write memory will be required. In any case, having the program stored on backup disk or on nonvolatile memory modules should be considered as a means of quickly restoring the program if necessary.

Finally, although no fixed rules exist for determining memory requirements, suppliers generally offer guidelines for making a close approximation. A simple rule of thumb, applied to relay equivalent circuits, is to allow ten words of memory for each internal or external output used. Eight to ten words is a good multiplier for function block instructions. This procedure is adequate when applied to simple to moderately complex logic. An additional 25-50 percent should be added to your estimate for more complex programs and expansion. Where large amounts of data need to be collected or data trending is required, consider rack installed computers, a hard disk module, or transferring the data to an external computer.

Software Considerations

The software language and the instruction set of a candidate PLC should be closely evaluated, since they will have significant impact on the ease of program development, maintenance, and troubleshooting. These, of course, will also have subsequent cost implications. Evaluating a PLC, based on the merits of its language and software capability should involve addressing the following considerations.

- ❏ Ease of use and implementation
- ❏ Ability to solve problems efficiently and accurately
- ❏ Application/program response-time constraints
- ❏ Alternative language solutions
- ❏ Suitable for group development
- ❏ Reuse of previously generated software

Small applications using low-end controllers, typically involve relay-replacement with discrete logic, timing, and counting. The choices of PLCs at this end of the spectrum will offer either ladder or Boolean programming, both of which are quite suited for this range of application. While both of languages are easily learned and require little training, ladder is more widely accepted, and its graphic presentation is perhaps easier to interpret and troubleshoot.

Applications of mid-range and high-end PLCs include a variety of problem-solving requirements that generally include some combination of discrete logic, analog or positioning control, arithmetic and data processing, or communications. The level of program complexity as well as the combination of problems to be solved will dictate what demands are placed on the programming language. The language and the instructions of a particular PLC will influence the efficiency in which the program is implemented and executed, as well as the overall response of the control system.

Programs of moderate complexity are generally easily implemented using the computer-oriented block functions. Block functions, found in many PLCs, simplify arithmetic, communications, data processing, and coding of control algorithms. However, it is important to evaluate the instruction set to see how major functions of an application will be efficiently implemented. In certain applications, alternatives or supplements to ladder programming should be evaluated. High-level languages with structured programming elements are more suitable for handling calculations, data processing, statistical analysis, or control algorithms such as for PID loops.

Ladder programs may also become difficult to work with in applications involving many sequential operations. Such operations may use numerous latch circuits to retain a sense of history of what has happened previously and what should be done next. Sequential flowcharting languages offers an alternative to ladders. These languages, which are introduced in chapter 12, are designed specifically to handle sequential control problems where the steps are sequential or time dependent, having complex interlocking logic.

Table 13-2. Central Processing Unit Checklist

General
- CPU Type/Architecture
- Scan Time/1K of Memory
- Networking Ability (proprietary, open system)
- Interrupt Processing (time-driven, I/O driven)
- I/O Scanning Methods
- On-line Program Changes/Merging
- Multiple CPUs Supported
- Redundant Systems
- Fault-Tolerant Designs
- PID Loops Supported
- Memory (RAM w/battery, EPROM, EEPROM)
- Application Memory Capacity (expandability)
- Data Table Size (fixed, expandable)

Power Supply
- Supply Voltage
- Voltage Range (+/- 15%)
- Maximum Current Delivered

Software
- Languages (ladder logic, high-level)
- Total Timers/Counters/Internal Relays
- Time Base Units (.01, .1, 1.0 sec)
- Arithmetic Instructions
- Data Transfer Instructions
- Flow Control Instructions (MCR, JMP,SUB)
- Comparison Instructions (basic, file)
- Drum Sequencers
- Logic Matrix Instructions
- File Manipulation
- ASCII Message Handling
- PID Loop Configuration Software
- Analog Alarms Configuration Software

Physical/Environmental
- Dimensions of CPU & I/O Racks
- Operating Temperature/Humidity
- Vibration/Shock Test
- EMI/RFI Test
- UL/CSA Test
- Regulatory Agency Approvals

13-5 Program Development and Operator Access Devices

Most PLC products offer a choice of devices for creating, editing, and monitoring the control program. These devices generally include proprietary industrial loaders, PC software packages, hand-held programmers, and operator access devices. As discussed in chapter 9, the programming system should provide a complete development and maintenance environment that supports program development, documentation, and extensive diagnostic tools.

Industrial Loaders

Industrial loaders, often called "intelligent CRTs," are vendor-specific devices that for many years were the main means for program development, on-line modification, and monitoring. These devices also offer off-line programming, hard disk storage, and in some cases limited documentation and graphics features. Advantages of these devices, which are still available from some vendors, have been their industrial ruggedness, and from a maintenance standpoint, their specific key functionality for programming and monitoring operations.

PC-Based Programming Systems

Desktop, laptop, and notebook style PCs are the primary development tools for PLCs. With many choices offered by PLC vendor and third-party companies, most program development and troubleshooting requirements can be conveniently satisfied. These devices, which are also available in ruggedized versions provide plant floor diagnostics and maintenance tools. With PC-based systems, users also have the benefit of many third-party developed maintenance and diagnostic utilities, documentation, and man-machine interface software. Hard disk storage also allows archiving of many PLC and other application programs.

Handheld Programmers

Handheld or calculator-styled devices are often the primary means for programming and monitoring for low-end PLCs. Although these low-cost devices were originally intended for use with low-end controllers, some are compatible with larger family members. Here, they are used primarily for making basic program changes and as an operator access device to allow monitoring or modifications to timer, counter, and general word locations. Handheld programmers offer users a convenient, low-cost means of making minor field program modifications.

Operator Access Device

Operator access device, sometimes referred to as a TCAM *(timer/counter access monitor)* is a device similar to handheld programming units, but without programming ability. They serve, instead, to provide a less complicated device with limited access to the PLC data table. The operator access device is typically used for monitoring and modifying a fixed range of word locations. Typically, the device is used for monitoring the changing values of timers, counters, and analog I/O modules, as well as for loading new setpoints.

Other Peripherals

While evaluating programming requirements, also consider peripherals that will aid the operator in interfacing with the controlled system. Commonly used peripherals include printers, video monitors, message display units, and many other devices used to generate reports, messages, or alarms, or that allow interactive communication between the operator and the control system. Typical interfacing requirements for these types of devices include RS232 or RS485 serial interfaces, BCD parallel I/O interfaces, or ASCII interfaces, each of which will have influence on the CPU selection. Constraints to be aware of include the maximum number of connections for such devices, distances, communications data rates and communications protocols, availability of required software drivers, and the ease of programming.

Table 13-3. Programming and Operator Interface Device Checklist

Industrial Loader/PC Development Systems	MMI/Operator Access Systems
- Physical Size & weight	- Physical Size
- Display Size	- Display Size and Type
- Ladder Matrix Size	- Keyboard Type
- PLC Interface (20 ma, RS-232, RS-422/RS485)	- Cabinet Mounting
- Operating System (MS-DOS, Windows, UNIX)	- Printer Interface
- Internal Diagnostics/Utilities	- Message/Alarm Handling Ability
- Storage Media (Floppy disk, Cassette tape)	-Fault Reporting and Logging Ability
- Fixed Disk Storage	- Report Generation Capability
- LAN Interface (direct connection/via interface)	- Operator Interface Screens
- Documentation Software (Integral, Third-Party)	- Third-Party MMI Systems
- Off-line Programming	- Network capability
- Program Merging	
- Program Text Editing (ASCII)	
- EPROM Programming Interface	
- Report Generation Capability	
Handheld Programmers	
- Physical Size	
- Display Size	
- Keyboard Type (Standard, Mylar)	
- Ladder Matrix Size	
- Intelligent Device (Integral operating system)	
- Diagnostic Capability	
- Printer Interface	

13-6 Understanding PLC Product Ranges

Before setting out to select a PLC, it will be helpful to understand the different categories of controllers and the features typically found within each. By narrowing the field to a particular class, the need to sift through a multitude of products can be avoided. Most major brands offer what is referred to as a "family" of PLCs. A family is intended to cover the full spectrum of features suited to handling the lowest to the most sophisticated control requirements. A family is considered such, since members have similar attributes such as instruction sets and memory organization, and share common resources such as the I/O system and programming equipment.

Product Segmentation

Figure 13-4 graphically illustrates how a typical PLC family would cover the product capability spectrum. The three major segments, *low-end controller*, *mid-range controller*, and *high-end controller* categories, are based on the conventional classification by I/O capacity. As the I/O capacity increases, so do memory capacity and functional capabilities, such as the variety of usable I/O modules, the available programming languages, and the diversity of the programming instruction set.

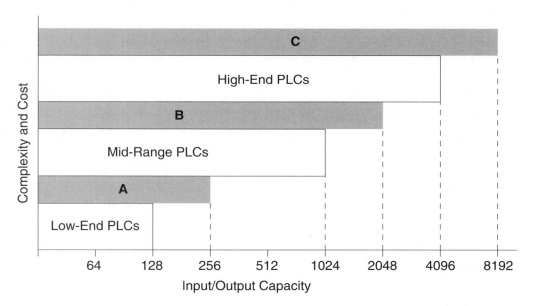

Figure 13-4. Illustration of PLC product spectrum

Gray areas (A, B, and C), shown overlapping the three major segments (1,2, and 3), reflect subcategories of products that have feature enhancements over the standard features of each of the major segments. Products in area A for instance, reflect enhancements to standard features of low-end controllers; products in area B, reflect enhancements to standard features of mid-range controllers. An example of an enhanced low-end PLC would be one that, because of its I/O count, would normally be classed in the low-end category, but having analog I/O, a selection of intelligent I/O, and an LAN interface places it in enhanced category A.

Product segmentation based on standard and enhanced features allows a selection of a product that closely matches system requirements without having to purchase from the next level of products, unless absolutely necessary. The characteristics of each of the standard and enhanced product categories outlined in the following discussions, although not etched in stone, will serve as a useful measure of what to expect of various products.

Low-end Controllers

Standard features listed in Table 13-4 are typical of low-end controllers. Generally, this category is referred to as *relay-replacers*, since they are mostly limited to digital I/O and basic instructions suited for timing, counting, and logic sequencing. A subcategory of this class includes PLCs having fewer than 64 I/O, called *microcontrollers*. Usually, micro-PLCs, or *bricks* as they are often called, are nonmodular, single-housing units that include the CPU, I/O, and in some cases the programming unit. Micro-PLCs are typically digital I/O controllers only. The micro-PLC is a low-cost relay-replacement solution in applications having a small fixed I/O requirement (24-32 I/O).

Table 13-4. Typical Features for Low-End PLCs

❑ 64 to 256 I/O maximum
❑ 4K-8K words of memory
❑ 256 internal output coils
❑ 64 timers and counters
❑ Digital I/O
❑ Limited Analog I/O
❑ Local I/O only
❑ Ladder or Boolean language
❑ Relay equivalent instructions
❑ Timer & counter instructions
❑ Basic comparison instructions
❑ Drum sequencer instructions
❑ Handheld programming unit

In many cases, products at the low-end will have their own I/O system and will not be compatible with the standard I/O used with larger family members. It may also be that programming of some smaller controllers is performed only with handheld programmers or limited-features programming package. While this particular group of PLCs are considered relay replacers, they offer a sizable advantage over relays in terms of flexibility, space requirements, energy consumption, ease of maintenance, and cost.

Enhanced Low-end Controllers

Enhanced low-end PLCs are represented by region A in Figure 13-4. I/O capacity is typically extended up to 256 I/O. PLCs in this class in many ways reflect a continuing trend away from large sophisticated controllers and toward multifunctional low-end PLCs. This class of PLC is best distinguished from its standard counterpart by basic hardware extensions, including memory and I/O capacity, processing speed, analog, and intelligent I/O. Intelligent I/O might include a high-speed counter module, serial communications module or port, and a LAN interface. To support these hardware extensions, the instruction set is also extended.

Applications of the enhanced low-end controllers are best identified as those small machines and processes requiring both digital and analog control, as well as the ability to incorporate basic arithmetic, data handling, inter-processor communication, and low-end operator interface devices. Distributed control of several small machines is a typical application for the enhanced low-end PLC. In such a configuration, the intelligent low-end PLCs may be supervised by a mid-range or high-end PLC that can download new recipes, schedule production runs, and collect data from each machine.

Mid-range Controllers

Features inherent to standard mid-range PLCs are listed in Table 13-5. In relation to low-end controllers, controllers in this class have greater hardware capacity and offer the ability to collect, manipulate, and output data to various peripheral and operator devices. The ability of mid-range controllers to utilize a full range of intelligent I/O modules and communicate with other devices and systems is probably the most significant enhancement over low-end PLCs.

Table 13-5. Typical Features for Mid-range PLCs

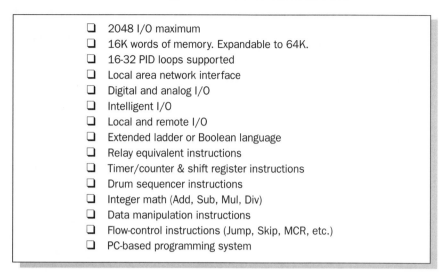

❑ 2048 I/O maximum
❑ 16K words of memory. Expandable to 64K.
❑ 16-32 PID loops supported
❑ Local area network interface
❑ Digital and analog I/O
❑ Intelligent I/O
❑ Local and remote I/O
❑ Extended ladder or Boolean language
❑ Relay equivalent instructions
❑ Timer/counter & shift register instructions
❑ Drum sequencer instructions
❑ Integer math (Add, Sub, Mul, Div)
❑ Data manipulation instructions
❑ Flow-control instructions (Jump, Skip, MCR, etc.)
❑ PC-based programming system

Mid-range controllers are first looked upon when physical requirements of an application, such as I/O device, exceed the physical resources of the enhanced low-end controller. With a typical capacity of 2048 I/O that can be configured either local or remote, this category of controllers can handle a wide range of applications requiring digital, analog, positioning control, and communications. In general, it is at this PLC category that most, if not all, of the available I/O modules of a particular family can be utilized. Extended hardware and software functionality, along with the ability to grow as requirements change, account for the fact that mid-range controllers are the most widely used PLCs.

Enhanced Mid-Range Controllers

The enhanced mid-range controller is the "workhorse" of most PLC families. Increased processing speed and instruction set extensions provide enhancement over the standard mid-range controller. While standard mid-range PLCs have extended memory and extended data manipulation instructions capable of supporting the available I/O modules, the extended resources (especially processing speed) of the enhanced mid-range PLCs may be required for stringent data processing and communications or if several of the more complex I/O modules are used.

High-end Controllers

Generally, high-end PLCs are selected for applications requiring the large I/O and memory capacity. It is likely, however, that these same applications will have need for and make good use of other standard high-end features such as remote I/O and an instruction set that facilitates extensive data manipulation, data acquisition, report generation, and communication. Other cases in which high-end PLCs are called upon include applications having high-speed requirements exceeding that of mid-range controllers or in which some other resource of the mid-range controller is marginally met or exceeded. Typical examples might include the number of PID loops supported, the need for floating point math, or the interrupt processing ability.

Table 13-6. Typical Features for High-end PLCs

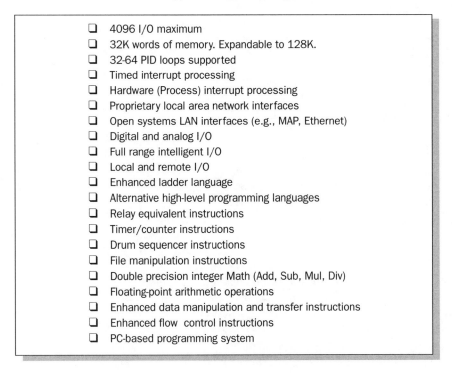

- ❑ 4096 I/O maximum
- ❑ 32K words of memory. Expandable to 128K.
- ❑ 32-64 PID loops supported
- ❑ Timed interrupt processing
- ❑ Hardware (Process) interrupt processing
- ❑ Proprietary local area network interfaces
- ❑ Open systems LAN interfaces (e.g., MAP, Ethernet)
- ❑ Digital and analog I/O
- ❑ Full range intelligent I/O
- ❑ Local and remote I/O
- ❑ Enhanced ladder language
- ❑ Alternative high-level programming languages
- ❑ Relay equivalent instructions
- ❑ Timer/counter instructions
- ❑ Drum sequencer instructions
- ❑ File manipulation instructions
- ❑ Double precision integer Math (Add, Sub, Mul, Div)
- ❑ Floating-point arithmetic operations
- ❑ Enhanced data manipulation and transfer instructions
- ❑ Enhanced flow control instructions
- ❑ PC-based programming system

Enhanced High-End Controllers

This category of extremely capable PLCs is hardly used in its full capacity in everyday PLC control applications, but instead is used considerably for supervisory and control operations involving a group of lower level controllers. This particular role in control hierarchy is considered the *cell level*, the level at which several controllers are monitored and/or coordinated by a single device (i.e., the *cell controller*). The main function is to coordinate the activities of a group of machines that perform different functions.

The requirements of the cell area of computer integration, as well as the type of device best suited (i.e., sophisticated PLC or computer), have been the subject of much discussion. Functional requirements, however, include but are not limited to 1) predictable I/O response characteristics, 2) priority interrupt structure, 3) mass storage, 4) communications and information processing, 5) high-level control language, and 6) a standard communications protocols.

While the enhanced high-end PLC is likely to eventually relinquish this position, it is very likely that the ultimate cell controller will embody this level of PLC technology with general-purpose computing technology.

Table 13-7. Typical Features of Enhanced High-end PLCs

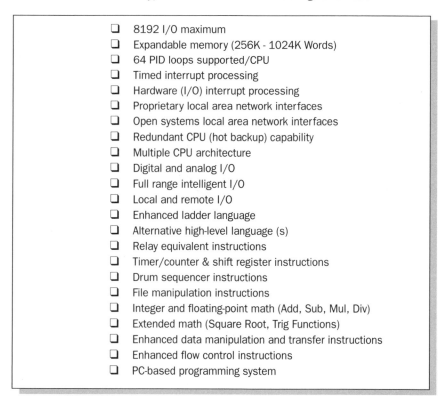

- ❏ 8192 I/O maximum
- ❏ Expandable memory (256K - 1024K Words)
- ❏ 64 PID loops supported/CPU
- ❏ Timed interrupt processing
- ❏ Hardware (I/O) interrupt processing
- ❏ Proprietary local area network interfaces
- ❏ Open systems local area network interfaces
- ❏ Redundant CPU (hot backup) capability
- ❏ Multiple CPU architecture
- ❏ Digital and analog I/O
- ❏ Full range intelligent I/O
- ❏ Local and remote I/O
- ❏ Enhanced ladder language
- ❏ Alternative high-level language (s)
- ❏ Relay equivalent instructions
- ❏ Timer/counter & shift register instructions
- ❏ Drum sequencer instructions
- ❏ File manipulation instructions
- ❏ Integer and floating-point math (Add, Sub, Mul, Div)
- ❏ Extended math (Square Root, Trig Functions)
- ❏ Enhanced data manipulation and transfer instructions
- ❏ Enhanced flow control instructions
- ❏ PC-based programming system

13-7 Evaluating the Intangible Factors

An evaluation of the hardware and software requirements previously outlined will narrow the selection to a few possible products. Eventually, two or more products or vendors will meet the functional requirements of the preliminary system design and a final decision can be made. At this point, several factors still remain, and when properly evaluated, can help lead to a final selection. The following points should be carefully considered.

Vendor Support

A company that is willing and capable of providing good technical support for years can make life after purchase much easier and less costly. It will also determine whether or not your investment will be with technology that provides a sound platform to build upon or that leads to an eventual dead end. Early on in your discussions with potential vendors, learn about their product design philosophies, future business directions, and intentions regarding various open systems standards. Include as part of the evaluation a visit to a local or regional technical center. Measure how well a company's technology philosophies and general directions accommodate those of your own organization. Be sure to get facts, not promises.

Field Support

The quality of after-sale support should be a primary concern for PLC purchasers. Vendor candidates should be closely scrutinized on this important point. Pre-sales support can offer a yardstick for predicting post-sales support. Once a controller has been purchased, it is most likely that some type of field support will eventually be required. Field support may involve clarification of user manuals, assistance with programming, installation assistance, and repair or replacement of failed components.

When evaluating this aspect of potential candidates, insist on knowing the level of the candidate vendors' local support, including sales, distributors, applications engineering, and field service engineering. Whatever the service requirement, qualified and prompt attention to your needs can mean the difference between a smooth flowing and timely executed project and a project plagued by annoying and costly setbacks that can lead to overall disaster. Some companies offer 24-hour technical support to help avoid such situations.

Technical Documentation

Supporting technical documentation, including programming, operation, and installation manuals, can prove to be an enormous assistance or a dreadful annoyance. Orderly and well-written user manuals minimize delays and avert costly misapplication. The quality of documentation will greatly influence whether or not you get off to a good start. Find out if vendors have publications detailing how your particular application might be approached, or brief examples of software coding. Such examples, referred to as *application notes*, may offer useful insights into how a particular product is already being applied to your application. These notes can also help you to avoid pitfalls.

Future Plant Goals

Finally, a consideration that may aid in firming up the selection process is that of your own company's intentions to standardize on the products of one or more vendors. Standardization on one or two product lines has become the choice of several companies using programmable controllers. This route offers many desirable benefits, the most of which stem from the family concept in which a complete range of products, from the low-end to high-end, have compatible architectures and share common system resources.

Product families share the same I/O system components and programming facilities and have common instruction sets. They also have similar memory organization and data structures that allow software created on one machine to be run on other machines included in the family. Usually some restrictions exist. This structure also simplifies access to the different PLCs by third-party software. A family of PLCs can also normally be connected to a local area network and have standard peer-to-peer communications interfaces. Some of the benefits to standardization are listed below.

❑ *Training cost and learning curves are reduced since new product training builds upon what has already been learned.*

❑ *Standard products can result in improved plant maintenance since more plant personnel are familiar with the same or similar systems.*

❑ *Use of common resources such as I/O modules and programming equipment reduces spare parts inventory requirements.*

❑ *Hardware design drawings and software routines can be standardized and generated for common use by different departments, resulting in reduced engineering cost.*

❑ *Communication between different plant systems over local area networks can be simplified, allowing greater plant integration.*

13-8 PLC Product Selection Summary

This chapter has offered a general outline for approaching the task of PLC selection. This process has been based primarily on determining physical and functional system requirements, based on obvious factors such as I/O capacity, memory capacity, and specific interfacing requirements.

Our last section, however, posed several final questions to be addressed prior to making a final selection. These intangible factors will, in the long run, have as much impact on overall success as will the more tangible items. The following outline summarizes the major considerations involved in PLC hardware configuration and selection.

Table 13-8. PLC Selection Criteria

Step 1: Understand the machine or process.
a. Involve people who know the process.
b. Learn from previously installed similar systems.
c. Decide how machine control can be improved.

Step 2: Determine the control strategy.
a. Individual machine control
b. Centralized control
c. Distributed control

Step 3: Determine input/output system requirements.
a. Total the number of digital and analog points.
b. Evaluate remote I/O opportunities.
c. Define special signal characteristics.
d. Evaluate specific control response needs.
e. Evaluate intelligent I/O opportunities.
f. Consider short term expansion requirement.

Step 4: Determine CPU requirements.
a. General requirements (i.e., timers, counters, etc.)
b. Input/Output capacities (digital, analog, etc.)
c. Processing speed requirements
d. Adequacy of program and I/O scan methods
e. Startup and runtime error diagnostics
f. Interrupt processing capability (time & I/O-driven)
g. Evaluate networking and internetting requirements

Step 5: Determine memory requirements.
a. RAM with battery backup
b. EPROM, EEPROM, or other nonvolatile storage
c. EPROM programming facilities (programmer, eraser)
d. Allow extra capacity for complex programming.
e. Consider short-term need for memory expansion.

Step 6: Evaluate software needs.
a. Alternative languages
b. Potential complexity of program
c. Language/application compatibility
d. Ease of software development
e. Ease of software maintenance and troubleshooting

Step 7: Determine programming and operator needs.
a. Desktop, laptop, notebook PC, or handheld programming device
b. Evaluate documentation features.
c. Evaluate monitoring/editing/archiving features.
d. Consider TCAMs for limited operator access.
e. Consider compatible third-party programming and MMI systems.

Step 8: Determine physical and environmental constraints.
a. Consider mounting space constraints.
b. Requirements for standards test (e.g., vibration, shock, EMI/RFI)
c. Requirements for test approvals (e.g., UL, CSA)
d. Harsh atmospheric or dangerous conditions
e. Regulatory agency test requirements (e.g., FDA)

Step 9: Evaluate the intangible factors.
a. Vendor credibility and technology directions
b. Vendor support organizations (e.g., distributors, technical support, etc.)
c. Your company's goals, such as for standards or plant integration
e. Determine your company's in-house ability to support product.
f. Product Availability
g. Worldwide product availability and support

14

PROGRAMMING AND DOCUMENTING THE CONTROL SYSTEM

Preliminary Documentation Review

Structured Program Development

Program Building Blocks

Documentation Requirements

The Documentation Package

The task of developing a control program has become much more intensive in its, demands due to higher requirements for automation flexibility and the PLC's increased number of relationships with other intelligent automation components. While program development need not be difficult, it involves much more than simply typing instructions. As a program developer you will have many alternatives to consider when developing the control program. Regardless of the size or complexity of the programming task, a structured development using predetermined design methodologies will produce the most effective solution.

This chapter presents a broad overview of the process of developing an application program, from conception and design to documentation. A structured approach to program development is introduced and several program building blocks are provided for frequently encountered situations. The intent of this chapter is not on writing a program, but on presenting a design methodology for program development and documentation.

14-1 Preliminary Documentation Review

As presented in the previous chapter, the conceptual design is a process in which the scope of a project is defined. During this phase of any project, various decisions are made concerning PLC hardware and system configuration. Many of these decisions will establish the groundwork for the programming tasks and such decisions will affect what hardware and software is required. If at all possible, the program developer should participate in this process as much as possible.

As a program developer, your first development step should be to acquire a complete understanding of the process or machine to be controlled and of the intended operational requirements. Reviewing existing documentation and consultation with system clients will enable you to gain this understanding. Early on, you will learn whether the project is a retrofit of an existing system or a new system altogether. The design approach to these two project types will differ slightly and will also affect what documentation is already available.

Retrofit and New Projects

In a retrofit or modernization project, the system owner (e.g., the plant) generally understands the machine or process and its control requirements. The sequence of operations is usually defined by an existing relay logic diagram. Relay logic can be translated into PLC ladder logic almost directly. However, the PLC will allow you to enhance the current method of control. New projects usually begin with control specifications being given to the persons responsible for the system design. These specifications should explain the intended process or machine operation. If your involvement begins after the conceptual design, you will need to thoroughly review any existing documentation. Look for possible errors and omissions resulting from the planning phase. Try to resolve any unanswered questions with those persons previously involved.

Project documentation which must be obtained and reviewed can usually be acquired from the client(s), or from the involved engineering disciplines. Available information should include one or more of the documents in the following list. From these documents you should be able to determine the desired function of each piece of equipment, and of the desired overall sequence of operation. In reviewing available documentation, you may find that modification to the conceptual design is required. Engineering organizations and plants should establish procedures for making changes to an initial system design.

❏ Relay Elementary Drawings
❏ Functional Specifications
❏ Motor and Electrical Devices List
❏ Piping and Instrument Diagrams
❏ Control System Arrangement Drawing
❏ Process Loop Diagrams
❏ Logic Gate Diagrams
❏ SAMA (Function Block) Diagrams

Relay Elementary Drawings

Relay elementary drawings, or *relay logic diagrams*, are schematic diagrams of hardwired electro-mechanical control circuits. These drawings, which are familiar to most plant engineers, electricians and technicians, are often the starting place for many retrofit jobs. Relay schematics show both power and discrete logic circuits for various control devices. These drawings are quite useful for identifying PLC discrete input and output devices such as various sensors, solenoid valves, pumps and motors. Required timing and counting circuits may also show up on relay logic diagrams. Although PLC control logic is often developed directly from relay diagrams, control enhancements are normally added. A typical relay logic diagram, with discrete I/O highlighted, is shown in Figure 14-1.

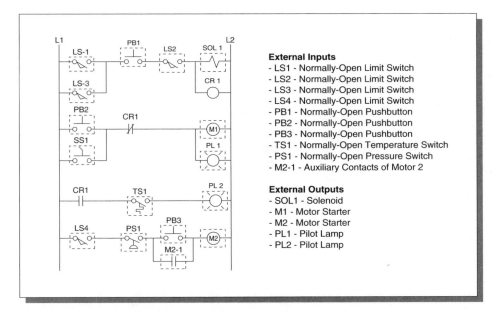

External Inputs
- LS1 - Normally-Open Limit Switch
- LS2 - Normally-Open Limit Switch
- LS3 - Normally-Open Limit Switch
- LS4 - Normally-Open Limit Switch
- PB1 - Normally-Open Pushbutton
- PB2 - Normally-Open Pushbutton
- PB3 - Normally-Open Pushbutton
- TS1 - Normally-Open Temperature Switch
- PS1 - Normally-Open Pressure Switch
- M2-1 - Auxiliary Contacts of Motor 2

External Outputs
- SOL1 - Solenoid
- M1 - Motor Starter
- M2 - Motor Starter
- PL1 - Pilot Lamp
- PL2 - Pilot Lamp

Figure 14-1. Portion of a relay logic diagram with discrete I/O highlighted

345

Functional Specifications

Functional specifications are written descriptions of the intended operation of individual pieces of equipment and of the overall sequence of operations of a machine or process. These specifications are often the result of a collaborative effort between the system owner (client) and the system developer. It is important that the final revision of this document be agreed upon by the system developer and the client. For this reason the development process normally involves two or more working meetings and reviews. Functional specifications often are the main tool for developing the control logic for each device, as well as the sequence of operations of an entire machine or process. A sample functional description for two devices is given in Table 14-1.

Table 14-1. Sample functional specification for two devices

Mixer-A Blender Motor	1) The blender motor mixes ingredient 1 and ingredient 2 in tank-A. 2) The blender motor is started and stopped from a local start/stop operator station mounted on the mixer tank 3) In automatic, the following permissives control blender motor-A: - Tank-A is not empty. - Tank-A drain valve is not open (energized) - The blender motor is not faulted (auxiliary contacts closed) - The emergency stop is not activated
Mixer-A Drain Valve	1) The drain valve, which uses a single spring return solenoid, allows the mixed product to drain into holding tank. - If the solenoid is energized, the drain valve is open. - I the solenoid is de-energized, the drain valve is closed. 2) The drain valve is manually opened and closed from Mixer-A local operator station. 3) The drain valve is permitted to open when the operator presses the start push-button and the following permissives are met: - If the blender motor is off - If the emergency stop push-button is not pushed.

Motor and Electrical Devices List

A *Motor and Electrical Devices List* is simply that, a tabular accounting of all motors and electrical devices pertinent to a machine or process. This list typically includes actuator devices such as motors, pumps, valves and compressors and sensors devices such as photoelectric and limit switches. Tag names are usually given for each device, and references to the location of the device on associated equipment is also provided. The M&EDL is eventually used to identify the I/O devices of the system. In the end, each device, that must be controlled, should have a corresponding functional description of its operation. If not already available, this document can be produced in conjunction with the system owner.

Piping and Instrument Diagrams

Piping and Instrument Diagrams (P&ID) graphically represent the major equipment of a given process, along with associated instruments. These drawings show equipment and associated piping for process equipment such as tanks, pumps, turbines, heaters and boilers. The P&ID also graphically represent physical connections of each process instrument (e.g., temperature, flow, pressure transmitters). The control strategy for devices such as recorders, analyzers, loop controllers and loop displays may also be shown on piping and instrument diagrams (See Fig. 14-2). All instruments input to the PLC and all final elements controlled by the PLC are also usually shown. Like the M&EDL, the P&ID can be used in the development of an I/O point list.

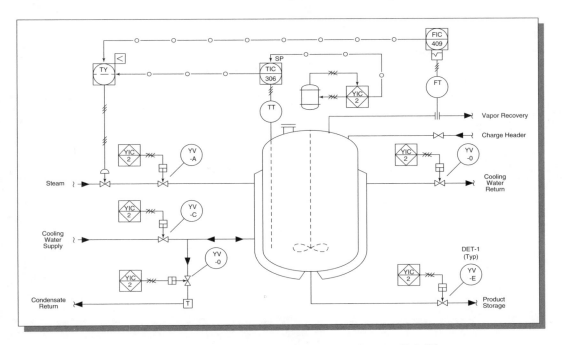

Figure 14-2. A typical piping and instrument diagram (P & ID)

Control System Arrangement Drawing

The *Control System Arrangement Drawing*, also referred to as System Layout Drawing, shows the layout of major electrical and electronic control equipment being supplied for a specific project. For example, a system integration company that provides a complete control system is often responsible for purchasing all PLC equipment, cabinet enclosures, man-machine interfaces, computer workstations, display panels, power supplies and other control and data acquisition equipment. Generally the automation company produces hardware layout drawings that shows placement and single line interconnections between the major control system components. As illustrated in Figure 14-3, network interconnections are also shown. If a system layout drawing is not already available, it should be produced as part of the overall documentation package.

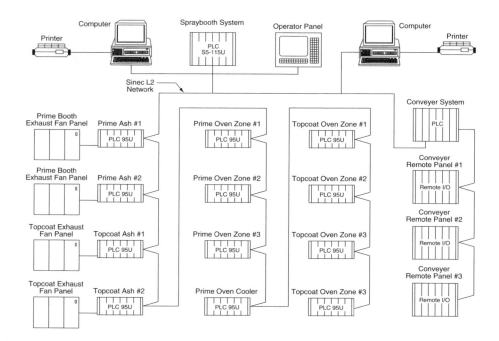

Figure 14-3. An example control system arrangement diagram

Process Loop Diagrams

Process Loop Diagrams are a type of wiring schematic similar to the elementary except it shows the wiring circuits for analog devices. A process loop consists of the control devices required to maintain stability in a single process variable. For example, the level control in a tank might consist of a level transmitter, a single loop controller, a current-to-pneumatic converter, and a final control valve. These diagrams may contain multiple inputs and outputs required to complete a closed loop or it may simply involve analog inputs or outputs that must be interfaced to the PLC. Figure 14-4 is a loop diagram showing termination, cabling and location information of a single instrument. Generally, loop diagrams are used to perform wiring checks for each instrument. For the program developer, loop diagrams convey closed loop control requirements analog signals that must be monitored.

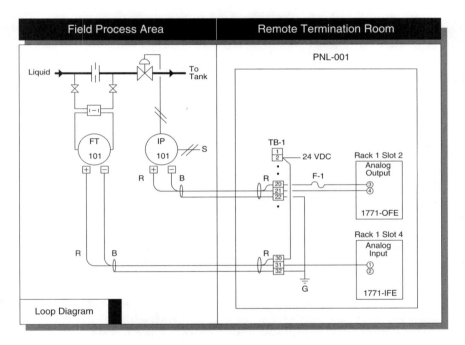

Figure 14-4. Example of process loop diagram

Logic Gate Diagrams

Some companies use *Logic Gate Diagrams* to graphically convey the operation of each subsystem or device. Logic diagrams use Boolean gate symbols, such as AND, OR and NOT, configured in series and parallel logic combinations. The gates describe the combination and sequential logic required to control digital I/O devices. Logic circuits show designation of real inputs, real outputs, timing delays and internal outputs that interlock various devices or subsystems. As shown in Figure 14-5, a single logic diagram may show the control logic for several devices. Most PLC programming packages support ladder logic programming that can be generated to correspond directly to a logic diagram. Some packages even allow program development using Boolean gate symbols.

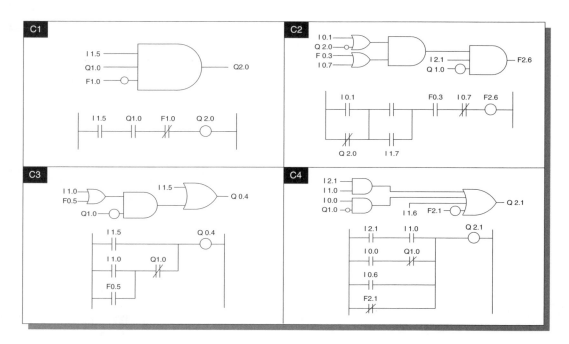

Figure 14-5. Logic diagram drawing showing equivalent ladder logic

Function Block Diagrams

Function Block Diagrams, sometimes referred to as *SAMA Diagrams*, are based on a set of block symbols developed by the Scientific Apparatus Manufacturers Association (SAMA). These symbols, which represent a variety of logic, control, and arithmetic functions, can be graphically arranged to convey both discrete logic and analog control strategies. Figure 14-6 illustrates a SAMA diagram for fuel and air control in furnace application. The diagram shows the inputs of the instrument, outputs to drive the final elements and the associated control logic. Similar to logic gate diagrams, the SAMA diagrams define control logic functions that can be used directly in program development. Some program development systems may even support program development using SAMA function blocks.

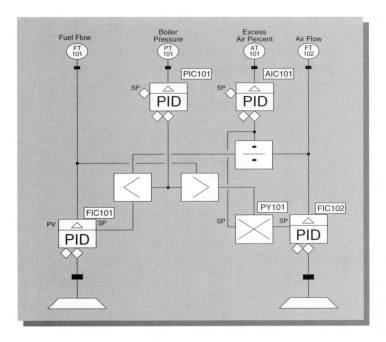

Figure 14-6. SAMA function block diagram showing fuel and
air control in a furnace application

14-2 Structured Program Development

The PLC has often been referred to as a distant relative to the general purpose computer. Despite its peculiar differences, however, it is indeed a computer — and in that light its program development must be approached in very much the same fashion. This is especially true since many computer-like enhancements in the programming environment and language choices have been integrated into the PLC. Furthermore, greater demands for flexibility are being placed on automation solutions. This latter factor alone calls for more stringent program-development, preparation and planning. Items that come to mind are *divide-and-conquer*, *structured programming*, and *good documentation*.

For creation of an effective application solution, the following program-development steps should be carried out in each project.

- ❑ Define the problem clearly and completely
- ❑ Define safety requirements
- ❑ Define operator interface requirements
- ❑ Develop program design strategy
- ❑ Develop I/O device list
- ❑ Allocate PLC system resources (e.g., I/O addresses)
- ❑ Develop control logic and write code
- ❑ Document the code
- ❑ Test and debug the code

Defining the Control Problem

Definition and understanding of the control problem is the first step in developing any application program. Since the control program will ultimately perform various levels of automatic control, over a machine or process, it is vital to understand and know the scope of what functions will come under the control of the PLC.

Whether the proposed system is a retrofit of an existing system or an entirely new system, you must start out by asking lots of questions regarding the scope of the task. Answers to these questions should lead to a definition of the control problem. If you have already reviewed existing documentation, you may already have in mind much of the basic purpose and design of the application — if not, that is where you should begin. With these documents and discussions with the system clients, a clear statement of the overall control objectives can be written. Remember, that without a clear and concise statement of objectives, you will have no measure of when the project is completed, nor a measure for its success.

Defining Safety Requirements

A second step in preparing for the control program, is to determine what components and functions to remain hardwired to ensure safety. In all cases, emergency stop circuits should be kept under complete manual control. Devices such as emergency stop push-buttons, rope switches or master control relays are expected to remove power and prevent harm to individuals and damage to equipment. For this reason, such circuits must operate even if PLC operation has failed. It may also be determined that equipment that is not switched frequently or is more or less standalone, may not require automatic control.

Defining Operator Interface Requirements

All machines and processes will involve a means by which an operator may interact with the controlled machine or process. This may be as simple as a single control panel with start and stop pushbuttons and some indicator lights, to as sophisticated as multiple computer-based operator interface systems with interactive graphic display systems showing visual views of the process with multiple display screens, and alarm and message screens. Whether, the operator interface involves a single or multiple stations, point-to-point or LAN communications, the required I/O data must be organized and grouped for efficient handling.

Developing a Program Design Strategy

The program design strategy is to define a methodology of structuring the control program. While this stage of development is not yet concerned with details of writing code, it is indeed the initial blueprint of a well designed program. Different program design approaches are used — for example, there's the traditional linear approach, where the entire program is written in one inline code block; or the more structured approach, that uses modular blocks of code to perform each tasks. In either case, the design strategy is best developed in two steps. The first step involves partitioning the machine or process into major units or functions, and each unit into subtasks and operations. The second stage is to develop the control logic of the individual subtasks and operations of each process unit. Such an approach is referred to as a *top-down, bottom-up design*.

Define Machine or Process Units. Any machine or process can be partitioned or subdivided into so-called machine or process units. Machine or process units generally refer to main equipment subsystems, each of which generally performs a logical piece of the whole process. This divide-and-conquer approach will enable you or the members of a development team to quickly grasp what has to be controlled, by allowing the entire system to be viewed as subsystems. Well planned partitioning allows for group program development and, more important, for easier adaptation of the program for modifications or future process expansion.

Define Subtasks and Operations. Machine or process units generally reflect the major steps required to produce a finished product, and therefore each can normally be further divided into functional *subtasks* that must be accomplished to complete the unit control function. Each subtask will normally consist of several *operations* involving individual devices, process loops, or other operations for which control logic must be developed. This simple concept is illustrated in Figure 14-7. In computer programming terms, this process is analogous to developing a system operations flowchart, that conveys the major procedures, subtasks, and operations for which a program must be created. Non-hardware related subtasks such as communications, alarm and fault processing should not be overlooked.

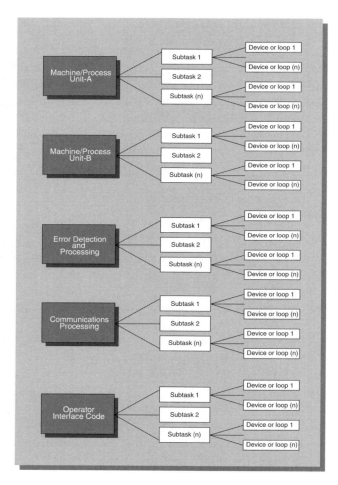

Figure 14-7. Illustration of process partitioning. A program of warehouse control, for instance, might include units for conveyor motor control, case brand detection, and tracking, sorter control, carrousel control, shrink wrapping, communications, and operator interface code.

Developing the I/O Device (Point) List

Once you have gained a thorough understanding of the project requirements, you are ready for the next step. The first tool that you will need in developing your program, is an *I/O point list*. The I/O list documents, in an orderly fashion, what devices must be monitored and controlled by the PLC. Development of the I/O point list involves two steps — first simply identifying what devices should be designated as inputs to the PLC and as outputs from the PLC and then the assignment of I/O addresses to these devices.

What devices are monitored and controlled by the PLC should be easily determined from one or more of the documents that were previously described. Both inputs to and outputs from the PLC are generally classified as digital or analog signals. The types of devices that either generate or are controlled by digital and analog signals are described in Chapter 6 and Chapters 7 respectively. Digital signals are normally found on existing *Relay Elementary Diagrams*, the *Motor & Electrical Devices List*, *Logic Gate Diagrams*, or stated implicitly in *Functional Specifications*. Analog devices will generally be located on *Loop Diagrams*, *SAMA Diagrams* or *P&IDs*.

Allocating I/O Addresses and other PLC System Resources

The address assignments of real inputs and outputs, are usually tabulated as shown in Table 14-3 on page 31. These addresses identify the physical terminal to which each input and output device is connected, as well as how each device is referenced in the control program. Generally, the table gives the type of device, its voltage level, its address, its function and perhaps a symbolic address (label) or device tag name. Such lists often may be generated using standard text editors or database programs. Some PLC programming packages also include symbolic address editors that allow creation of the I/O point address list along with I/O nicknames that may be substituted in the program for absolute addresses.

A planned grouping of associated I/O devices is recommended for the addressing. This grouping will allow more efficient monitoring and manipulation of groups of I/O. For instance, if 16 motors are to be started sequentially, their starting sequence can be viewed by monitoring a single I/O register. As a program developer, the I/O point list will remain an important tool for you — it must be continually updated as program development progresses. Also, since it is likely that new devices will be added, you may want to leave spaces in your address assignment to accommodate any late arrivals.

Developing the Control Logic

The second stage of control strategy development deals with developing control logic for the subtasks of each process unit. In other words, the definition of how specific operations (e.g., *devices, process loops, error processing*) will be implemented or controlled. A given subtasks, for instance, may require control of both digital and analog devices. Completion of the task may also involve performance of data processing, error checking, and perhaps communications functions. One-by-one, the control logic for each of these operations must be developed. This is the bottom-up aspect of the control strategy implementation.

Development of the control logic, is actually the design basis for the PLC program code. In your control logic design, you may want to use either logic gate diagrams and/or flow charts — whichever is more suitable. Logic diagrams are often used for discrete logic development, while analog loop control is often represented using flow charts or SAMA diagrams. To many, this process may be seen as an extra or even unnecessary step. What it does, however, is establish the control requirement for each device or loop — thereby simplifying the coding process. It also establishes a standard documentation component that may be used later by others. In some organizations, logic diagram development is required. Figure 14-8, shows a relay logic circuit and its equivalent Boolean gate logic implementation.

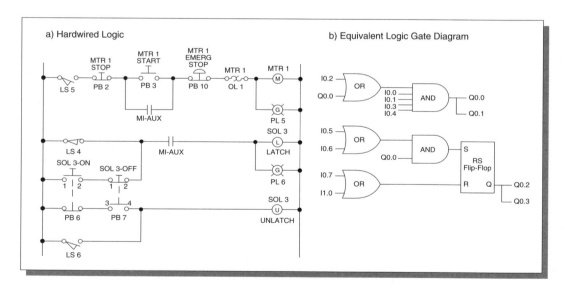

Figure 14-8. Logic diagram (b), created directly from hardwired logic diagram (a)

Writing the Program Code

Coding is the process of writing control logic, using the appropriate instructions from a given instruction set, to achieve the desired control results. This simple definition however implies that any method is valid as long as the desired results are achieved. The fact is, however, that a well written program is not only one that achieves the desired results, but is one that is easily interpreted, modified and maintained throughout its life cycle. These results can only be achieved by following a coding standard or at minimum, a consistent coding style. A few helpful coding design guidelines are presented in the following discussions.

Use Consistent Techniques. While our discussion thus far has presented one PLC program design methodology, there are other ways to approach the problem. The point here, is that the application should be approached in a structured manner, and rely on predictable methods. Just as we suggested starting out by partitioning the process in a logical and predictable fashion, each aspect of the program organization, implementation and documentation should reflect the pattern or style you have decided on. Always do similar things in a similar fashion. If giving symbolic names to I/O or memory locations, use similar names for similar devices or locations. Also, let control logic for similar devices use similar methods, so as to be immediately recognizable. Motor control logic, for example, should be similar or the same for all motors.

Modularize Functionality. Modularity is the "jewel in the crown," of a well-written program. This technique, involves writing modular units of code, each of which perform a small piece of the overall task. This concept is typical in conventional computer programming, where a complete program is composed of a collection of procedures. The procedure is analogous to our process subtasks shown back in Figure 14-7. In Figure 14-9, on the following page, the entire program is divided into blocks containing the logic for a given set of devices or operations required to complete a unit function. The main program determines when and how often the each block is called. If the logic of a given unit is complex, its operations may be further divided into smaller blocks.

Most PLCs programming environments have resources to facilitate the coding of modular blocks of code. Some allow the creation of function blocks, files or subroutines that can be called and processed repetitively throughout the program, either conditionally or unconditionally. Advantages of modular code include the ability to test and debug each module as it is developed and easy duplication or modification for reuse for the same or a similar function. Although these techniques are often implemented in a high-level language subset or an alternative language such as C, some ladder instruction sets allow subroutines and/or subprograms that can be used to write modular code.

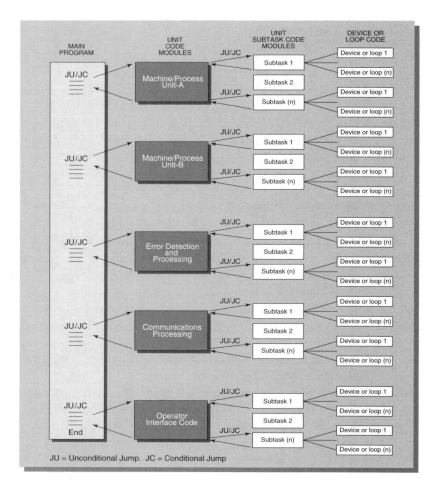

Figure 14-9. Illustration of program design with modularized functionality

Structure Process Data. Good organization of program and process data values is as important to a well-structured program as is the actual coding. Modularly grouped data will aid in efficient program processing. It will also simplify data manipulation and help to ensure that others can easily interpret various techniques you might employ. Where possible, use data files that you may access as a block of data and easily use indexed addressing techniques.

If data files are not possible with your CPU, simply use contiguous word locations to group related data. If you have you ever seen how data points scattered throughout memory effect update times on an operator screen, then you will appreciate data grouping. When data from many locations are to be transmitted over a serial link or network, grouping the data in one or more files first, will greatly enhance the overall response. In many cases, the data stored in the PLC will form a database that will be accessed by another controller or by a host computer. If you name data locations, using symbolic tags, always use meaningful names and assign similar names to similar data values. Typical data groupings are listed below.

- ❏ Program Constants
- ❏ Timer/Counter Presets
- ❏ Analog Presets (e.g., alarm limits, setpoints)
- ❏ Analog loop Parameters
- ❏ Machine Setup Data
- ❏ Process Recipes
- ❏ Product Tracking Data
- ❏ Fault and Status Indicators (Bits, Bytes, Words)

Testing and Debugging the Code

All software programs in development have one thing in common, bugs. Although debugging is discussed here, after code development, it is a process that is required throughout the development process. Some bugs are simply syntax or addressing errors and they are part of the normal process of program development. The modular approach by which you have thus far designed your program, however, should have greatly reduced the introduction of structural errors. Such errors could make future modifications and expansion difficult or impossible without restructuring the entire program.

The modular approach will also greatly simplify the testing process. For example, when the initial skeleton code for the overall sequencing of the major functions written, it would be a good idea to test and ensure its correct operation before proceeding further. Also, just as the code was developed for each process unit, and for each device or operation of each subtask, the testing and debugging for each of these should be performed in a modular fashion. Each piece of code should be tested several times and under different conditions, for correct operation.

Modular code will also simplify the debugging process. Most programming systems have utilities that can reveal the actual step that has caused a program to stop. One technique is to run one section of the program at a time, using a temporary end program instruction. Some systems allow you to create variable status charts, that may be viewed in conjunction with the associated control logic. It is possible to observe changing variables in one window, while the status of the control logic is viewed in another. Such utilities allow you to troubleshoot the system by simulating or activating inputs, and observing the results while the program executes. This troubleshooting method will verify that the program performs each function as intended.

Documenting the Code

Documentation is a vital part of the program development process. No program is complete until it is properly documented. For the developer, documentation should be an ongoing process of compiling, organizing and recording information pertaining to the various elements of the program. Although our mention of documentation thus far has been in reference to tools that aid the developer, to every extent possible, documentation should be end-user-oriented. The latter part of this chapter has been completely devoted to this aspect of documentation so that it might be thoroughly presented.

Summary of Programming Steps

While you may be tempted to take a free-form approach to programming, there is still absolutely no substitute for thoughtful planning and preparation. Remember, the application program you produce will eventually be relied on daily to perform correctly and reliably. Although the structured approach to programming presented here does not guarantee success, it does lay the groundwork for a sound program — one that is easily put into operation and later maintained. If you had to make a list of the essential steps involved in developing an application program, from start to finish, it would very likely resemble the entries of Table 14-2.

Table 14-2. Summary of programming steps.

STEP	PROGRAM DEVELOPMENT FUNCTIONS
1	- Review any existing documentation.
2	- Clearly understand the scope of the automation problem.
3	- Identify major steps of process or elements of machine.
4	- Allocate PLC resources (i.e., I/O, internal coils, timers, counters, loops).
5	- Define the overall sequence of operations on paper.
6	- Define functional specification for each device.
7	- Design program flow for sequencing of major machine/process subfunctions.
8	- Design control logic for each device.
9	- Write and document the code for controlling each loop or device.
10	- Write and document the code for overall program sequencing.
11	- Write and document code for operator interface .
12	- Test and debug the code for each device or loop.
13	- Test and debug the complete application program.
14	- Be prepared to support your program.

14-3 Program Building Blocks

As you develop different programs, you will begin to notice that many pieces of equipment require similar control and that many of your programming implementations can be reapplied. Once the code is developed and debugged, you will want to save any routines that are suitable for possible reuse. Most program developers accumulate and save such routines or "building blocks" into a library. This section will present several small pieces of code that are commonly required when programming the controller. For convenience, these examples are implemented using the most basic ladder instructions.

Example A: Internal Coils

Internal coils are driven by conditional logic, like output image table addresses, but they are not directly associated with an external device. Internal coils are used to store intermediate logical results or to simply to indicate the occurrence of an event or condition. Figure 14-10, illustrates two common uses of internal coils. The first case shows how a logic rung that exceeds the number of allowed series contacts might be altered. The same might be done for a parallel circuit. In Figure 14-10, an internal coil stores the logic result of a combination of contacts that are needed throughout the program. Now, contacts from that coil may be used repeatedly throughout the program instead of rewriting the code.

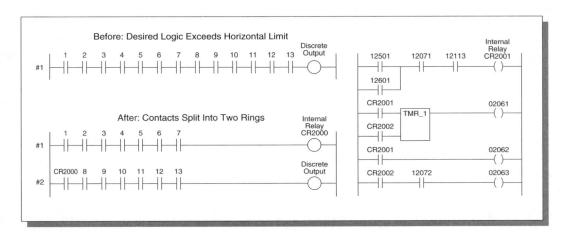

Figure 14-10. Using internal coils

Example B: Exclusive-OR Logic

The Exclusive-OR circuit in Fig. 14-11 allows an output (external or internal) to be energized if either of two separate input conditions is activated, but not if both inputs are activated simultaneously. In an Exclusive OR, the logic is simply that the output will be TRUE if A OR B occurs, but not if both occur.

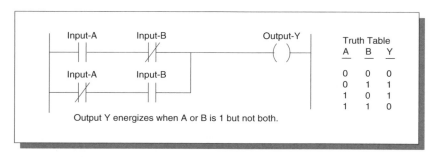

Figure 14-11. Exclusive-OR program logic

Example C: Start/Stop Logic

The Start/Stop logic shown in Fig. 14-12 may be used to start or stop a motor or other device, or to simply provide the enable/disable signal for some process or function. The input conditions that drive the start/stop circuit, are typically a START push-button, STOP push-button and an emergency (E-STOP) stop push-button. There may also be other permissive conditions, for example time delays.

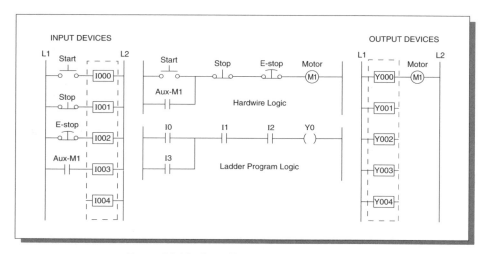

Figure 14-12. Start/Stop logic implementation

Notice, that the inputs STOP and E-STOP are programmed normally-open. This is true since stop switches are wired normally-closed to ensure a safe stop when the contacts of the switch open. While the STOP, and the E-STOP push-buttons, are not pushed, there input statuses are 1, hence the Examine-ON contacts will close immediately and allow logic continuity to start the motor. Since the START push-button (wired normally-open) is a momentary device and allows continuity only when closed, a contact from the motor output is used to seal-in the circuit. The seal-in contact is usually a wired input to the PLC from auxiliary contacts of the motor starter.

Example D: System Startup Alarm

The startup alarm logic, is used as a safety measure to sound an alert prior to starting a system. Normally, such an alarm is initiated when an operator enables the system. In a warehouse for instance, an alarm usually sounds for about ten seconds, prior to starting the first conveyor motor. In this example, the SYSRUN signal is enabled and latched in after a momentary START push-button is depressed.

In Fig. 14-13a, SYSRUN enables an on-delay timer, preset for 10 seconds. The alarm logic allows the horn to sound while SYSRUN =1 and the timer is not timed out (DN=0). When the timer times out, the done bit energizes and opens the alarm circuit. The startup alarm circuit may also be implemented using an off-delay timer as shown in Figure 14-13b. The timer is enabled (EN=1) when SYSRUN is enabled, and starts timing for 10 seconds when the START push-button is released. The alarm sounds while the timer is enabled (EN=1) but is not timed out (DN=0). After the timer times out 10 seconds later, the alarms shuts off.

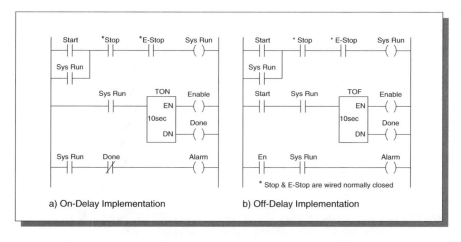

Figure 14-13. System start-up alarm program logic

Example E: Rising Edge One-Shot

Rising edge detection is a logic circuit used to detect each OFF-to-ON transition of a given signal. In Figure 14-14, when TRIGGER makes a low-to-high transition, the output ONESHOT goes high for one scan and then goes off. The one-shot goes off after one scan, even if the trigger signal stays high for more than one scan. The FLAG output, which follows the trigger, remains high whenever the trigger is high. Therefore whenever ONESHOT goes high initially, it is immediately reset during the next scan, by the normally-closed contact of FLAG. Hence, ONESHOT detects the leading edge of the TRIGGER. ONESHOT is triggered again only after the TRIGGER goes off and goes on again.

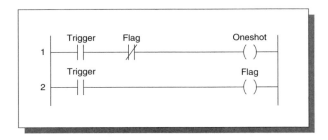

Figure 14-14. Rising edge one-shot program logic

Example F: Falling Edge One-Shot

The falling edge one-shot logic, shown in Figure 14-15, functions just the opposite of the leading edge one-shot — it sets an output high for one scan when the triggering signal makes a high-to-low transition. While the trigger is true, both the ONESHOT and FLAG coils are de-energized. When TRIGGER first makes a high-to-low transition, ONESHOT energizes. In the second rung, the FLAG energizes and will cause ONESHOT to de-energize on the next scan. ONESHOT will energize again only when the trigger has made a low-to-high and then a high-to-low transition.

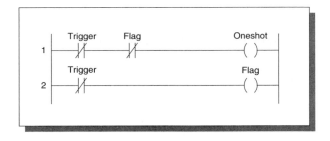

Figure 14-15. Falling edge one-shot program logic

Example G: Toggle Pushbutton

Often, it is desirable to have a single push-button perform both the START (*enable*) and STOP (*disable*) functions. A switch functioning in this manner is called a toggle switch. As shown in Figure 14-16a, when the push-button (SS-PB) is pressed for the first time, TOGGLE goes high and latches ON. When the button is released, FLAG2 goes OFF, so that the next time that the push-button is pressed, FLAG1 will go high, causing the TOGGLE output to go OFF. The internal coil (FLAG2) follows the SS-PB and therefore causes a one-shot on FLAG1 each time SS-PB makes an off-to-on transition. TOGGLE is the START/STOP output. A timing diagram shows the operation of the circuit.

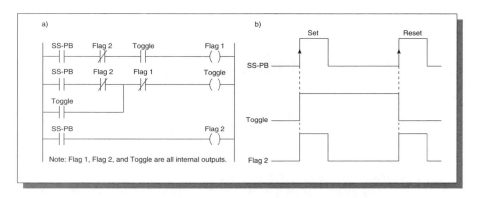

Figure 14-16. Toggle pushbutton program logic

Example H: Self-Restarting Timer

Logic for a self-restarting timer, also referred to as repeat cycle timer, is shown in Figure 14-17. This technique, which uses an on-delay timer, is applied when a one-shot (one-scan) pulse is generated at a fixed time period is required. When the timer expires it is automatically restarted. Each time the timer times out, the examine-off contact of the timers own timed-out coil breaks the logic continuity to the timer, thereby resetting the timer. The timer's coil, now off, causes the timer to restart on the next scan. A one scan pulse is generated each time the timer times out. The repetition of this pulse is determined by the preset value of the timer.

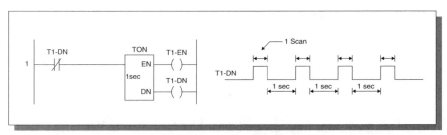

Figure 14-17. Self-restarting timer program logic

Example I: Periodic Pulse Width Modulation

The logic circuit shown in Figure 14-18, is composed of two on-delay timers (T1 and T2), that generate a periodic output pulse of any width (duration). T1 determines how long the pulse is ON and T2 determines how long the pulse is OFF. The durations for which the pulse is ON and OFF are independent and may be set with different times. In this example both timers are set for 1 second, which keeps the pulse ON for 1 second and OFF for 1 second. This circuit, which is used in many ways, is often used to ensure that some event occurs at a fixed interval and duration. One example may be to output a new message to a scoreboard display every 1 second. Another use is shown in the following example.

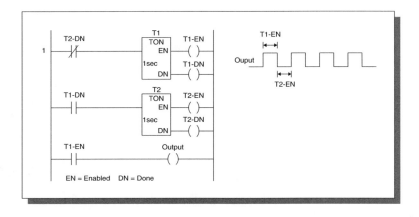

Figure 14-18. Periodic pulse-width modulation program logic

Example J: Alarm Indicator Flasher

The flasher logic, shown in Fig. 14-19, illustrates how the periodic pulse of Example I is used to pulse an alarm output ON and OFF at a fixed interval. A contact (of T1) from the oscillator circuit of Example I, is programmed in series with each alarm condition. As long as the alarm condition is TRUE, the alarm indicator output will be energized (ON) for T1 and de-energized (OFF) for T2. The output in the case of a flasher is a pilot light; however it could to a buzzer or horn alarm. Note that any number of alarm indicators could be made to pulse, using the same circuit. A contact of the flasher would simply be placed in series with each alarm indicator circuit.

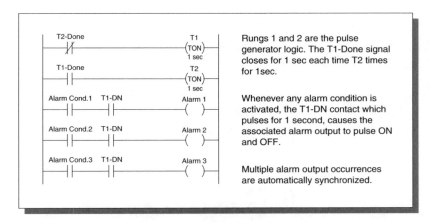

Figure 14-19. Alarm indication and synchronization program logic

Example K: Sequential Motor Starter

Sequential motor starting, as illustrated in Figure 14-20, shows how several motors are energized sequentially, as opposed to all at once. This is typical of starting the motors of a long conveyor system. For simplicity this example uses a separate on-delay timer to delay the start of each motor. Using a unique timer for each motor might be impractical for starting a large number of motors. Other techniques may be used that do not require as many timers as motors (e.g., shift registers, or the self-restarting timer circuit).

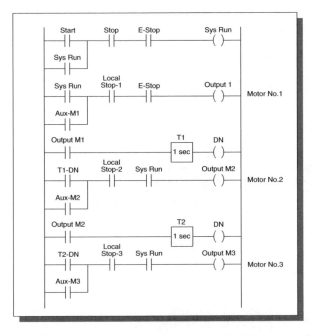

Figure 14-20. Example of sequential motor starting program logic

Example L: Timing For Long Durations

In some applications, a given timing function may require timing for durations that, for certain PLCs, cannot be achieved using the maximum timer presets. This problem can be cured by simply cascading the output of one timer into a second timer, or by using a single timer in conjunction with one or more counters. Often a timer is used with a counter to record the length of time a piece of equipment has been in operation. In figure 14-21, timer T1 begins timing when the motor contact M1 is energized. T1 will continually restart at the end of every 60 seconds and C1 counts the number of minutes the motor has been in operation. C2 tracks the number of hours.

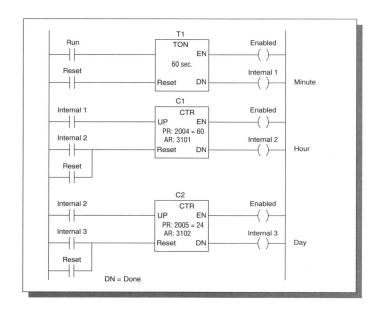

Figure 14-21. Example program logic for timing for long durations

Example M: Counting Beyond Maximum Count

In some applications, it may be necessary to count events that will exceed the maximum value that can be held in a 16-bit word. The maximum count in most controllers is either 9999 (BCD) or 32767 (decimal). In either case, extending the count may be achieved by cascading two counters (C1 and C2) in which the output of C1 is input to the UP-line of C2. The solution requires presetting C1 to 9999, and C2 to 32767. C2 will increment each time 9999 counts occur. On the first time counter 1 reaches 9999, C2 will register 1 and C1 will register 0000 on the very next count. The combined count in the two word locations is 10,000. The technique is illustrated in the following sequences of Figure 14-22.

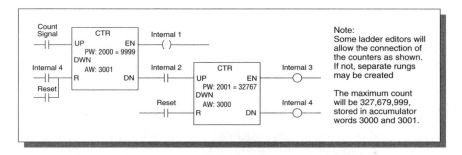

Figure 14-22. Example program loic for counting beyond the maximum count

Example N: A 24-Hour Clock

The 24 hour clock has many applications, but is often used to determine when an event should occur (e.g., when a report is generated, or heater turned ON). The logic used to implement the clock is shown in Fig. 14-23. It consists of an on-delay timer and three counters: the timer is given a preset time of 60 seconds, C1 counts 60 seconds, C2 counts 60 minutes, and C3 counts 24 hours. The time can be displayed by outputting the accumulator register values of each counter, to seven-segment BCD displays. This technique is not required in those PLCs that generate a 1-second clock pulse. If a system seconds pulse is available it can be used instead of the timer.

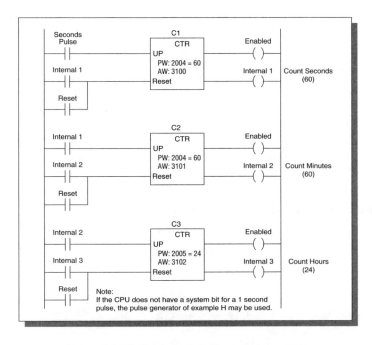

Figure 14-23. Program logic for a 24-hour clock

14-4 PLC Documentation Requirements

Documentation may be defined as an organized collection of recorded information concerning the operation of a machine, process or system. This broad definition however is normally thought of as manuals, pamphlets, and various drawings detailing the operation of some machine or piece of equipment. While this basic form of documentation of the PLC's operation is provided in the vendor's operation and installation manuals, documentation as described here is concerning the PLC as a control system applied to a particular application.

For a computer-based control system such as a programmable controller, documentation should provide information regarding both the hardware and software components of the system, that aid in the design, programming, installation, start-up, operation and maintenance of the control system. Its development should be started at the outset of a project, to serve as a working tool for the program developer. Early development of the documentation will also help to avoid allowing this task to be put off and eventually becoming an unwelcome burden as the programming task nears completion.

Documentation Benefits

Proper documentation will not only serve as a useful reference tool for the developer during the programming phase but for all others that will come in contact with the system at a later date. These tools will be required by installation, operator, maintenance and other personnel. Obtaining a complete documentation package, should be a primary concern to the end-user — having as much importance as any other component of the total system. Several benefits stemming from good documentation are listed below:

- *Allows project information to be communicated in a standard and simplified form.*

- *Allows the system to be easily installed, diagnosed for malfunctions, and expanded or altered.*

- *Allows individuals other than original designers, to answer questions, diagnose problems or make modifications.*

- *Provides base of structured training material for operator and maintenance staff.*

- *Establishes useful plant conventions that reduce future engineering, design, installation and maintenance cost.*

- *Allows completed designs to be easily re-used.*

14-5 The PLC Documentation Package

What actually constitutes a PLC documentation package, will naturally depend on who's putting the package together and what requirements may exist. For instance, the package provided by one systems integrator or individual may differ from that of another. Still yet, one plant facility may specify documents that adhere to its internal standards, that may differ from that of another plant within the company. What is important, is that the end-users receive whatever documents they deem necessary. As a general rule, a minimum set of documents should include the following items:

- ❑ System Abstract
- ❑ System Arrangement Diagram
- ❑ I/O Address Assignments
- ❑ I/O Device Wiring Diagram
- ❑ Internal Output Address Assignments
- ❑ Word Storage Assignments
- ❑ Program Hardcopy and Backup

System Abstract

The *system abstract* should provide a brief description of the design intent and the philosophy and strategies employed in a particular control system. Generally, such a description is formulated by the control engineer performing the work. The system abstract should make a clear statement of the control requirements, a synopsis of the control philosophy, specific design strategies used to implement the solution, and a clear statement of the major objectives that must be achieved. Such a document will serve to quickly convey the scope and general design strategies used in a particular application. In short, the system abstract is an introduction.

The control philosophy, should describe the choice of control scheme, such as distributed versus centralized control, why it was selected, and how this approach fits into the plant's present control strategies and directions. For instance, individual machines of a packaging line will each be controlled separately and configured such that they can be eventually linked over a local area network.

Specific design strategies should briefly outline the functions of major hardware components of the system and why each was selected, as well as, any special software techniques that were used. Brief functional descriptions should include components such as each CPU, remote I/O subsystems, intelligent I/O modules, computer links and operator interfaces. A software overview might include a brief description of items such as special techniques, software modules or subroutines, operator screens, data acquisition and report generation.

Finally, with all applications, whether performed in-house or by contractors, it is of extreme importance to make a clear statement of strategic and functional objectives for the project. This statement will provide a yardstick for measuring the success of the intended objectives once implemented. It will also serve as a means for knowing exactly when a project is completed.

PLC System Arrangement Diagram

This second documentation component, referred to as the *PLC System Arrangement Diagram*, is the visual counterpart of the System Abstract. It provides a second level of detail, that includes block diagram of each major component, simplified interconnection of these components, block diagrams of the major PLC components (e.g., module types within I/O racks. Like any good picture, the PLC system arrangement diagram casts a great deal of light upon its verbal counterpart — the system abstract.

With a good system arrangement diagram, a control system that spans for miles, can be depicted within the borders of a D-size drawing. As illustrated in Figure 14-24, in addition to referencing locations, this diagram can be used to show what modules are installed in each CPU and I/O rack, as well as the addresses in these racks. Installed spare modules, or open module slots might also be shown. The system arrangement should also include other equipment, such as host computers, operator workstations, and printers. Tie-ins to other plant systems, such as to a "backbone network" or to other networks, should also be shown. Local area networks references should include network numbers, network node addresses, network cable types and distance between nodes.

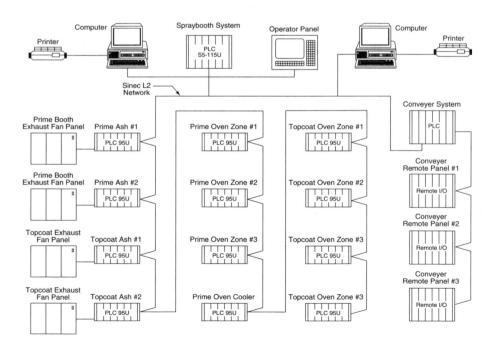

Figure 14-24. A PLC system arrangement diagram

I/O Address Assignments

This particular document, which should be created early on in the design phase of a project, is a listing of each of the real input/output addresses that will be installed in the PLC. The I/O assignment table lists each input and output address, along with the field device to which it is associated. Unused addresses are also usually listed. While this document is an essential programming reference, it is also used extensively during installation and start-up.

The *I/O Assignment Document* must be well organized, to serve as a useful design and programming aid, as well as for future use. Adopt assignment practices that can be established as plant conventions and that perhaps can be easily committed to memory. Typical conventions are to allocate consecutively assign addresses according to device groups. For example, when assigning inputs, assign all limit switches, then selector switches, then push-buttons, leaving spares in between for additional devices in each group. Use a similar convention with outputs — all motors, solenoids, pilot lights and alarms. This same convention could be used but slightly modified by assigning groups of inputs and outputs according to machine or process subsystems.

In general, as illustrated in Table 14-3, address assignment should list each input/output address, the module type (e.g., 120 VAC), connected device identification (e.g. PB100, LS100) and functional description of the input or output device. Other items that might be listed include, device location, device wire number, tag name or symbolic address, and whether the device is wired normally-open or normally-closed.

Table 14-3. Sample Input/Output Address Assignment Document.

Device	I/O Address	Symbol Name	Description
AUX-M1	I20.0	INGR_A_MTR_FBK	Ingredient A Feed Pump Motor Starter Auxiliary Contact
LS1-A	I20.1	INGR_A_INVLV_OPN	Ingredient A Intake Valve Open
LS2-A	I20.2	INGR_A_FLVLV_OPN	Ingredient A Feed Valve Open
PB1-A	I20.3	INGR_A_STR_PB	Ingredient A Motor Start Pushbutton
PB2-A	I20.4	INGR_A_STP_PB	Ingredient A Motor Stop Pushbutton
M1-A	Y37.0	INGR_A_MTR_COIL	Ingredient A Feed Pump Motor Coil
PL1-A	Y37.1	INGR_A_STR_PL	Ingredient A Motor Start Pilot Light
PL2-A	Y37.2	INGR_A_STP_PL	Ingredient A Motor Stop Pilot Light
	F20.0	INGR_A_MTR_FLT	Ingredient A Motor Fault
AUX-M2	I21.0	INGR_B_MTR_FBK	Ingredient A Feed Pump Motor Starter Auxiliary Contact
LS1-B	I21.1	INGR_B_INVLV_OPN	Ingredient A Intake Valve Open
LS2-B	I21.2	INGR_B_FLVLV_OPN	Ingredient A Feed Valve Open
PB1-B	I21.3	INGR_B_STR_PB	Ingredient A Motor Start Pushbutton
PB2-B	I21.4	INGR_B_STP_PB	Ingredient A Motor Stop Pushbutton
M2-B	Y37.3	INGR_B_MTR_COIL	Ingredient A Feed Pump Motor Coil
PL1-B	Y37.4	INGR_B_STR_PL	Ingredient A Motor Start Pilot Light
PL2-B	Y37.5	INGR_B_STP_PL	Ingredient A Motor Stop Pilot Light
	F20.1	INGR_B_MTR_FLT	Ingredient A Motor Fault
AUX-M3	I40.0	AGIT_MTR_AUXC	Agitator Motor Starter Auxiliary Contact

I/O Device Wiring Diagrams

The *I/O device wiring diagrams* show actual wiring connections between field input/output devices and corresponding input/output modules. This document, which is used primarily by electricians during installation, normally provides schematic diagrams for I/O power supply connections, I/O device power wiring circuits, and input/output wiring from the device to the input or output module. Figure 14-25 and 14-26 illustrate typical I/O device wiring diagrams. Typical nomenclatures include line numbers, device names, wire numbers, termination number and actual input/output addresses.

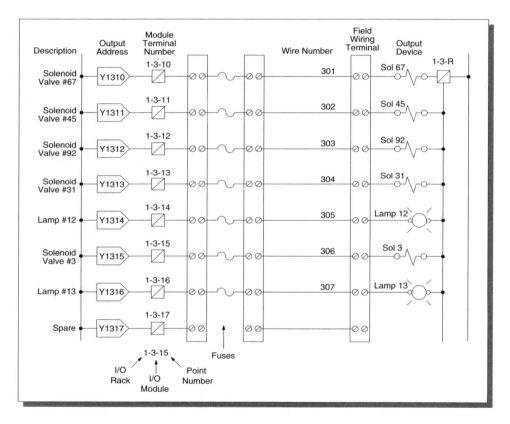

Figure 14-25. Typical output wiring diagram

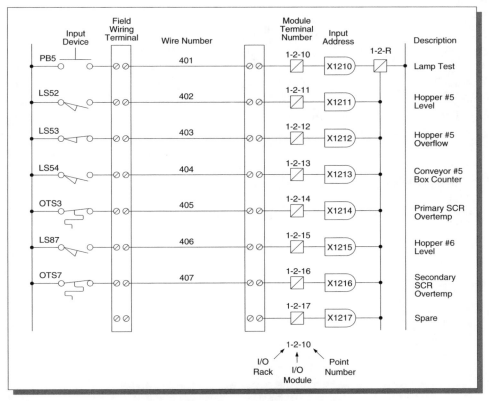

Figure 14-26. Typical input wiring diagram

Internal Output Address Assignment

Internal outputs are the software equivalent of control relays. In the control program, they provide many of the same functions, including interlocking sections of control logic, status signals indicating the occurrence of some event, such as "system ready," or to flag various alarms and fault conditions. In some controllers, internals are used as outputs to timers and counters to signal when the preset value has been reached. The many ways in which internals are used, warrant special care for how their use is allocated and documented. Just as with real I/O addresses, it is a good practice to document the used and unused internal outputs. This practice will avoid redundant usage and allows usable addresses to be quickly located as needed.

When assigning internals, consider allocating a consecutive group of words for each part of a machine or process, or for different program functions. For example a block of internals for analog alarm status or fault and diagnostic bits. Often this same information must be sent over a serial link to an operator interface device or to some other host device. If, for instance, a block of internal outputs are used for diagnostics and alarms, transferring this data will be much more efficient and programming required to manipulate and monitor these bits can be greatly reduced. Figure 14-27, illustrates a typical form for documenting internal output address assignments.

Internal Address	Symbol Name (Label)	Description

Figure 14-27. Sample form for internal output address assignments

Word Storage Assignments

The *word storage area* of the PLC memory is where all data is treated as 16-bit units of information. Typical data stored in this area include timer and counter preset and accumulated values, general presets, recipe data, constant values, analog I/O data, BCD and other types of I/O data. Like with internal outputs, the use of this area of memory is generally user definable. Its use must be well thought out and documented if the program is to be easily interpreted or modified at a later date.

Like with internal outputs, when assigning word memory always allocate blocks of words for different uses. Groupings may be based on machine or process function, or on software functions. Process functions might include temperature setpoints, actual temperature readings or motor speeds. Typical software groupings, are timer/counter presets, general presets, constant values, analog I/O, BCD I/O, intelligent I/O and so on. Again, grouping blocks of words will allow efficient program manipulation and local or network data transfers.

Program Hardcopy and Backup

A fundamental and most essential documentation component is an accurate printout and software backup of the control program. While this may seem a reasonable expectation, it is not unusual, in many situations, that the last program printout or software backup does not reflect those most recent and so-called "minor changes," that were made directly in the PLC. Working with a less than accurate or up-to-date hardcopy, presents a serious handicap for anyone having to diagnose malfunctions or make program changes. Although it may seem impractical or inconvenient to reprint or make a backups after small on-line alterations, it is important to avoid the easy habit of not doing so. If online changes are made, then an updated backup copy of the program on floppy disk, tape or EPROM should be made immediately.

In addition to maintaining an updated hardcopy of the program, another practice well worth adhering to is that of recording each program change — specifying the modification, why it was made, and the date of the change. If this feature is not part of a utility program, a history of program changes can be recorded on a separate log or can be written directly on the updated program printout. Another security practice, is to keep a copy of the last program listing just prior to the most recent changes. This practice will allow a place to return to if the most recent modifications result in malfunctions.

15 INSTALLATION, START-UP AND MAINTENANCE

Enclosure Selection and Layout

System Power and Safety Circuitry

Input/Output Installation

System Start-up

Maintenance and Troubleshooting

An important design criterion of PLCs, set forth in the beginning, was that they be easily installed and maintained by those same individuals who had maintained electromechanical control systems. The result was a system composed of modular plug-in type components each capable of performing its function without additional complex custom interfaces. Each components was designed using reliable solid-state circuitry incorporating diagnostic indicators that signal correct as well as malfunctioning operation.

These inherent characteristics of PLCs, having been enhanced over time, still maintain the original design intentions of ease of maintenance and installation. This concept alone has been perhaps the most influencing factor in the widespread utilization of programmable controllers. This chapter provides a fairly detailed approach to the tasks associated with installation, start-up and maintenance of a PLC system. Over time, these fundamental practices have proven to ensure a smooth installation and a reliable operating control system.

15-1 Enclosure Selection and Layout

Proper consideration given to the placement and interconnection of PLC and ancillary equipment inside the enclosure will simplify installation, start-up, and maintenance and will ensure the best possible machine operation. The enclosure layout should conform to the manufacturer's guidelines, national and local electric codes, and should consider the effects of heat, electrical noise, and mechanical vibration. A good design will also consider system safety and ease of maintenance.

Selecting An Enclosure

The PLC system components, including processor, power supply, and I/O racks, are normally mounted inside a metal enclosure designed to meet electrical and environmental standards of the National Manufacturers Association (NEMA). NEMA specifications address traditional factory environments of electrical noise, extreme temperatures, high levels of moisture, and various atmospheric dust and contaminants, all of which the controller should be protected against for optimum performance. Table 15-1 suggests minimum requirements for a PLC enclosure.

Table 15-1. Minimum Requirements for PLC Enclosures

❑ Protection from dust, dirt and other contaminants
❑ A shield against electromagnetic interference
❑ Conformance to electrical standards
❑ Adequate space for PLC and ancillary equipment
❑ Easy access to system components and wiring
❑ A secure vertical back panel for mounting components
❑ A means by which unauthorized access can be restricted (e.g., lock)

When determining the enclosure size, allow extra space for isolation transformers, fusing, disconnect switch, terminal strips, and wire ducts. Also consider any surrounding free space requirements of the CPU and I/O chassis. Although the NEMA-12 enclosure is the most commonly used and meets the needs of most applications, the range of extreme conditions existing in plants, may require different levels of protection and construction. Table 15-2 lists various NEMA enclosures and the applications in which they are used. Specifying the appropriate enclosure will provide the best protection and will prevent overpaying for an enclosure that exceeds the environmental requirements.

Table 15-2. NEMA Enclosure Classifications and Descriptions

TYPE	DESCRIPTION	TYPICAL APPLICATIONS
NEMA-1	General Purpose	Protects against accumulating dust, but is not dust tight. Indoor use where atmospheric conditions are normal.
NEMA-2	Drip-Tight Indoor	General purpose applications; indoor use where condensation may be severe.
NEMA-3,3R,3S	Dust, Rain-Proof Sleet Resistant	Where wind blown dust or weather hazards such as rain, sleet or snow exist. Outdoor use: underground, subways, tunnels etc.
NEMA-4,4X	Water-Tight/Corrosion Resistant	Protects against large amounts of spray, typically dairies, breweries, etc. Corrosion-proof normally required in food processing or similar industries.
NEMA-5	Dust-Tight	Indoor use for protection against dust and falling dirt.
NEMA-6	Submersible	For applications such as mines, quarries, and manholes. Selection depends on submersion time and pressure.
NEMA-7	Hazardous Locations	Indoor use. Locations Class I, Groups A to D, as defined by the National Electric Code (NEC).
NEMA-8	Hazardous Locations defined by the NEC.	Indoor/Outdoor use. Locations Class I, Groups A to D as
NEMA-9	Hazardous Locations	Indoor use. NEC classified locations, Class II, Groups E to G.
NEMA-10	Underground Use	Meets applicable requirements of the Federal Mine Safety and Health Administration (MSHA).
NEMA-11	Oil Immersion	Protects against oil immersion, corrosive liquids and gases. Primarily intended for indoor use.
NEMA-12	Drip Resistant	For indoor use primarily to provide a degree of protection against dust, falling dirt, and dripping noncorrosive liquids.
NEMA-13	Oil Tight	Applications involving machine tools and other locations where oil, coolants, water, filings, or lint might infiltrate the enclosure via mounting holes, conduit, or other obscure entry points.

Preliminary Layout Considerations

With a properly designed enclosure layout, components are easily accessed and maintained while adverse environmental and electrical noise conditions are minimized. Table 15-3 offers suggestions for the location and physical aspects of the PLC enclosure that will ensure safety and convenience of the control system.

Table 15-3. PLC Enclosure Design and Placement Considerations

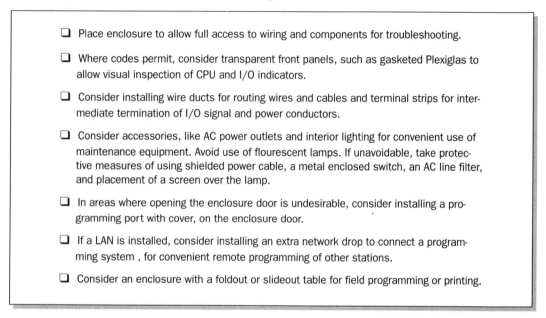

❑ Place enclosure to allow full access to wiring and components for troubleshooting.

❑ Where codes permit, consider transparent front panels, such as gasketed Plexiglas to allow visual inspection of CPU and I/O indicators.

❑ Consider installing wire ducts for routing wires and cables and terminal strips for intermediate termination of I/O signal and power conductors.

❑ Consider accessories, like AC power outlets and interior lighting for convenient use of maintenance equipment. Avoid use of flourescent lamps. If unavoidable, take protective measures of using shielded power cable, a metal enclosed switch, an AC line filter, and placement of a screen over the lamp.

❑ In areas where opening the enclosure door is undesirable, consider installing a programming port with cover, on the enclosure door.

❑ If a LAN is installed, consider installing an extra network drop to connect a programming system , for convenient remote programming of other stations.

❑ Consider an enclosure with a foldout or slideout table for field programming or printing.

Enclosure Environmental Considerations

The influence of temperature, humidity, electrical noise, and vibration are all factors to be considered when deciding on the best placement of the enclosure as well as the placement of each component inside the enclosure. Environmental elements may also necessitate conditioning (i.e., heating, cooling) of the air inside the enclosure. The guidelines in Table 15-4 are concerned with providing favorable environmental conditions for the controller.

Table 15-4. PLC Environmental Considerations

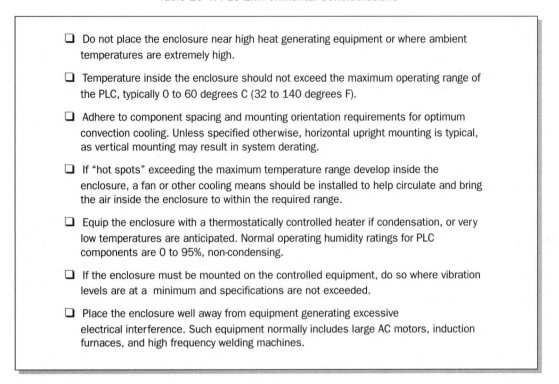

❑ Do not place the enclosure near high heat generating equipment or where ambient temperatures are extremely high.

❑ Temperature inside the enclosure should not exceed the maximum operating range of the PLC, typically 0 to 60 degrees C (32 to 140 degrees F).

❑ Adhere to component spacing and mounting orientation requirements for optimum convection cooling. Unless specified otherwise, horizontal upright mounting is typical, as vertical mounting may result in system derating.

❑ If "hot spots" exceeding the maximum temperature range develop inside the enclosure, a fan or other cooling means should be installed to help circulate and bring the air inside the enclosure to within the required range.

❑ Equip the enclosure with a thermostatically controlled heater if condensation, or very low temperatures are anticipated. Normal operating humidity ratings for PLC components are 0 to 95%, non-condensing.

❑ If the enclosure must be mounted on the controlled equipment, do so where vibration levels are at a minimum and specifications are not exceeded.

❑ Place the enclosure well away from equipment generating excessive electrical interference. Such equipment normally includes large AC motors, induction furnaces, and high frequency welding machines.

While PLCs are designed to operate at temperatures between 0 and 60 degrees C, their design is also intended to allow convection cooling (i.e., such that a vertical column of air is drawn in an upward direction over the surface of the components). To maintain inside enclosure temperatures within limits, the temperature gain resulting from component heat dissipation must be held within manufacturer's sepcifications. A system arrangement of large power supplies or several heat producing I/O cards may require air cooling. When using a fan, the air should be filtered to prevent dirt or other contaminants from entering. Dust buildup will obstruct the heat dissipation of components and can be especially harmful on heat sinks when thermal conductivity to the surrounding air is lowered.

The basis for the cooling system selection will depend on the amount of cooling air required to compensate for the temperature gain inside the enclosure, due to the influence of the ambient temperature and heat dissipation of the enclosed components. Before deciding on a temperature conditioning system, consult enclosure manufacturers as well as the PLC vendor for heat gain information (normally given in watts for each component). They may also have curves that show permissable ambient temperature as a function of the known power dissipation.

Placement of Controller Components

Generally, installation manuals will provide layout suggestions, as well as any mounting restrictions such as for orientation or minimum distance spacing between components. Although there may not be any rigid rules governing the exact placement of CPU racks, power supplies, and I/O racks, commonly used practices listed in Table 15-5 will help minimize the effects of heat generated inside the enclosure.

Table 15-5. Placement of PLC Components Inside the Enclosure

❑ Large power supplies, in separately encased units, generate large amounts of heat and are therefore mounted above all other components. Good placement for such power supplies is toward the top of the enclosure with a clearance of 7-10 inches, or adjacent to other components, using sufficient spacing.

❑ The CPU rack should be placed in a convenient working location; normally at a medium height.

❑ Local I/O racks are normally placed in any desired arrangement within the allowable cable distance and adhering to spacing requirements. The racks are normally placed below or adjacent to the CPU rack or an externally mounted power supply.

❑ Remote I/O racks and power supplies are placed in an enclosure located near the controlled equipment. Racks are placed inside the enclosure in any desired arrangement, adhering to the manufacturer's spacing requirements.

Table 15-6. Placement of Ancillary Equipment Inside Enclosure

❑ Incoming line devices, such as isolation or constant voltage transformers, and power disconnects are normally located in a corner position at the top or bottom of the enclosure. This location keeps power wiring inside the enclosure as short as possible, thereby minimizing the transmission of electrical noise.

❑ Electromechanical components such as relays and motor starters, are generally grouped together and placed nearby the incoming line devices. If these devices are mounted above the controller, a good practice is to use a separation barrier.

❑ Fans or blowers should be placed close to the heat generating devices. A fabric or other reliable filter type should be used to prevent conductive particles or other contaminants from entering the enclosure.

❑ Consider a central ground bus for PLC chassis and other inactive metal components.

❑ Do not place heat generating devices directly below the I/O or CPU chassis.

In general, other electrical components inside the enclosure are grouped together and placed away from the controller components. This separation will minimize the effects of noise or heat generated by these devices. Placement of ancillary electrical hardware, such as magnetic starters, relays and transformers, is illustrated in Figure 15-1.

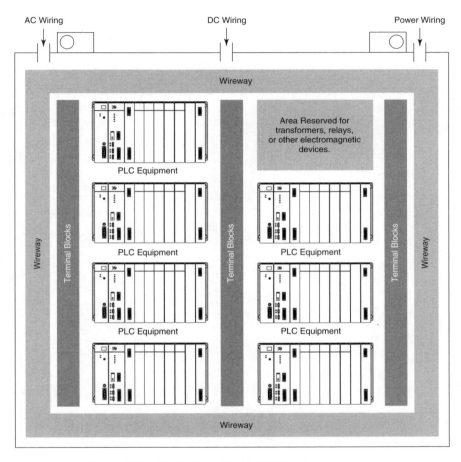

Figure 15-1. Illustration of typical PLC enclosure layout

15-2 System Power and Safety Circuitry

PLC power supplies are generally designed to accept power from either a 115 VAC or 230 VAC source (50hz/60hz) and will accept an input typically within a range of plus or minus 10 percent of the rated input voltage. The desired operational voltage is normally switch or jumper selectable. Power connections are normally made (using stranded or solid, #12 or #14 wires) to a terminal strip located on the power supply which is labeled L1 (hot side of AC line), N or L2 (neutral side of AC line), and GND (ground conductor).

A major consideration for each installed PLC power supply is that the current consumption of the installed modules does not exceed that which the power supply is rated for. Overloading the power supply can be avoided by predetermining power requirements based on a calculation of the power consumption for each module installed in a rack. A typical power supply connection is illustrated in Figure 15-2.

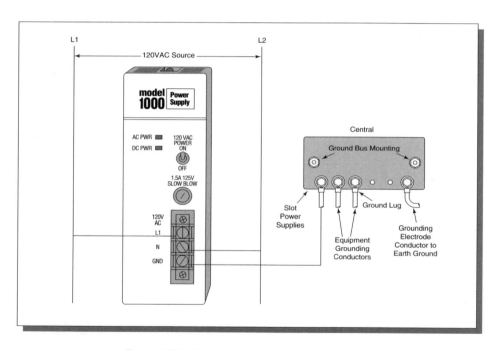

Figure 15-2. Typical PLC power supply connection

A Common AC Power Source

When supplying power to the PLC, it is recommended that the same AC power source be used for the CPU power supply and its associated I/O devices. This practice minimizes line interference caused by other equipment and allows the system to take advantage of the line monitoring function of the PLC's power supply. Generally, the power supply monitors the line voltage and detects when it falls below the specified range. In such a case, the power supply signals the CPU to stop receiving input data and to turn all outputs OFF. This feature prevents the possibility of reading faulty input signals if at some point the AC source to the I/O devices were to become unstable while the AC source to the CPU remained stable. This connection is illustrated in Figure 15-3.

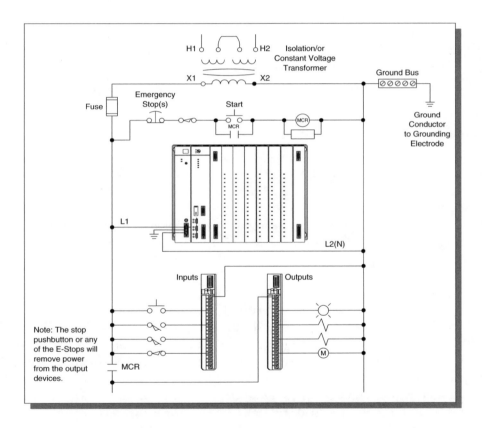

Figure 15-3. Connecting the AC power source to the PLC inputs and outputs

Isolation Transformers

Isolation transformers are often used in PLC systems. Their function is to isolate the PLC from electrical disturbances generated by other equipment on the plant's power distribution system. Although the PLC is designed to operate in harsh environments, other plant equipment may generate considerable amounts of electromagnetic interference that may result in intermittent misoperation of the controller if not isolated. A normal practice is to place the PLC power supply and I/O devices on a separate transformer, that may also serves as a step-down transformer to reduce the incoming voltage to the desired level.

Separate transformers for each PLC may not always be practical, for instance with several small controllers. However, controllers should not be placed on the same circuit with heavy equipment that is likely to introduce noise or large voltage variations when started or stopped. Although isolation transformers are adequate in most situations, highly unstable line conditions may warrant use of a constant voltage transformer (CVT).

Constant Voltage Transformers

As mentioned earlier, the power supply operates within a typical margin of plus or minus 10 percent of its rated voltage. This ability allows the power supply to continue to operate while the line voltage may fluctuate within the operating range. If voltage fluctuations exceed this range for a duration greater than the supply is designed to sustain, then a system shutdown will be caused. In areas where excessive line voltage variation or extended brownouts are anticipated, installing a constant voltage transformer may be required to minimize nuisance shutdowns of the PLC.

The CVT is installed in the incoming line as shown in Figure 15-3. Its function is to stabilize the input voltage to the power supply by compensating for voltage changes at its primary in order to maintain a steady voltage at its secondary. Generally, the controller's power supply and all the input devices are connected on the secondary side of the transformer, while the output devices are connected ahead of the transformer. This arrangement allows for a lower rated constant voltage transformer. The rating of the CVT in units of volt-amperes (VA) should be selected based on the worst-case power requirement of the connected load (typically 2.5 to 3 times the rated load).

Safety Considerations

A most vital consideration during installation planning must be the safety of personnel and the avoidance of equipment damage. Since solid-state control devices can fail in what might be unsafe conditions, reliable non-semiconductor mechanisms must be incorporated in each design to allow unconditional stopping of the machine or process in emergency situations. It is also vital to ensure that the machine will assume a safe state in case of failure, and that safe mechanisms are employed during machine operation. To ensure that the programmable controller system is configured with adequate protective measures for safety, always consider the points listed in Table 15-7.

Table 15-7. General Safety Considerations

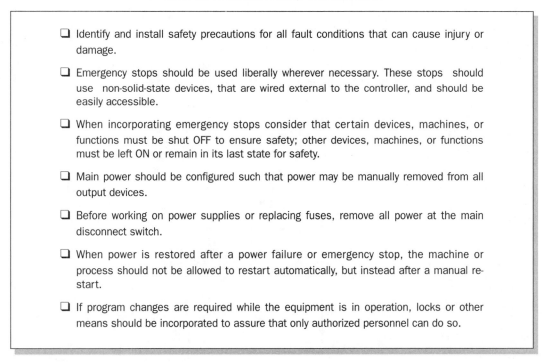

❑ Identify and install safety precautions for all fault conditions that can cause injury or damage.

❑ Emergency stops should be used liberally wherever necessary. These stops should use non-solid-state devices, that are wired external to the controller, and should be easily accessible.

❑ When incorporating emergency stops consider that certain devices, machines, or functions must be shut OFF to ensure safety; other devices, machines, or functions must be left ON or remain in its last state for safety.

❑ Main power should be configured such that power may be manually removed from all output devices.

❑ Before working on power supplies or replacing fuses, remove all power at the main disconnect switch.

❑ When power is restored after a power failure or emergency stop, the machine or process should not be allowed to restart automatically, but instead after a manual restart.

❑ If program changes are required while the equipment is in operation, locks or other means should be incorporated to assure that only authorized personnel can do so.

Power and Safety Circuitry

In addition to following the manufacturer's installation guidelines, it may be useful to refer to the installation guidelines for programmable controllers as recommended in the NEMA ICS 3-304 Programmable Control Standards. The specific article is "ICS 3-304.81 Safety Recommendations." Although specific design practices for safe power delivery and removal will depend upon the application, some examples of typical design practices used in PLC installations are described in Table 15-8 on the following page.

Table 15-8. Typical Power and Safety Circuit Practices

❑ Use of a main disconnect switch to remove all incoming power to the PLC.

❑ Use of an isolation transformer to provide noise-free power lines and complete isolation from other equipment.

❑ Use of a Master Start/Master Stop relay circuit on the AC power line side of the controlled output devices. This circuit is illustrated in Figure 15-3.

❑ Have power to input devices wired such that field inputs can be activated and monitored whenever the CPU has power. This method allows input statuses to be examined in a failure situation while outputs are disabled. See Figure 15-3.

❑ Use of the PLC fault relay (if available) to signal an alarm to alert the operator or related equipment, in the event of a CPU shutdown.

❑ Use of safety relay or limit switch contacts in series with critical loads, to allow removal of power from the load when a machine is not operating or when it is necessary for the operator to reach into the machine. Power must be removed by a non-semiconductor switch or a physically-wired relay contact, placed to interrupt the output. See Figure 15-4a.

❑ Use a bypass for PLC outputs in machine loading or setup operations, as shown in Figure 15-4b, when an operator must come in close proximity to the machine while using a "JOG" or "INCH" button.

❑ Provide a means for removing power from critical output loads if an emergency condition occurs during machine operation. As shown in Figure 15-4c, the emergency stop circuit is wired external to the PLC and electromechanical relay contacts are used to disconnect critical loads that could cause injury or damage.

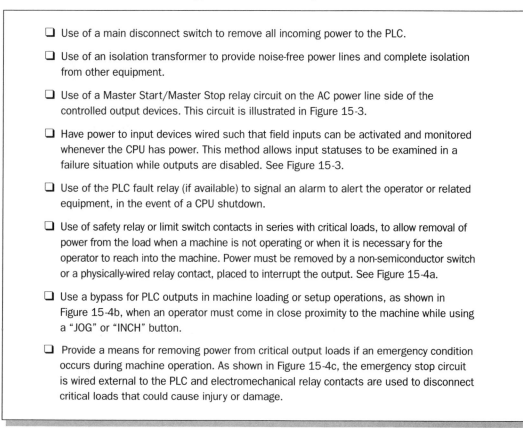
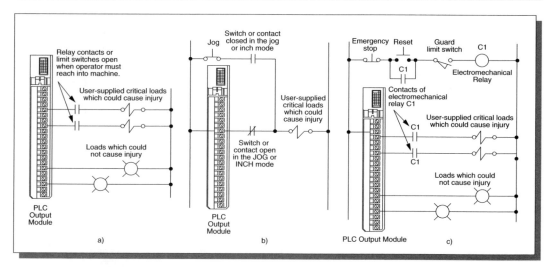

Figure 15-4. a) Operator Safety Switch Shut-Off
b) Machine Setup Jog Switch c) Emergency Stop switch circuit

System Grounding

A good grounding system is a major consideration for any electrical system and therefore should be properly planned for your PLC installation. A properly installed grounding system will provide a low-impedance path to earth ground, which will give all PLC internal filtering devices a good ground return for reference. The earth ground of the building site should provide reliable grounding for the PLC; however, if excessive ground current is present, a separate grounding electrode should be installed.

The complete PLC installation, including enclosures, CPU and I/O chassis, and power supplies, should all be connected to a single low-impedance ground. These connections should exhibit very low DC resistance and low high-frequency impedance. A common practice, is to provide a central ground bus bar as a single point of reference inside each enclosure, to which all chassis and power supplies are connected. The ground bus is then connected to the building's earth ground. The practices described in Table 15-9 will help establish a well-grounded system.

Table 15-9. PLC equipment grounding Practices

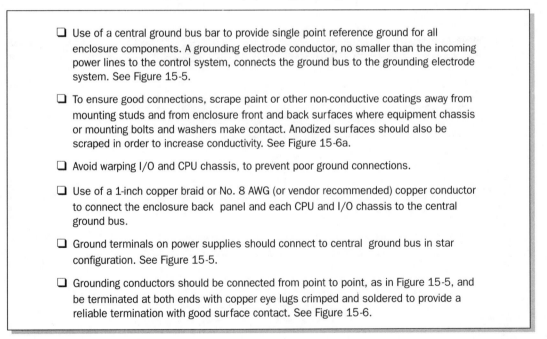

❏ Use of a central ground bus bar to provide single point reference ground for all enclosure components. A grounding electrode conductor, no smaller than the incoming power lines to the control system, connects the ground bus to the grounding electrode system. See Figure 15-5.

❏ To ensure good connections, scrape paint or other non-conductive coatings away from mounting studs and from enclosure front and back surfaces where equipment chassis or mounting bolts and washers make contact. Anodized surfaces should also be scraped in order to increase conductivity. See Figure 15-6a.

❏ Avoid warping I/O and CPU chassis, to prevent poor ground connections.

❏ Use of a 1-inch copper braid or No. 8 AWG (or vendor recommended) copper conductor to connect the enclosure back panel and each CPU and I/O chassis to the central ground bus.

❏ Ground terminals on power supplies should connect to central ground bus in star configuration. See Figure 15-5.

❏ Grounding conductors should be connected from point to point, as in Figure 15-5, and be terminated at both ends with copper eye lugs crimped and soldered to provide a reliable termination with good surface contact. See Figure 15-6.

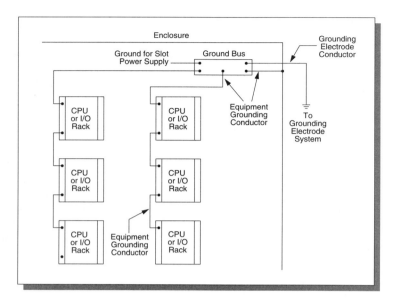

Figure 15-5. Illustration of PLC grounding system

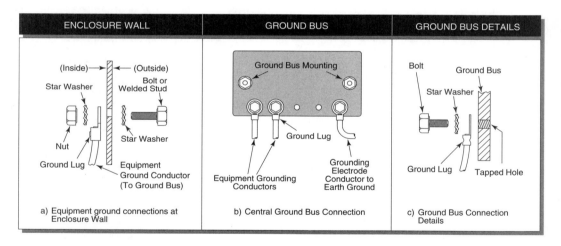

Figure 15-6. Illustration of making ground connections

15-3 Input/Output Installation

With the possible exception of designing and writing the control program, planning for and actually installing the I/O system are perhaps the most time-consuming and critical tasks of the overall job of putting a PLC into commission. While small systems with as few as 64 I/O are easily designed and installed, large systems with hundreds of I/O will require many hours of careful attention to detail from project beginning to completion.

The guidelines for I/O installation involve many details that are normally prepared during the design phase of a project. A complete set of documents with precise information should include I/O connection and wire routing diagrams, and arrangement diagrams (i.e., panel equipment and duct layouts, equipment locations). These documents will help to assure that this major portion of the control system is installed accurately and as intended.

I/O Module Grouping

Module grouping is planned placement of common or similar I/O modules within a rack. The intent is to achieve an arrangement that a) simplifies wiring, allowing bundling of signal wiring for each module; b) enhances wire routing, so as to minimize noise-related problems; c) produces a well-structured I/O to memory relationship, allowing easy and efficient I/O manipulation for control and diagnostic purposes; and d) produce an orderly appearance, allowing fast visual troubleshooting. Table 15-10 offers suggestions for grouping I/O modules that, if carefully planned and executed, will produce the benefits as mentioned.

Table 15-10. I/O Module Grouping Practices

❑ With large I/O systems especially, group different I/O types into separate racks while separating inputs and outputs. For example, AC inputs, AC outputs, DC inputs, DC outputs, Analog inputs, and Analog outputs. See Figure 15-7

❑ If complete rack separation is not practical, separate I/O within the rack. For example, AC I/O, DC I/O, and Analog I/O. Where possible separate groups using and empty slot. See Figure 15-7 on the following page.

❑ If intelligent I/O modules can be placed in racks other than the CPU rack, then wherever practical, these modules should be grouped in a separate rack. Alternative placement of certain of these modules that may carry low-level voltages and/or low currents is with analog I/O modules.

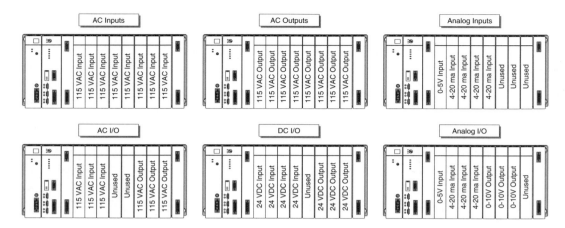

Figure 15-7. Illustration of I/O module grouping

Raceway and Wiring Layout

The raceway and wiring layout is concerned with the proper routing of field power and signal wiring to the PLC enclosure and inside the enclosure. The major concern is to provide proper separation of high-energy conductors, carrying high voltages and or high currents; low-energy conductors, carrying low voltage and/or low current; and the PLC component interconnection cables. Wiring inside the enclosure will be largely influenced by the arrangement of I/O racks and the grouping of various modules within these racks. If grouping I/O modules, as discussed under I/O Module Grouping, was considered during the planning stage, wire routing will be simplified and will certainly help to reduce the effects of electrical noise, like that resulting from cross-talk, electrostatic and magnetic coupling. Table 15-11 offers some general guidelines for PLC wire routing.

Wire and Terminal Labeling

A most important phase I/O installation is that of clearly and systematically identifying each wire to be connected and the terminal to which it is connected. A reliable labeling method such as shrink wrap wire markers or tape should be used to label each wire. Wiring connectors for input/output modules usually include spaces for stick-on type or insert labels for identifying each I/O address and device connected. For the best results, labels should be typed or printed clearly in ink.

Good wire and terminal identification will not only simplify and speed up installation, but it will greatly aid in future troubleshooting and maintenance. No identification standards, exist for PLC systems, yet many companies have their own standards, which contractors and in-house engineering must adhere to. Often, wire numbers are the same as the input/output addresses, perhaps with a prefix to indicate some specific location such as building or device. Such conventions are time savers and quite beneficial during installation.

Table 15-11. General Wire Routing Guidelines

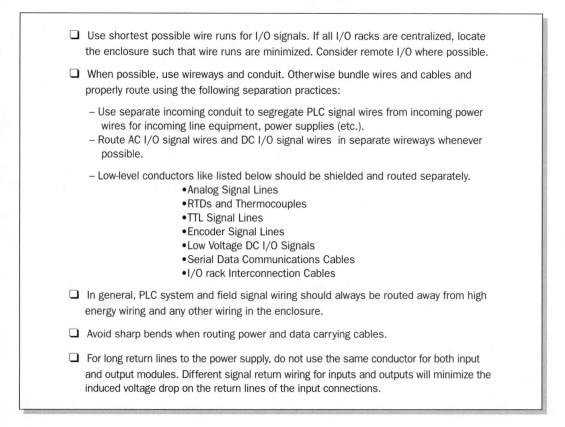

❑ Use shortest possible wire runs for I/O signals. If all I/O racks are centralized, locate the enclosure such that wire runs are minimized. Consider remote I/O where possible.

❑ When possible, use wireways and conduit. Otherwise bundle wires and cables and properly route using the following separation practices:

  – Use separate incoming conduit to segregate PLC signal wires from incoming power wires for incoming line equipment, power supplies (etc.).
  – Route AC I/O signal wires and DC I/O signal wires in separate wireways whenever possible.

  – Low-level conductors like listed below should be shielded and routed separately.
    • Analog Signal Lines
    • RTDs and Thermocouples
    • TTL Signal Lines
    • Encoder Signal Lines
    • Low Voltage DC I/O Signals
    • Serial Data Communications Cables
    • I/O rack Interconnection Cables

❑ In general, PLC system and field signal wiring should always be routed away from high energy wiring and any other wiring in the enclosure.

❑ Avoid sharp bends when routing power and data carrying cables.

❑ For long return lines to the power supply, do not use the same conductor for both input and output modules. Different signal return wiring for inputs and outputs will minimize the induced voltage drop on the return lines of the input connections.

Wire Bundling

Wire bundling is a technique commonly used to simplify wire routing and I/O module connections. This method involves gathering the conductors to be connected to each module and tie- wrapping them into separate bundles for routing to the module. If wires are pre-bundled prior to entering the enclosure, then each bundle must first be labeled and its wires properly identified. Bundles are then routed through wireways with bundles of similar signal characteristics.

Prewired Enclosures

Many companies prefer to have their PLC enclosures prewired and pretested by an equipment panel builder. While the control program is being developed, the panel is built concurrently and can arrive at the installation site by the time programming has been completed. Given the appropriate documentation, the panel builder can provide a completely wired panel according to specifications.

Such panels are typically equipped with premounted auxiliary equipment such as transformers, external power supplies, circuit panels, wire ducts, lighting, and AC outlets. CPU and I/O racks are mounted with all interconnect cables installed. All input/output signals and power wires are prewired to terminal strips and to I/O module connectors. If the panel is pretested with power applied, all that remains at installation is to supply field power and route field device wires from the devices to the appropriate prelabeled termination points.

I/O Wiring Procedures

After all I/O modules have been installed in their correct slot locations, the final installation step is the actual wiring of each field device to the appropriate module for termination. By now, decisions should have been made regarding the type of conductors each module would require. If single conductors are used, they should be bundled into groups for each module, to simplify handling and connection.

If all cables and/or single conductors have been prebundled and labeled, each should be verified prior to wiring each module. Each conductor should also be labeled according to its termination point. Each module should have been identified, and each I/O

Table 15-12. Guidelines for Connecting I/O modules

❑ Prior to beginning, remove or lock-out power from power supplies and I/O.

❑ Loosen terminals on all I/O module connectors or on pre-wired enclosure terminal strips.

❑ Starting with the first rack, locate the wire bundle or multi-conductor cable for each module and according to routing paths, route the wires to the appropriate module. If wire ducts are not used, make necessary turns at right angles, allowing adequate length to tie the bundles in a straight neat fashion.

❑ Starting with the first module, locate from the bundle or cable, the wire that connects to the lowest terminal. At the point where the wire is at a vertical height equal to the termination screw, bend the wire at a right angle towards the terminal and cut such that the wire extends 1/4 inch under the terminal.

❑ Strip about 3/8 inch of insulation from the conductor exposing the end of the wire. Place the wire under the pressure plate of the terminal and tighten the terminal screw. Gently pull the wire to ensure a good connection.

❑ When using a multi-conductor shielded cable, cut back the braided and foil shield, pull back the drain wire and connect to the chassis ground terminal of the connector. If the cable uses a DB-type connector, the drain wire can be soldered to the connector case.

❑ Repeat the wiring steps for each wire in the bundle or cable until completing the module.

❑ Repeat the steps until all modules and I/O racks are completely wired.

point should have been labeled to correspond to the wire number and device to be connected. If intermediate terminal strips are used, all terminals should be labeled and verified. Once these steps have been performed, the guidelines described in Table 15-12 should be used to connect each module.

Special I/O Wiring Practices

Fusing AC Outputs. PLC output module circuits generally incorporate fuses to protect each output device and its wiring against short circuits and overloads. In some controllers, especially single-board microcontrollers, this fusing may not be internal and is expected to be provided by the user during installation. In such cases, a properly rated fuse should be selected according to the manufacturer's specification. External fusing for output circuits is typically installed at an intermediate terminal strip between the module and the field wiring.

Using Interposing Relays. AC and DC output module circuits are designed to drive various output devices directly. However, in some cases the AC or DC load may have a continuous current draw that exceeds the maximum current deliverable by the module's output circuit. For instance, a 115-volt AC output circuit having a continuous ON-state rating of 1 ampere at 60 degrees C would not meet the requirements of a NEMA size 5 AC starter. The inrush current also would not be sustained by the solid-state output. In such a case, an interposing relay capable of switching the higher current is wired in series with the device, as illustrated in Figure 15-8. The output circuit drives the relay, which in turn switches the output device. This practice is quite common in the utilities industry.

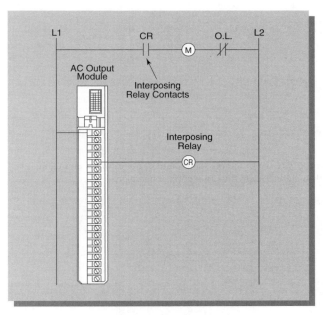

Figure 15-8. Using an interposing relay

Using Shielded Cable. Low-voltage wiring (less than 24 volts) used with TTL, analog, thermocouple, and other low-level signals is normally routed in separate conduit or wireways and away from high energy wiring and noisy devices. This physical separation provides a measure of protection against the noise generated by these sources. Reducing the effects of noise through physical distance can be further enhanced byshielded twisted-pair conductors to connect these low-level control signals. Shielded conductors should also be used for wiring that enters harsh-noise areas to allow monitoring and control of the connected devices.

A ground connection (to the single-point ground) for the shielded cable is shown in Figure 15-9, with the shield connected at one end only — typically at the signal originating end. Care should be taken to ensure that shield continuity is maintained for the entire length of the cable, that the cable is routed away from high noise areas, and that the shield is insulated on both ends.

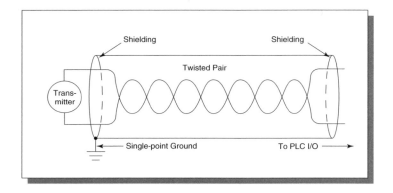

Figure 15-9. Using shielded cable

Connecting Leaky Inputs. Many electronic input devices with transistor or triac outputs exhibit a characteristic, referred to as leakage current, that may need to be considered when they are connected to PLC input modules. When a transistor or triac is switched OFF, a small amount of current, usually on the order of a few milliamperes, is still conducted by the device.

This so-called leakage current, is typically exhibited by two-wire proximity, photoelectric and other such sensors. The leakage may have little or no effect, depending on the characteristics of the input module to which the device is connected. A minimal effect of this leakage current is to cause the input circuit's LED indicator to flicker; however, a large enough conducting current can activate the input circuit, causing a false input signal. A normal solution to this problem is to connect a pulldown resistor across the input as shown in Figure 15-10. This practice is typical when connecting a PLC output to a PLC input.

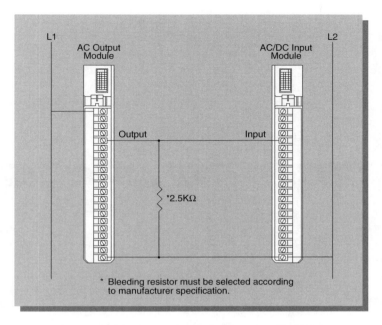

Figure 15-10. Connecting leaky inputs to the PLC

Suppressing Inductive Loads. Noise suppression is normally needed for inductive loads such as relays, solenoids, motor starters, and any of these devices when operated by "hard contacts," like pushbuttons or selector switches wired in series or in parallel. In PLC applications, suppression may also be required for these devices when they are connected as outputs or when they are connected to the same power source as the PLC. When inductive loads are switched OFF, high-transient voltages are generated, and if not suppressed, can reach several thousand volts across the leads that feed power to the device or between both power leads and chassis ground. The result is a "showering arc" effect that could couple with the adjacent wiring, finding its way back to the PLC.

Suppression techniques prevent the transient spikes from traveling back into the PLC wiring. The suppression circuit, typically an RC network or metal-oxide varistor (MOV), limits the magnitude of the transient voltage, as well as the rate of change of current through the inductor. Suppression circuits or devices achieve best results when applied as closely as possible to the noise source.

Suppression for small AC devices, such as solenoids, relays, and motor starters up to NEMA size 1, can be accomplished by placing an RC (resistor-capacitor) network across the device; larger contactors of Size 2 and above will require a metal-oxide varistor in addition to the RC network. For inductive DC output devices, a diode, with the appropriate breakdown voltage and current rating, or a varistor is suitable — a surge suppressor can also be used. Figure 15-11 illustrates several examples of suppressing inductive loads.

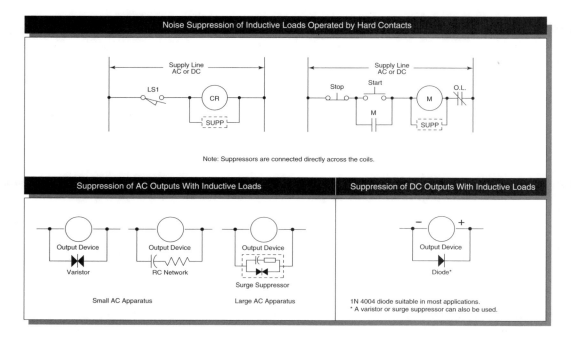

Figure 15-11. Noise suppression of inductive loads

15-4 The System Start-up

Once the field installation of the programmable controller is complete, then comes the task of system start-up. Like other aspects of the system design, programming and installation, a well thought out plan of approaching and implementing each start-up task will result in a smooth and orderly execution and the best possible results. In general, the PLC start-up consists of the following items:

- ❑   Pre-start-up Inspection
- ❑   Input Wiring Inspection
- ❑   Output Wiring Inspection
- ❑   Pre-start-up Program Inspection
- ❑   Dynamic Program Testing

Depending on the size of the installation, several individuals and organizations may be involved — all must be aware of the plan, its timing, and their responsibilities. If certain lines will be completely or partially shutdown for an extended period, preparations for temporary operations may need to be made. As part of a planned strategy for start-up, someone, such as the project manager, should be responsible for coordinating the activities and providing a checklist of responsibilities and scheduled events.

Pre-start-up Inspection

Before getting started with the various system checks, and before power is applied, a thorough visual inspection of the system hardware and interconnections is recommended. If carefully performed, these procedures will isolate wiring and other mistakes that could result in personal injury or equipment damage. The time required to perform these checks will vary depending on the size of the system. However, this time, if wisely invested, will significantly reduce the total start-up time. Table 15-13 offers some suggestions for the pre-start-up inspection.

Table 15-13. Pre-start-up Inspection Checklist

❑ Use a system arrangement diagram, to verify that all PLC, network, and other control system related components are in place and securely mounted.

❑ Verify that CPU and I/O modules are securely in place and are installed in the correct slots.

❑ Check all incoming power connections including main disconnect, transformer, fusing, main power supply, input/output device power, master control relay and emergency stop circuits.

❑ Verify that each CPU-to-I/O rack communications cable is installed and correctly correspond to rack address assignments, if applicable.

❑ Use an I/O address assignment listing, to verify that a connection is made at the module end and at the device end for all listed inputs and outputs.

❑ To ensure safety, disconnect and if necessary, lockout all output actuator devices such as motors and solenoids that can result in machine motion.

❑ Apply power to the system and verify that the proper input voltage is at the CPU power supply terminals, and that the DC voltages are within range.

❑ Verify that the emergency stop circuit functions properly and will disconnect power to the entire system and/or the output devices.

Input Wiring Inspection

The input wiring inspection is performed with power applied to the CPU and input devices. If the output devices are powered by the same circuit feeding the inputs, which is typical with a small PLC, then it is important to ensure that output power is removed or that all rotating equipment or other motion-causing devices are disconnected. Performance of this test may require at least two individuals, one to manually activate each device, while the other observes the associated LED status indicator or image table address, using the programming system. For long distances, hand radios may be required.

When performed, the input wiring inspection verifies that the connection from each device to input terminal is correct, that the device functions properly, that each input circuit is operational, and that information received by the module is received by the CPU. The input wiring can usually be checked without the use of a programming terminal, however, the programming device makes it possible to verify that the CPU actually receives the input status. This is true, since status change on the programming terminal reflects what the CPU sees.

Table 15-14. Guidelines for Input Wiring Inspection

❑ Place the CPU in a mode that inhibits program execution (e.g., STOP, DISABLE, or PROGRAM).

❑ Apply power to the CPU and input devices, leaving power to the output devices disconnected if possible. Clear the CPU memory.

❑ Verify that all power supply, CPU and I/O communication diagnostic indicators are signaling correct operation.

❑ Manually activate each input device and use an I/O assignment listing, to verify that the corresponding input status LED correctly reflects the change. A programming device may also be used, to verify that the corresponding address reflects the correct state.

Output Wiring Inspection

The output wiring inspection can be performed with power applied to the controller and to input and output devices. Motion-causing devices should be disconnected. The most desirable way to disconnect a device is so that the output can still be tested. For instance, disconnecting motor leads at the starter or at the motor, still allows operation of the starter coil. Performance of the output wiring inspection verifies that the connection between each output terminal and device is correct, and that each output circuit is operational. Like the input wiring test, this test may require at least two individuals. Output tests normally involves the following guidelines, and one of the example testing methods.

Table 15-15. Guidelines for Output Wiring Inspection

❑ Disconnect all outputs that will cause mechanical motion.

❑ Verify operation of emergency stop circuit.

❑ Apply power to the controller and input/output system and clear memory.

❑ Method 1: Starting with the first output , use the PLC I/O Force or similar forcing function to set each output to '1' and observe the status LED of the related output address, for an ON state. The output device should energize unless purposely disconnected. Clear each forced output before proceeding to the next.

❑ Method 2: If forcing is not available, a monitor/modify utility is usually available that allows the contents of an address to be modified by simply writing a new value to the location. With no program loaded, and the CPU in the RUN or (required mode), test each output by writing a '1' to the location being tested. Observe the output device and corresponding LED indicator.

Regardless of the testing method used, it is recommended that only one output be tested at a time. If forcing is used, each forced output should be cleared before moving to the next, or all cleared upon completion. If the test rung method is used, only one rung should be programmed at a time. While testing the outputs, if a device fails to energize or the appropriate status indicator fails to illuminate, it may be that the incorrect address was referenced, field wiring is incorrect, the field device or output module is defective, or some other fault exists. Diagnosing such failures are discussed later in this chapter.

Pre-start-up Program Check

A final and most vital step prior to dynamic testing of the control program is that of reviewing the program to be loaded into memory. To perform this review, a complete documentation package including I/O address assignments, memory data table assignments, wiring diagrams, and a hardcopy of the program will be required. If the program is long and complex, it may be advisable to involve not only the control programmer, but also an individual who was either involved with formulation of the intended control logic or who is very familiar with how the machine or process should operate. Table 15-16 offers a checklist for pre-start-up program inspection.

Table 15-16. Guidelines for Pre-start-up Program Check-out

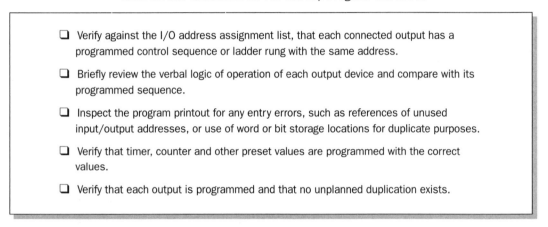

> ❏ Verify against the I/O address assignment list, that each connected output has a programmed control sequence or ladder rung with the same address.
>
> ❏ Briefly review the verbal logic of operation of each output device and compare with its programmed sequence.
>
> ❏ Inspect the program printout for any entry errors, such as references of unused input/output addresses, or use of word or bit storage locations for duplicate purposes.
>
> ❏ Verify that timer, counter and other preset values are programmed with the correct values.
>
> ❏ Verify that each output is programmed and that no unplanned duplication exists.

While each of the inspection items listed here can be performed manually, many systems offer various software cross-reference checks that can be performed automatically using an off-line program development system. Either way, if carefully performed, this final program inspection can reduce the number of program-related problems.

Dynamic Program Testing

The dynamic check-out is a procedure by which the control program is verified for correct operation of individual outputs and eventually for complete program operation. This check-out assumes that all equipment and wiring checks have been performed, the wiring is correct, hardware components and emergency stops have been manually checked and are functioning correctly, and the software has been thoroughly reviewed for accuracy. At this point, it can be assumed that it is safe to gradually bring the total system under full automatic control.

Although it may not be necessary with small systems, it is always a good practice to start a large system in sections. Larger systems generally use remote subsystems to control different sections of the machine or process. Each subsystem can be temporarily disabled either by locally removing power or by disconnecting the communications link with the CPU. Bringing one subsystem on-line at a time will allow the total system start-up to be performed with maximum safety and with fewer problems. The steps outlined in Table 15-17 suggest possible procedures for dynamic system check-out.

Table 15-17. Guidelines for Dynamic Program Check-out

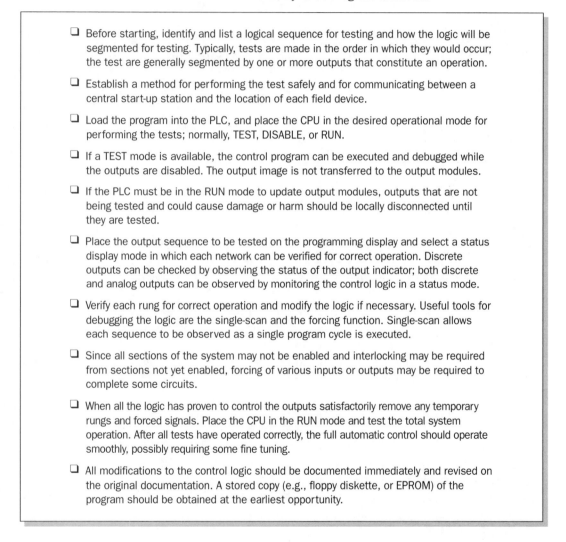

❑ Before starting, identify and list a logical sequence for testing and how the logic will be segmented for testing. Typically, tests are made in the order in which they would occur; the test are generally segmented by one or more outputs that constitute an operation.

❑ Establish a method for performing the test safely and for communicating between a central start-up station and the location of each field device.

❑ Load the program into the PLC, and place the CPU in the desired operational mode for performing the tests; normally, TEST, DISABLE, or RUN.

❑ If a TEST mode is available, the control program can be executed and debugged while the outputs are disabled. The output image is not transferred to the output modules.

❑ If the PLC must be in the RUN mode to update output modules, outputs that are not being tested and could cause damage or harm should be locally disconnected until they are tested.

❑ Place the output sequence to be tested on the programming display and select a status display mode in which each network can be verified for correct operation. Discrete outputs can be checked by observing the status of the output indicator; both discrete and analog outputs can be observed by monitoring the control logic in a status mode.

❑ Verify each rung for correct operation and modify the logic if necessary. Useful tools for debugging the logic are the single-scan and the forcing function. Single-scan allows each sequence to be observed as a single program cycle is executed.

❑ Since all sections of the system may not be enabled and interlocking may be required from sections not yet enabled, forcing of various inputs or outputs may be required to complete some circuits.

❑ When all the logic has proven to control the outputs satisfactorily remove any temporary rungs and forced signals. Place the CPU in the RUN mode and test the total system operation. After all tests have operated correctly, the full automatic control should operate smoothly, possibly requiring some fine tuning.

❑ All modifications to the control logic should be documented immediately and revised on the original documentation. A stored copy (e.g., floppy diskette, or EPROM) of the program should be obtained at the earliest opportunity.

The start-up recommendations and practices that have been presented in this section are mainly to highlight general practices that will aid in the safe and orderly start-up of any PLC system. However, before attempting to start-up a particular PLC you should be aware of specific requirements and procedures that are outlined in the manufacturer's product installation manual.

15-5 Maintenance and Troubleshooting

This section will examine some fundamental aspects of maintaining and diagnosing problems related to the PLC. Thus far, you have seen that a PLC is comprised of modular components, including the software program. This aspect of the PLC along with the fact that it is a solid-state design makes for a system that requires little maintenance and that, with a few basic troubleshooting skills, can be easily diagnosed for problems.

If individuals responsible for troubleshooting failures related to programmable controller systems are aware of certain basic operational principles and inherent diagnostic features of these devices, the task of diagnosing problems will become simpler and almost second nature. Before this can happen, however, a second ingredient is required — that is, a systematic approach to troubleshooting. After several successes with troubleshooting PLC system malfunctions, one will soon become aware that most malfunctions develop externally to the PLC.

Preventive Maintenance

Historically, PLCs perform reliably once installed and fully debugged. This reliability is related to their inherent rugged design and the fact that they are almost totally solid state. If the installation has taken into consideration items such as the enclosure, good grounding practices, any extreme environmental conditions, or harsh electrical noise, chances for some of the most common malfunctions will have been greatly reduced.

Although there are no PLC components that require regularly scheduled maintenance, a certain amount of routine preventive maintenance is required to ensure good operation. Establishing a regular schedule for performing a few basic checks will provide years of trouble-free operation. As a minimum, the preventive measures presented in Table 15-18 should be considered in all installations.

Spare Parts

Spare parts for each installed controller should not be an afterthought, but considered when the system is initially configured. Although this proposition may seem costly, the financial investment will prove negligible if extended downtimes due to component failure can be avoided. Having the right back-up components in a failure situation could mean a shutdown of only minutes instead of hours or days. A typical PLC spare parts list is suggested in Table 15-19.

A good rule of thumb is to stock at least 10 percent of the number of each component used or a minimum of one spare of each component. Some plants choose to stock a full set of CPU boards and at least one each of every other module. Often this same system is made operational and used as a training setup. This is a particularly good idea since those modules held as spare stock are thereby continually being tested.

Table 15-18. Preventive Maintenance Checks for PLCs

❑ Install the PLC components in an enclosure suitable for the environment

❑ Establish a regular schedule to inspect the I/O and processor units. Communications cables in tact and LEDs responding properly.

❑ Filters should be cleaned or replaced periodically.

❑ Verify that emergency batteries and power packs are fully charged, and check for battery-low indicators on CPUs. Although low batteries may work for weeks or months, it is best to change them immediately.

❑ Enclosure doors should be kept closed to avoid build-up of dirt and dust on components. A buildup of dirt and dust on components will obstruct good heat dissipation and may cause short circuits.

❑ The enclosure should be kept clean and free from any articles or debris that could obstruct air flow. Do not allow drawings, manuals, and other paper articles to accumulate.

❑ Check terminations periodically for good connections and modules to see if they are securely seated. This check should be performed more frequently in areas where the controller is subjected to continuous vibration.

❑ Care should be taken to ensure that after a system is installed, heavy noise-generating equipment is not moved too closely to the PLC enclosure.

❑ If an output fuse blows, be sure to replace it with the manufacturer recommended replacement. If a fuse continues to blow, ensure that the module's output current is rated properly for the device.

Table 15-19. Typical PLC Spare Parts List

SPARE PART	QUANTITY
Central Processor Module	1 ea
Other CPU Modules	1 ea
CPU Power Supply	1 ea
I/O Processor Module	1 ea or 10%
CPU Chassis	1 ea
I/O Expansion Chassis	1 ea
I/O Power Supply	1 ea
Programming Cables	1 ea
Programming Device	1 ea
Discrete Input Modules	1 ea or 10%
Discrete Output Modules	1 ea or 10%
Analog Input Modules	1 ea or 10%
Analog Output Modules	1 ea or 10%
Intelligent Modules	1 ea
Memory Backup Battery	1 ea or 10%
Power Supply Fuses	5 ea

Using Diagnostic Indicators

Use of the diagnostic indicators of PLC components is perhaps the fastest means of pinpointing system failures or malfunctions. In fact, PLC diagnostic indicators are equally useful in helping to isolate problems that occur both internally to the PLC or from an externally connected device. Since each modular component incorporates diagnostic or status indicators that signal correct or malfunctioning operation, defective components are quickly identified and easily replaced.

Table 15-20. Typical PLC Status Indicators and Functions

PLC COMPONENT	STATUS INDICATOR	NORMALLY INDICATES
CPU	RUN	- CPU in RUN mode (Program in cycle)
	PROGRAM	- CPU in PROGRAM mode
	TEST/DISABLE	- Program executing , outputs disabled
	FORCE	- I/O points are being forced
	CPU READY	- Processor diagnostic tests passed
	MEM ERR	- Parity or checksum error detected
	BATT LOW	- Backup battery needs replacement
Power Supply	AC OK	- AC power ON and within range
	DC OK	- DC voltages are present and within range
I/O Processor	COMM OK	- I/O communication link and data is OK
Discrete Inputs	Power	- Input power is applied at device
	Logic	- Input signal of "1" is recognized
Discrete Outputs	Logic	- Output is commanded to energize
	Blown Fuse	- Module or circuit has blown fuse

It should be noted that in the list of examples given in Table 15-20, an illuminated indicator signals that the specified condition exists; however, indicators such as "MEM ERR"and "I/O COMM" may be inverted on some PLCs. For instance, if the indicator was "MEM OK," the LED would remain ON until an error occurred. If the I/O communication indicator was "COMM ERR," then the LED would remain OFF until the error occurred.

Diagnosing Input Malfunctions

Discrete input modules generally incorporate a power indicator for each input circuit. When illuminated, it indicates that the input signal is present at the module's input. Recall that each input circuit has both a power side and a logic side, electrically isolated from one another. Some systems therefore add a second indicator, a logic indicator, that when illuminated verifies that the input signal has been received and processed by the logic or processor side of the circuit. On such a module, when both power and logic indicators fail to match, it is signaling that the module is unable to transfer the incoming signal to the processor correctly.

If an input is malfunctioning, the first check is to see if the power indicator is responding to the field device. If the input device is activated but the power indicator does not illuminate, then suspect field wiring or the device. First check the input voltage at the input terminal. If the input voltage, wiring, and device are OK, the input module should be replaced. If the input indicators are illuminated and according to the programming device the processor is not recognizing the input, then the input module may have a fault, or you may be examining the wrong address. If a replacement module fails to eliminate the problem and other modules are working, the I/O rack slot may be at fault. A general input diagnostic flowchart is shown in Fig. 15-12.

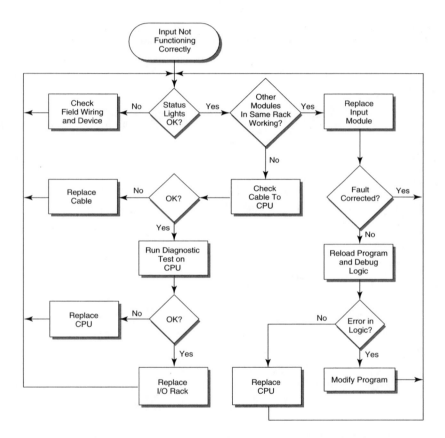

Figure 15-12. Troubleshooting flowchart for PLC inputs

Diagnosing Output Malfunctions

Discrete output modules generally incorporate a logic indicator for each circuit. When ON, it indicates that the module's logic side of the circuit has recognized a command from the processor to turn ON. In addition to logic indicators, output modules will usually incorporate a blown fuse indicator for each circuit or one indicator that is shared by all circuits. The blown fuse indicator signals that an output circuit has been shorted, or has overdrawn the maximum current.

Like input circuits, output circuits also have a logic and power side. Therefore, some output modules will also have both a logic indicator and power indicator. When ON, the power indicator signals that the power side of the circuit recognizes the logic command from the processor, and in response switches power to the output device. Like the power and logic indicators of the input module, if both are not ON simultaneously, the output module is malfunctioning. If the module only has one status LED, you may only assume that the addressed output and device is being commanded to turn ON.

If an output is malfunctioning, the first check is to see if the output device is responding to the LED status indicators. Then verify that all the CPU and I/O rack LEDs are OK. If an output rung is energized, the indicator is correct, the output voltage is correct, and the device is not responding, then the field wiring or device should be checked; but first, check for a blown fuse or simply replace the module. If, according to the programming device, an output device is being commanded to turn ON, but the indicator is OFF, then the module should be replaced. A general output diagnostic flowchart is shown in Figure 15-13.

Module Replacement

When diagnosing input/output malfunctions, the best approach is to quickly isolate the problem either to the module itself or to the field wiring and. If both power and logic indicators are available, then module failure becomes readily apparent. Normally, the first test is to replace the module or take a voltage measurement at the proper input terminal. If the proper voltage is measured at the input terminal and the module is not responding, then the module should be replaced. A proper voltage level at the output terminal while the output device is OFF indicates a fault in the field wiring or device. If an output rung is activated and the LED indicator is OFF, then the module should be replaced.

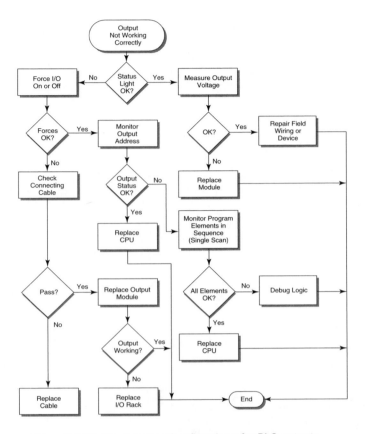

Figure 15-13. Troubleshooting flowchart for PLC outputs

If a malfunction cannot be traced to the I/O module, then the module connectors should be inspected for poor contact or misalignment. Finally, check for broken wires under connector terminals and cold solder joints on module terminals. Almost always, if other points on a module are working correctly or other modules in the rack are working, then the first step should be to replace the module.

If a module has to be replaced, you should make sure that the module being installed is of the correct type. Some I/O systems allow modules to be replaced while power is still applied, but others may require that power be removed. In the case of discrete outputs, if replacing a module solves the problem, but the failure reoccurs in a relatively short period, you should check inductive loads that may be generating transients spikes and may require external suppression. If the module fuse blows again after it is replaced, it may be that the module's output current limit is being exceeded or that the output device is shorted.

APPENDIX: A

ASCII Characters with Binary/Octal/Hexadecimal Equivalents

ASCII CHAR	DEC	BINARY	OCT	HEX	ASCII CHAR	DEC	BINARY	OCT	HEX
NUL	0	00000000	000	00	space	32	00100000	040	20
SOH	1	00000001	001	01	!	33	00100001	041	21
STX	2	00000010	002	02	"	34	00100010	042	22
ETX	3	00000011	003	03	#	35	00100011	043	23
EOT	4	00000100	004	04	$	36	00100100	044	24
ENQ	5	00000101	005	05	%	37	00100101	045	25
ACK	6	00000110	006	06	&	38	00100110	046	26
BEL	7	00000111	007	07	'	39	00100111	047	27
BS	8	00001000	010	08	(	40	00101000	050	28
HT	9	00001001	011	09	)	41	00101001	051	29
LF	10	00001010	012	0A	*	42	00101010	052	2A
VT	11	00001011	013	0B	+	43	00101011	053	2B
FF	12	00001100	014	0C	,	44	00101100	054	2C
CR	13	00001101	015	0D	—	45	00101101	055	2D
SO	14	00001110	016	0E	.	46	00101110	056	2E
SI	15	00001111	017	0F	/	47	00101111	057	2F
DLE	16	00010000	020	10	0	48	00110000	060	30
DC1	17	00010001	021	11	1	49	00110001	061	31
DC2	18	00010010	022	12	2	50	00110010	062	32
DC3	19	00010011	023	13	3	51	00110011	063	33
DC4	20	00010100	024	14	4	52	00110100	064	34
NAK	21	00010101	025	15	5	53	00110101	065	35
SYNC	22	00010110	026	16	6	54	00110110	066	36
ETB	23	00010111	027	17	7	55	00110111	067	37
CAN	24	00011000	030	18	8	56	00111000	070	38
EM	25	00011001	031	19	9	57	00111001	071	39
SUB	26	00011010	032	1A	:	58	00111010	072	3A
ESC	27	00011011	033	1B	;	59	00111011	073	3B
FS	28	00011100	034	1C	<	60	00111100	074	3C
GS	29	00011101	035	1D	=	61	00111101	075	3D
RS	30	00011110	036	1E	>	62	00111110	076	3E
US	31	00011111	037	1F	?	63	00111111	077	3F

ASCII CHAR	DEC	BINARY	OCT	HEX	ASCII CHAR	DEC	BINARY	OCT	HEX
@	64	01000000	100	40	`	96	01100000	140	60
A	65	01000001	101	41	a	97	01100001	141	61
B	66	01000010	102	42	b	98	01100010	142	62
C	67	01000011	103	43	c	99	01100011	143	63
D	68	01000100	104	44	d	100	01100100	144	64
E	69	01000101	105	45	e	101	01100101	145	65
F	70	01000110	106	46	f	102	01100110	146	66
G	71	01000111	107	47	g	103	01100111	147	67
H	72	01001000	110	48	h	104	01101000	150	68
I	73	01001001	111	49	i	105	01101001	151	69
J	74	01001010	112	4A	j	106	01101010	152	6A
K	75	01001011	113	4B	k	107	01101011	153	6B
L	76	01001100	114	4C	l	108	01101100	154	6C
M	77	01001101	115	4D	m	109	01101101	155	6D
N	78	01001110	116	4E	n	110	01101110	156	6E
O	79	01001111	117	4F	o	111	01101111	157	6F
P	80	01010000	120	50	p	112	01110000	160	70
Q	81	01010001	121	51	q	113	01110001	161	71
R	82	01010010	122	52	r	114	01110010	162	72
S	83	01010011	123	53	s	115	01110011	163	73
T	84	01010100	124	54	t	116	01110100	164	74
U	85	01010101	125	55	u	117	01110101	165	75
V	86	01010110	126	56	v	118	01110110	166	76
W	87	01010111	127	57	w	119	01110111	167	77
X	88	01011000	130	58	x	120	01111000	170	78
Y	89	01011001	131	59	y	121	01111001	171	79
Z	90	01011010	132	5A	z	122	01111010	172	7A
[	91	01011011	133	5B	{	123	01111011	173	7B
\	92	01011100	134	5C	|	124	01111100	174	7C
]	93	01011101	135	5D	}	125	01111101	175	7D
^	94	01011110	136	5E	~	126	01111110	176	7E
_	95	01011111	137	5F	DEL	127	01111111	177	7F

APPENDIX: B

Centigrade/Fahrenheit Temperature Conversion Chart

-100 to 30			31 to 71			72 to 212			213 to 620			621 to 1000		
C	<->	F	C	<->	F	C	<->	F	C	<->	F	C	<->	F
-73.0	-100	-148.0	-0.6	31	87.8	22.2	72	161.6	104	220	428	332	630	1166
-68.0	-90	-130.0	0.0	32	89.6	22.8	73	163.4	110	230	446	338	640	1184
-62.0	-80	-112.0	0.6	33	91.4	23.3	74	165.2	116	240	464	343	650	1202
-57.0	-70	-94.0	1.1	34	93.2	23.9	75	167.0	121	250	482	349	660	1220
-51.0	-60	-76.0	1.7	35	95.0	24.4	76	168.8	127	260	500	354	670	1238
-46.0	-50	-58.0	2.2	36	96.8	25.0	77	170.6	132	270	518	360	680	1256
-40.0	-40	-40.0	2.8	37	98.6	25.6	78	172.4	138	280	536	366	690	1274
-34.4	-30	-22.0	3.3	38	100.4	26.1	79	174.2	143	290	554	371	700	1292
-28.9	-20	-4.0	3.9	39	102.2	26.7	80	176.0	149	300	572	377	710	1310
-23.3	-10	14.0	4.4	40	104.0	27.2	81	177.8	154	310	590	382	720	1328
-17.8	0	32.0	5.0	41	105.8	27.8	82	179.6	160	320	608	388	730	1346
-17.2	1	33.8	5.6	42	107.6	28.3	83	181.4	166	330	626	393	740	1364
-16.7	2	35.6	6.1	43	109.4	28.9	84	183.2	171	340	644	399	750	1382
-16.1	3	37.4	6.7	44	111.2	29.4	85	185.0	177	350	662	404	760	1400
-15.6	4	39.2	7.2	45	113.0	30.0	86	186.8	182	360	680	410	770	1418
-15.0	5	41.0	7.8	46	114.8	30.6	87	188.6	188	370	698	416	780	1436
-14.4	6	42.8	8.3	47	116.6	31.1	88	190.4	193	380	716	421	790	1454
-13.9	7	44.6	8.9	48	118.4	31.7	89	192.2	199	390	734	427	800	1472
-13.3	8	46.4	9.4	49	120.0	32.2	90	194.0	204	400	752	432	810	1490
-12.8	9	48.2	10.0	50	122.0	32.8	91	195.8	210	410	770	438	820	1508
-12.2	10	50.0	10.6	51	123.8	33.3	92	197.6	216	420	788	443	830	1526
-11.7	11	51.8	11.1	52	125.6	33.9	93	199.4	221	430	806	449	840	1544
-11.1	12	53.6	11.7	53	127.4	34.4	94	201.2	227	440	824	454	850	1562
-10.6	13	55.4	12.2	54	129.2	35.0	95	203.0	232	450	842	460	860	1580
-10.0	14	57.2	12.8	55	131.0	35.6	96	204.8	238	460	860	466	870	1598
-9.4	15	59.0	13.3	56	132.8	36.1	97	206.6	243	470	878	471	880	1616
-8.9	16	60.8	13.9	57	134.6	36.7	98	208.4	249	480	896	477	890	1634
-8.3	17	62.6	14.4	58	136.4	37.2	99	210.2	254	490	914	482	900	1652
-7.8	18	64.4	15.0	59	138.2	37.8	100	212.0	260	500	932	488	910	1670
-7.2	19	66.2	15.6	60	140.0	43.0	110	230.0	266	510	950	493	920	1688
-6.7	20	68.0	16.1	61	141.8	49.0	120	248.0	271	520	968	499	930	1706
-6.1	21	69.8	16.7	62	143.6	54.0	130	266.0	277	530	986	504	940	1724
-5.6	22	71.6	17.2	63	145.4	60.0	140	284.0	282	540	1004	510	950	1742
-5.0	23	73.4	17.8	64	147.2	66.0	150	302.0	288	550	1022	516	960	1760
-4.4	24	75.2	18.3	65	149.0	71.0	160	320.0	293	560	1040	521	970	1778
-3.9	25	77.0	18.9	66	150.8	77.0	170	338.0	299	570	1058	527	980	1796
-3.3	26	78.8	19.4	67	152.6	82.0	180	356.0	304	580	1076	532	990	1814
-2.8	27	80.6	20.0	68	154.4	88.0	190	374.0	310	590	1094	538	1000	1832
-2.2	28	82.4	20.6	69	156.2	93.0	200	392.0	316	600	1112			
-1.7	29	84.2	21.1	70	158.0	99.0	210	410.0	321	610	1130			
-1.1	30	86.0	21.7	71	159.8	100.0	212	414.0	327	620	1148			

Temperature Conversion Formulae $C = 5/9 \, (F - 32)$ $F = 9/5 \, C + 32$

The numbers in the center of each column represent the Fahrenheit or Centigrade temperature to be converted.
When converting Fahrenheit to Centigrade, the equivalent temperature is found to the left of the center.
When converting Centigrade to Fahrenheit, the equivalent temperature is found to the right of the center.

APPENDIX: C
NEMA Enclosure Classifications.

TYPE	DESCRIPTION	TYPICAL APPLICATIONS
NEMA-1	General Purpose	Protects against precipitative dust however is not dust tight. Indoor use where atmospheric conditions are normal.
NEMA-2	Drip-Tight Indoor	General purpose applications, indoor use where condensation may be severe.
NEMA-3,3R,3S	Dust,Rain-Proof / Sleet Resistant	Where wind blown dust or weather hazards such as rain, sleet or snow exist. Outdoor use: underground, subways, tunnels etc.
NEMA-4,4X	Water-Tight / Corrosion Resistant	Protects against large amounts of spray; typically dairies, breweries, etc. Corrosion-proof normally required in food processing or similar industries.
NEMA-5	Dust-Tight	Indoor use for protection against dust and falling dirt.
NEMA-6	Submersible	For applications such as mines, quarries, and manholes. Selection depends on submersion time and pressure.
NEMA-7	Hazardous Locations	Indoor use. Locations Class I, Groups A to D, as defined by the National Electric Code (NEC).
NEMA-8	Hazardous Locations	Indoor/Outdoor use. Locations Class I, Groups A to D as defined by the NEC.
NEMA-9	Hazardous Locations	Indoor use. NEC classified locations, Class II, Groups E to G.
NEMA-10	Mine Use	Meets applicable requirements of the Federal Mine Safety and Health Administration (MSHA).
NEMA-11	Oil Immersion	Protects against oil immersion, corrosive liquids and gases. Primarily intended for indoor use.
NEMA-12	Drip Resistant	For indoor use primarily to provide a degree of protection against dust, falling dirt, and dripping non-corrosive liquids.
NEMA-13	Oil Tight	Applications involving machine tools and other locations where oil, coolants, water, filings, or lint might infiltrate the enclosure via mounting holes, conduit, or other obscure entry points.

GLOSSARY

A

ac: See *alternating current*.

accumulator word: A memory storage location used to hold the current value of a timer or counter instruction. Also see *preset word*.

ac input: Reference to any discrete ac signal, or device whose signal is input to the programmable controller or similar control system using an ac input module.

ac input device: Devices that generate a discrete ac signal and are interfaced to a programmable controller or similar control system via an ac input interface, such as 120 VAC, 230 VAC, or 24 VAC.

ac input module: An input module designed to provide the required interface for connecting ac input devices to the PLC. The module converts AC signals to the appropriate logic level for use by the processor. Standard ac input voltage ratings include 12-24 VAC, 24-48 VAC, 115 VAC, and 230 VAC.

ac output module: An output module designed to provide the required interface for connecting the PLC to field devices that are turned on or off by switching an ac voltage. Standard ac output voltage ratings include 12-24 VAC, 24-48 VAC, 115 VAC, and 230 VAC.

actuator: 1) A device that performs an action in response to an electrical signal. A solenoid is an example of an actuator. **2)** The mechanism of a switch, that when moved as intended, will operate the switch contacts.

address: 1) A reference number that identifies a unique bit, byte, word, or double word memory location. **2)** An identifying number designating a unique system entity, that is known to all other similar entities in the system.

address, terminal: Typically a 4, 5, or 6-digit number that identifies a terminal to which a unique input or output device is connected. For every terminal address, a corresponding bit location is reserved in the input/output image table of the programmable controller memory.

alarm: An audible or visible signal that indicates an abnormal or out-of-limits condition.

alphanumeric characters: Character set that includes letters of the alphabet, numeric digits, and some special characters.

alphanumeric display: A type of device that is capable of displaying messages utilizing a fixed set of letters of the alphabet, numeric digits, and special characters.

alternating current (AC): Current flow in which the charge flow reverses periodically.

ASCII: See *American Standard Code for Information Interchange.*

analog: Data in the form of continuously variable physical quantities, such as speed or pressure, expressed as a function of varying current or voltage; contrasts with digital, which pertains to data represented by discrete states, such as on or off.

analog channel: A channel on which the information transmitted can take on any value between the limits defined by the channel.

analog control: The ability to process analog input and output signals for the purpose of providing smooth and continuous control of some process variable.

analog data: See *analog.*

analog input: Reference to any continuous current or voltage input signal; or a device that generates a signal that is input to a programmable controller or similar control device using an analog input module. A signal that represents temperature is an analog input.

analog input devices: Devices that measure analog quantities, such as temperature and pressure, generate a continuous current or voltage signal, and are interfaced to a programmable controller or similar control device using an analog input module such as 4-20 ma or -10 VDC -to- +10 VDC.

analog input module: An input module designed to provide the required interface for connecting field devices that generate analog signals, to the PLC. The module employs an analog-to-digital converter to convert the incoming signal to a binary value that represents the analog signal present at the input. Standard voltage ratings include + -10 VDC, +-5 VDC, 4 -to- 20 ma, 0 -to- +10 VDC, and 0 -to- +5 VDC.

analog I/O: The class of input and output devices that can be interfaced to a programmable controller, or similar control device, using analog input and output modules.

analog output: Reference to any continuous current or voltage signal output from the processor; or a device that requires a varying signal for control and is interfaced to the programmable controller using an analog output module.

analog output devices: Devices that require a continuous current or voltage signal for control and are interfaced to a programmable controller or similar control device using an analog output module, such as 4-20 ma or -10 VDC -to- +10 VDC.

analog output module: An output module having one or more output channels that provide the required interface between a programmable controller, or similar control device, and field devices that are controlled by an analog current or voltage. The module employs a digital-to-analog converter to generate a proportional output current or voltage based on the numeric value received from the processor. Standard voltage ratings include +- 10 VDC, +-5 VDC, 4 -to- 20 ma, 0 -to- +10 VDC, and 0 -to- +5 VDC.

analog signal: Signal that is continuous and changes smoothly over a given range, rather than switching suddenly between certain levels (as with discrete signals).

analog-to-digital converter: A component that converts a sampled analog signal to a digital code that represents the same sampled analog signal.

application: The system or problem to which a computer is applied. Typical applications include: control, data acquisition, and data processing.

application engineers: Engineers who normally specialize in the application of a particular technology, manufacturing process, or technique for a particular industry. Examples of application engineers are those that specialize in the application of technologies such as robots, PLCs, computers, machine vision, and automatic guided vehicles or industry techniques such as plastics extrusion, steel making, materials handling, or food packaging.

application memory: That part of a total system memory that is available for the storage of the user application program and associated data.

application program: 1) The set of instructions written by the user for control, data acquisition, or report generation. This software is stored in the application memory. **2)** A prepackaged, canned software program designed to perform a particular function and to operate under a given operating system. Spreadsheets are application programs.

arithmetic capability: The ability to perform such math functions as addition, subtraction, multiplication, division, and square roots.

American Standard Code for Information Interchange: ASCII, pronounced "askey". The standard 7 or 8-bit code used for exchanging alphanumeric information between intelligent devices and associated equipment and for representing 128 data and control characters. Of the 128 possible codes, 32 are reserved for upper-case alphabets and a few punctuation marks. A second group of 32 is used for numbers 0-9, spacing, and additional standard punctuation and symbols. Rarely used punctuation marks and lowercase alphabets are assigned a third group of 32 codes. A final group of 32 codes is assigned as machine or control commands. This group includes non-printable codes such as line (LF) or carriage return (CR).

ASCII module: An I/O module that serves as a means for accepting ASCII input to the processor from devices such as a bar code reader, for outputting messages from the processor to devices such as an alphanumeric display, or for bi-directional flow of ASCII data between an intelligent data terminal and the PLC.

B

backplane: The printed circuit board located on the inside back panel of a CPU or I/O rack housing designed for inserting various types of input/output modules. The backplane includes a data bus, power bus, and mating connectors for accepting various types of plug-in type modules.

backup: A device or system that is kept available to serve as a replacement for a primary device or system that may fail in operation. Also see "hot backup."

batch process: A process consisting of a finite number of steps, whereby some operation is performed on one or more ingredients or inputs in order to produce a finished product.

battery back-up: A battery or set of batteries installed for the purpose of providing power to RAM memory in case of a system power outage.

BCD: See *binary coded decimal*.

BCD input: Reference to BCD input data or to a device that generates a BCD value that can be interfaced to a programmable controller or similar control device using a BCD or standard discrete input module.

BCD input devices: Devices that generate a BCD value at their output and can be interfaced or input to a PLC or similar control device using a BCD input module or parallel digital input signals, 4-wires per BCD digit. Typical devices that output BCD values are bar code readers and thumbwheel switches.

BCD input module: An input module designed specifically for interfacing BCD input devices to a programmable controller.

BCD I/O: Collectively, the class of input and output devices that can be interfaced to a programmable controller or similar control device using BCD input and output modules or using parallel digital I/O.

BCD output: Reference to BCD output data or a device that requires a BCD value for operation and can be interfaced to a programmable controller or similar control device using a BCD output module.

BCD output devices: Devices that require a BCD value to control their operation and can be interfaced to a programmable controller or similar control device by using a BCD output module or by using parallel digital output signals, 4-wires per BCD digit. Typical devices that are driven by a BCD value are 7- segment LED displays and message display units.

binary: 1) Pertaining to the base 2 numbering system. **2)** Having the characteristic or property of only two possible choices, states, or conditions (e.g., on/off, true/false, 1 or 0, extended/retracted).

BCD output module: An output module designed specifically for interfacing devices that are driven by a BCD value.

binary coded decimal (BCD): A coded number system in which each decimal digit from 0 to 9 is expressed by a 4-bit binary number. BCD is a method by which decimal numbers, easily handled by humans, can be input to digital machines in a format (binary) that is readily usable by the machine. On the other hand, the machine can output binary information in a decimal format. The four positions of a BCD number each have a weighted value of 1,2,4, and 8, respectively, starting with the least significant bit. A thumbwheel switch is a BCD device; when connected to a programmable controller, each decade (0-9) requires four wires. Decimal 91 = 1001 0001 in BCD

bit: 1) Abbreviation for binary digit. **2)** A single digit in a binary number.

bit status: The on/off state of a particular bit location in memory.

bleeding resistor: A resistor connected across a power source to improve voltage regulation, to drain off the charge remaining in capacitors when the power is turned off, or to protect equipment from excessive voltages if the load is removed or substantially reduced.

block: Refers to a group of memory word locations handled as a unit.

block length: The total number of words in a given block of data.

block transfer: The act of moving a block of data words from one area to another or the instruction or technique used to move a block of words.

Boolean: The logic or arithmetic processes used in the algebra developed by George Boole.

Boolean programming: A programmable controller programming technique that uses Boolean operators, AND, OR, and NOT, to develop control logic sequences,

branch: 1) A parallel path of logic in a ladder diagram rung. **2)** An alternative path in a software program.

C

centralized control: A control design approach in which the entire machine or process control is handled by a single programmable controller or other control system.

closed-loop system: A control system designed with feedback-type control such that the output is used to modify the input. The output is fed back and compared to the input to generate an error signal (actual value minus the desired value). The error signal is used to generate a new adjusted output signal.

coil: 1) The element energized by the input signal to a relay. **2)** Refers to the output symbol in a ladder diagram program. The Ladder energize output symbol, -( )-, used to reference a connected output device in a ladder diagram program, is also referred to as a coil.

common mode interference: A form of interference which appears between the terminals of any measuring circuit and ground.

common mode rejection: The ability of a circuit to discriminate against common mode voltage, usually expressed in decibels.

common mode voltage: A signal of the same polarity on both sides of a differential input, often caused by a common path.

condition instructions: Any instructions that are evaluated and must be met prior to causing any action to take place as a result of those conditions. The "Examine ON -] [-" and "Examine OFF -]/[-" Ladder instructions allow the on/off status of inputs and outputs to be examined; they are condition instructions.

constant voltage transformer: A special purpose transformer designed to compensate for voltage changes at its input (primary) to maintain a steady non-fluctuating voltage at its output (secondary).

contact address: An identifier number placed over a programmed contact in a Ladder program. The number identifies the unique memory location of the status being examined.

contact: 1) One of the conducting parts of a relay, switch, or connector that are engaged or disengaged to open or close the associated electrical circuits. **2)** In reference to a Ladder program, the juncture point that provides a complete path when closed. See *ladder contact*.

contact matrix: See *ladder matrix*.

contact symbology: The conventional relay logic symbols, used to express the control logic in a Ladder program (e.g., normally open contact -] [-, normally-closed contact -]/[- ,and coil -( )-).

continuos current rating: An ac output module rating that defines the maximum current that can be safely supplied to the load by a single output channel when the output is in the ON state. This rating, also known as the ON-state current rating, is typically specified based on an ambient temperature of 0-60 degrees centigrade.

continuous process: A process in which raw materials enter one end of the system and a finished product exits at the other end.

control logic: 1) The combination of conditions that must be satisfied to control a particular device or perform a particular function. Each step, event, or sequence is defined by either a single instruction or a combination of expressions. **2)** Refers to the entire program logic or relay logic that will control a given machine or process.

control panel: See *operator control panel*.

control program: A sequence of instructions that prescribes the series of steps to be taken by a programmable controller, computer, or similar device to control a machine or process.

control sequence: The operating order for a piece of equipment, based on an established set of conditions.

control variable: 1) A quantity, condition, or part of a system that is subject to manipulation, regulation, or control by a computer, programmable controller, or similar control device. **2)** The process variable regulated by the process control loop.

counter: 1) An electromechanical relay-type device that counts the occurrence of some event. The event to be counted may be pulses developed from operations such as switch closures, interruptions of light beams, or other discrete events. **2)** A programmable controller eliminates the need for hardware counters, by using software counters. The software counter can be given a preset count value and will count up or down, depending on program.

counter accumulated value: The current count or value stored in the accumulator word of a software counter.

counter, down: A programmable controller software counter that decrements its accumulated value by one for each off-to-on transition of its count-down pulse.

counter preset: The value stored in a software counter preset word. This value determines the value to which the counter will count up or down to and the point at which the counter output will energize.

counter, up: A programmable controller software counter that increments its accumulated value by one for each off-to-on transition of its count-up pulse.

counter, up-down: A programmable controller software counter that combines the actions of both the up-counter and down-counter. An up/down counter can be used for production accounting of good parts and rejected parts.

CPU diagnostics: Error-checking routines that the processor performs while the system is running (run-time error checking) to test its own integrity. CPU diagnostics typically include memory test, backup battery test, and program execution time out-of-range test.

cross talk: A condition involving the signal of one circuit or conductor appearing on a nearby circuit or conductor as interference.

CRT programmer: A programming device containing a cathode ray tube.

cursor: The intensified or blinking element on a display screen. Typically an underscore dash or filled in square, the cursor normally indicates the position at which the next character entered will appear on the screen or the position of a data entry field.

current loop: A two-wire communication link in which the presence of a 20 milliamp current level indicates a binary "1" (mark), and its absence indicates no data, a binary "0" (space).

D

daisy chain: A method of propagating signals along a bus connecting two or more system components. This method is a bus line that is interconnected with units in such a manner that a signal passes from one unit to the next in a serial fashion.

data acquisition: The process of collecting data from the system through some manual or automatic means for the purpose of producing printed reports for operating, supervisory, maintenance, or accounting disciplines.

data highway: A means of transmitting frames between stations interconnected by a data transmission line. A data highway consists of a data circuit and the physical and data link layers of the stations connected to the data circuit.

data manipulation instructions: Those instructions that allow operations on data such as the comparison of two values, number conversions, and the transfer of data from one place to another.

data table: 1) An area allocated in memory for the storage of any data associated with executable programs. **2)** As used in reference to programmable controllers, that part of the application memory that contains I/O image tables (status), internal storage bits, data storage for timers and counters, setpoints, recipes, and any other data associated with the control program.

data transfer: The process of moving information from one location to another, such as word address-to-word address or device-to-device.

data transfer instructions: Those PLC instructions that allow the programmer to move data internal to the programmable controller memory as well as read and control data I/O such as analog, BCD, encoder, and other numerical I/O modules.

dc: See *direct current*.

dc input module: An input module designed specifically to interface devices that generate discrete dc signals to the PLC. The module converts dc signals originated in various devices to the appropriate logic level for use by the processor. Standard dc input voltage ratings include 12-24 VDC, 24-48 VDC, 115 VDC, and 230 VDC.

dc input: Reference to any discrete dc signal or to a device that generates a signal that is input to the programmable controller using a dc input module.

dc output module: An output module designed to provide the required interface between the PLC and field devices that are turned on or off by switching a dc voltage. Standard dc output voltage ratings include 12-24 VDC, 24-48 VDC, 115 VDC, and 230 VDC.

dc outputs: General reference to any discrete device that is driven by the PLC via discrete dc output modules.

debugging: The process of detecting, isolating, and correcting errors or malfunctions in software programs or hardware devices.

decade: A group assembly of ten units (e.g., a single thumbwheel switch that counts from 0 to 9). With a 4-decade thumbwheel the count can be incremented from 0000 to 9999.

de-energize: To de-activate or turn OFF.

derivative control action: That component of control action for which the output is proportional to the rate of change of the input. Also referred to as rate action.

differential input: The difference between the instantaneous values of two voltages both being biased by a common mode voltage.

digital: Information in the form of a discrete number of codes. Contrast with analog.

digital device: A device that processes digital signals.

digital I/O: The class of input and output devices that can be interfaced to a programmable controller or similar control device using digital input and output modules.

digital signal: A signal that is meaningful only when in either of two possible states, ON or OFF. A digital signal does not have in-between states or values.

digital-to-analog converter (D/A): A device that accepts at its input a numerical value expressed as a digital code and whose output is the equivalent analog signal level.

direct current (dc): A unidirectional current in which the changes in value are either zero or so small that they may be neglected. The term normally means a steady-state or non- pulsating current.

disable output: A state of a PLC's CPU that prevents a designated output or all outputs from being energized by the program. This debug feature is normally used during startup of the controller or troubleshooting and protects against unsafe conditions.

discrete: The characteristic of being distinct in nature such as on or off, open or closed, extended or retracted.

discrete inputs: Those on/off type ac or dc signals or those devices that generate such signals that are input to a PLC using digital input modules. Pushbuttons, limit switches, proximity switches, and selector switches are all discrete inputs.

discrete I/O: The class of input and output devices that are interfaced to the programmable controller using discrete input and output modules.

discrete outputs: Those devices that are driven by a discrete signal and are interfaced to the programmable controller using a discrete output module.

distributed control: A design approach in which factory or machine control is divided into several subsystems, each managed independently by a unique PLC or other control system, yet all interconnected to form a single entity. Individual subsystems may be interconnected via communications networks.

distributed processing: A design approach in which processing tasks are handled by two or more processors within a single system. For example, a PLC with intelligent I/O might have peripheral communications, PID control, axis positioning, BASIC programming, and other such functions performed by these intelligent microprocessor-based modules that can function independently of the central processor.

documentation: 1) An orderly collection of information normally regarding hardware and software systems and in the form of tables, listings, cross-references, and drawings that provide valuable reference material for design, installation, startup, and maintenance of the system. **2)** Handbooks and operator and service reference manuals.

double precision: 1) The use of two memory word locations to represent a number. **2)** In floating-point arithmetic, the use of additional bytes or words, in which a number is represented, to double the number of bits in the mantissa.

downtime: The time when a system is not available for production due to required maintenance (scheduled or unscheduled).

dynamic start-up: That part of the controller start-up procedure in which the system is checked under program control.

E

edit: To deliberately modify a stored program.

EEPROM: See *Electrically Erasable Programmable Read Only Memory*.

EIA: See *Electronic Industries Association*.

electrical isolation: The physical separation of two electrical circuits.

electrical noise: See *noise*.

Electronic Industries Association (EIA): An agency that sets electrical/electronic standards.

elementary diagram: A wiring diagram of an electrical system in which all devices are drawn between two vertical lines that represent the hot and neutral power conductors.

emergency stop: 1) A condition under which all power is disconnected from the system. **2)** A manually or automatically operated device that causes all power to be removed from a system given certain potentially hazardous or unsafe conditions.

EMI: See *electromagnetic interference*.

enclosure: An encasement for equipment designed to provide a degree of protection against a specified environment, and to protect personnel against accidental contact with the enclosed equipment.

encoder: A device capable of translating from one method of expression to another method of expression. A shaft encoder, for instance, translates each rotation of a shaft to a fixed number of pulses.

encoder counter module: A programmable controller input module, also referred to as high-speed pulse counter module, designed to read position information encoded as a fixed number of digital pulses output from encoder devices.

energize: To activate or to turn ON.

EPROM: See *Erasable Programmable Read Only Memory*.

engineering units: Units of measure as applied to a process variable, e.g., degrees, feet/second, psi, etc.

Erasable Programmable Read Only Memory (EPROM): A nonvolatile memory that can be re-programmed only after first erasing the contents by exposing the chip to ultraviolet light.

examine-OFF: A Ladder instruction used to examine the status of the referenced bit address for an OFF (0) state. If the referenced bit is OFF (0), the programmed contact will provide logic continuity.

examine-ON: A Ladder instruction used to examine the status of the referenced bit address for an ON (1) state. If the referenced bit is ON (1), the programmed contact will provide logic continuity.

external output: A term that pertains to connected field output devices such as motors, solenoids, and alarms. This term is used to make a distinction from "internal outputs" that are internal to the processor memory and that are not directly associated with a field output device. Also see *internal output*.

external suppression: A PLC output wiring method for providing protection against transients and surges generated when switching inductive or capacitive loads. The suppression device is connected in parallel with the load.

F

fail-safe: A device or system that has inherent to its design the capacity to fail without causing danger to personnel or major damage to itself or plant equipment.

fast input module: A PLC I/O module designed specifically for reading discrete input signals of very short pulse duration (e.g., on the order of microseconds). The fast input module captures and stretches the input signal for at least one program scan. Sometimes referred to as an *electronic input module* or the *pulse stretcher input module*.

fault: Any malfunction that interferes with normal operation.

fault contact: A PLC diagnostic feature that incorporates a set of relay contacts on the CPU so that in a given CPU fault situation, the contacts will open or close depending on normal state of the contacts. Fault contacts normally work in conjunction with the run-time error checking routines and/or watchdog timer.

fault relay: See *fault contacts*.

fault tolerance: That characteristic of a system that allows it to perform its assigned function in the presence of one or more faults in the hardware or software components.

feedback: The part of a closed-loop system that automatically puts information back into the system concerning the variable being controlled.

feedback control: A system control obtained when a portion of the output signal is operated upon and fed back to the input in order to obtain a desired effect.

final control element: The last system element that responds quantitatively to a control signal and performs the actual control action (e.g., valves, solenoids, and servo motors).

force function: A PLC function that allows the user to override the normal status of inputs and outputs. This feature allows setting an input or output to ON (1) or resetting an input or output to OFF (0), by forcing a 1 or 0 into the desired I/O image table location.

force OFF: 1) The use of the forcing function to override the actual status of a connected input device and to have it appear to the program as off, regardless of the actual input state. **2)** The use of the forcing function to override the actual status of a connected output device and to have it turn OFF, regardless of the result of programmed logic.

force ON: 1) The use of the forcing function to override the actual status of a connected input device and to have it appear to the program as ON, regardless of the actual input state. **2)** The use of the forcing function to override the actual status of a connected output device and to have it turn ON, regardless of the result of programmed logic.

frequency: 1) In ac signaling, the number of complete cycles transmitted per second, expressed in hertz (cycles per second). **2)** The number of cycles an event occurs over a specified time period. The reciprocal of frequency is called the period.

function block instructions: PLC instructions that allow users to handle operations not easily handled by ladder diagram relay-type instructions. The block format is typically such that it only requires entry of certain parameters that will allow the particular instruction to operate. Arithmetic, data transfer, data manipulation, and communication operations are normally incorporated in function block instructions.

G

galvanic isolation: Isolation that allows a signal to pass from its source to a measurement system without electrical or physical connection between the two circuits.

global outputs: An output signal that is available to all network stations; normally used in reference to programmable controller networks.

gray code: A binary code in which sequential numbers are represented by binary expressions, each of which involves no more than a single bit change (from 1-to-0 or 0-to-1) at any position as the binary value increases by one.

ground loop: Unexpected voltage drops due to current flowing in a ground wire.

ground potential: With respect to the earth, a zero voltage drop.

ground, signal: Conductor that establishes the electrical ground reference potential for all interchange circuits, except the frame-grounding circuit.

H

hand-held programmer: A small, low-cost, calculator-style programming device normally used with small PLCs. Hand-held programming devices are also used for a more convenient means of data entry/editing and monitoring for larger PLCs.

hard copy: An actual printout of a program or data that is also stored in some form of memory (soft copy).

hardware: Physical entities such as programmable controllers, computers, printers, or tape readers; contrasted to software.

hardwired: Pertains to a fixed wiring of electrical components.

hardwired logic: Logic control functions that are determined by the way devices are connected. Hardwired interconnections are wired for a specific purpose and, contrasted to programmable logic or software solutions, are relatively unalterable.

hertz (Hz): A unit of frequency equal to one cycle per second.

high density I/O module: Typically, a programmable controller I/O module containing 16 or more input/output circuits on a module the same size as would normally hold 8 circuits.

high-speed counter module: A PLC input module designed to interface to devices that generate high-frequency pulse trains, that cannot be read by standard discrete input modules and counted by standard software counters.

high = true: A signal type in which the higher of two voltages indicates a logic ON (1) state; equivalent to positive logic. Also see *low = true*.

host computer: 1) The primary computer attached to a network for the primary purpose of providing services such as computation, data base access, and access to special programs or programming languages. **2)** An intelligent device or information processor that provides support services or supervision to other computers, controllers, terminals, and other subordinate devices.

hot backup: A term that refers to a standby processor in a redundant programmable controller system. If the primary or master controller fails, the secondary or backup controller, which has the identical control program, takes over operations. Also see *redundant PLC*.

hot standby: See *hot backup*.

I

image table: See *I/O image table*.

immediate input instruction: A programmable controller instruction that allows critical input signals to be read on demand or when a change of state occurs instead of waiting until the normal I/O scan, which is typically at the end of program scan. Also see *I/O scan*.

immediate I/O instructions: Programmable controller instructions that provide the ability to read an input or control an output on demand, prior to the normal I/O scan. This feature is a form of interrupt to the program execution to act on critical inputs or outputs.

immediate I/O update: A programmable controller processor feature that allows reading or controlling of inputs and outputs immediately, as opposed to waiting until a predetermined I/O update time (typically at the end of each program scan).

immediate output instruction: A programmable controller instruction that allows a critical output device to be updated on demand or when the program commands it to change state, instead of waiting until the normal I/O scan, which is typically at the end of each program scan.

indicator, blown fuse: A programmable controller output module diagnostic indicator that illuminates when there is a blown fuse in an output circuit.

indicator, I/O status: An LED indicator typically on PLC discrete I/O modules to indicate if the signal is present at the input terminals, in the case of input modules, and at the output terminals, in the case of an output modules.

indicator, logic: An LED indicator sometimes found in addition to the status indicator on discrete I/O modules. Whereas the status indicator is based on the power side of the input or output circuit, the logic indicator diagnoses the logic side of the input or output circuit. In the case of input modules, it indicates that the CPU has recognized the signal in the case of an output, it signals if the connected device is being commanded to turn on.

indicator, power: See *indicator, I/O status*.

individual control: A control scheme in which an individual machine or process is not integrated into the control scheme of any other machines or processes.

inductive load suppression: A programmable controller output wiring practice that is intended to protect the output module circuitry and CPU against large surges of current that will be present after turning off inductive devices such as motor starters, relays, and solenoids. Typically an MOV (Metal Oxide Varistor) is wired across the load device.

initialize: 1) To preset to certain states or values. **2)** To execute a special software routine to set certain flags states or certain memory locations to zero or some other starting value.

input: Information sent to a computer, programmable controller or similar processor from connected devices, via some input interface.

input delay: A programmable controller input module specification that defines the duration for which an input signal must exceed the ON threshold before being recognized as a valid input signal. The actual delay, a result of filtering circuitry, is to protect against recognizing contact bounce or line noise as valid input signals. See *contact bounce*.

input devices: Any connected equipment that will supply information to the programmable controller, computer, or similar device. Each type of input device has a unique input interface to the processor.

input image table: An array of memory bit locations set aside in a programmable controller memory for storing the status of connected digital inputs. The number of bits allocated in the image table is normally equal to the maximum number of digital inputs. A controller with a maximum of 64 inputs would require an input image table of 64-bits or four 16-bit words. Each connected input has a bit in the input image table that corresponds exactly to the terminal to which the input is connected. On each processor scan, the input image table is updated to reflect the current status of the device (ON = 1, OFF = 0). Also see *output image table* and *I/O scan*.

input module: An interface module designed to input information into a programmable controller or similar control device.

input/output (I/O): 1) Generally, the devices that communicate with a computer, programmable controller or similar device. **2)** The data involved in such communication. **3)** The process of sending information from an external device to a computer or programmable controller (input) or from a computer or programmable controller (output) to an external device.

input/output system: Those components such as cables, I/O processor modules, power supplies, racks, and I/O modules designed to read data into or output data from a programmable controller or computer.

input signal: A current or voltage signal applied to a device, element, or system.

input table: See *input image table*.

integral control action: That component of control action, whereby the output is proportional to the time integral of the error signal. Also referred to as *reset action*.

intelligent CRT: See *intelligent terminal*.

intelligent I/O module: Input/output module designed with integral processor and memory that allow specific control, communications, arithmetic, or some other processing function, independent of the main processing unit. Intelligent I/O modules are a form of distributed processing that unburdens the main CPU from having to perform these tasks. Example intelligent I/O include BASIC or other language modules, PID control, temperature control, axis positioning, and many others.

intelligent terminal: A terminal that contains an integral microprocessor, dynamic memory, communications capability, and mass storage memory devices. Intelligent terminals are often used as front-end processors or programming devices.

interface: The common boundary between two devices or two systems that allows the necessary interaction between the two.

interference: In electrical systems, the presence of undesirable energy in a circuit, caused by external sources. See *noise*.

interlock: To arrange the control of machines or devices so that their operation is interdependent to assure proper coordination and safe operation.

internal output: A bit output that is used strictly for internal purposes (does not drive a field device). It provides interlocking functions like a hardwired control relay; however, normally closed and normally open contacts from an internal output may be used as often as required. Also called *internal storage bit*, *internal coil*, or *flag bits*.

interrupt: An efficient method of requesting the immediate attention of a central processor to gain some type of service. Interrupts are usually classified as hardware (e.g., process signal, I/O module with interrupt lines) or software (e.g., timed interrupts).

I/O: See *input/output*.

I/O address: A unique number assigned to each input and output. The address number is used when programming, monitoring, or modifying a specific input or output device.

I/O address assignments: 1) The memory addresses that have been assigned to individual connected input and output devices. **2)** A document that lists memory locations allocated for storing status of input/output devices connected to a programmable controller system. The document should reflect used and unused I/O addresses.

I/O address, real: A memory location in the I/O image table that corresponds directly with a connected input or output device and holds the status of that device. The I/O address is used in the control program when a particular device status is to be examined or controlled. Contrasted to internal storage addresses.

I/O channel: 1) A single input or output circuit on an I/O module. **2)** A port that provides a communication link to one or more input/output subsystems.

I/O cross reference: A document that lists input/output addresses cross referenced by the program line numbers in which the address is used.

I/O forcing: See *forcing function*.

I/O grouping: An installation technique that involves grouping I/O modules of like signals and voltage levels in an I/O rack. This procedure is an attempt to manage the duct and wiring layout such that cross-talk or other forms of interference will be minimized.

I/O image table: An area allocated in programmable controller memory systems to store the actual status of connected input and output devices. Ones and zeros are placed in memory locations corresponding with each input and output depending on the ON (1) or OFF (0) status. The I/O image table is updated on every processor scan. Also see *input image table* and *output image table*.

I/O interface: 1) Input/output circuitry designed to allow field signals to be input or output from the processor. **2)** The circuitry required to allow various devices to either send or receive information from a programmable controller, computer, or similar device.

I/O, local: Programmable controller input/output subsystems that are restricted to a distance local to the central processing unit, typically within a few feet; contrasted to remote I/O, which typically can be located at distances of one mile or more.

I/O module: A plug-in type assembly that contains more than one input or output circuit; normally 2,4,8,16, or 32 circuits. A module usually contains two or more identical circuits.

I/O, remote: A programmable controller capability of locating input/output subsystems at long distances from the central processing unit, typically up to one mile or more.

I/O rack: The housing in which I/O modules are installed. Also called *I/O chassis* or *I/O base*.

I/O scan: The programmable controller processor function of continuously revising each and every bit of the input image table after reading the input modules and controlling the connected output modules based on the latest status of the output image table. Also referred to as I/O update. Also see *I/O scan time*.

I/O scanner: An I/O system processor module responsible for handling I/O communication between the central processing unit and an I/O rack.

I/O scan time: The time required to read all inputs and update outputs in local and remote I/O racks. The I/O scan time is added to the program scan time to give the total processor scan time. Also referred to as *I/O update time*.

I/O terminal: That part of an I/O module or I/O module connector to which field devices are wired.

I/O update: See *I/O scan*.

I/O update time: See *I/O scan time*.

I/O wiring diagram: An electrical wiring diagram that gives interconnection details concerning the control power and terminal address to which each field device is connected.

isolated I/O module: An input or output signal has a separate positive and negative lead wire, thereby electrically isolating it from other circuits on that module. Isolated I/O modules are designed to allow connection of devices that are powered from different sources, to reduce the effects of noise, and faulty readings related to ground loops.

isolation transformer: A transformer inserted in a system to separate one section of the system from undesired influences of the other sections. A programmable controller is typically placed on an isolation transformer to segregate it from other plant influences, such as large motors or arc welding equipment.

J

jumper: **1)** A short length of cable used to make electrical connections within, between, among, and around circuits and their associated equipment; usually a temporary connection. **2)** A direct electrical connection between two or more points on a printed-circuit or terminal board.

K

K: **1)** Abbreviation for kilo. **2)** A prefix used with various units of measurement to designate quantities of 1000. Example: kilometer, or 1000 meters. **3)** Used as a unit measurement for memory in units of 1024 storage locations. Typically, the expression is used in reference to the number of bytes or number of words of memory. *1K =1024, 2K = 2048, 4K = 4K = 4096*, etc.

keying: A protective technique used to ensure that only certain types of modules can be installed in a slot according to how the backplane connector for that slot is keyed.

L

ladder diagram: An industry standard for representing relay-logic control systems. Also referred to as relay ladder diagram, relay logic diagram, or simply relay diagram.

ladder diagram programming: The oldest and most widely used method of programming PLCs; a graphic programming method that uses symbols and format similar to a relay ladder diagram.

ladder element: The symbolic program elements used in a ladder program. The elements include contacts, coils, and branch ties.

ladder listing: A hard copy of a ladder diagram program.

ladder matrix: A rectangular array of programmed contacts, formed by maximum number of series contacts, that can be programmed across a row and the number of parallel branches allowed in a single ladder rung.

ladder network: See *ladder rung.*

ladder rung: A single Ladder diagram network that performs the desired the control logic.

latching relay: A relay that maintains its activated state until released mechanically or electrically.

latch output: A ladder program output instruction that retains its state even though the conditions that caused it to latch ON may go OFF. A latched output must be unlatched.

leakage current: A characteristic of both transistor and triac output devices whereby a small current flow is still present at the output of the device even after it is switched off.

leaky inputs: Input devices that exhibit a leakage current; a characteristic of transistors and triacs. See *leakage current.*

LED (light-emitting diode): A semiconductor device that emits light when current passes through it. LEDs are normally used as diagnostic and status indicators.

LED display: An illuminating visual readout composed of LED alphanumeric character segments.

load: 1) The power used by a machine or device. **2)** A device intentionally placed in a circuit or connected to a machine or apparatus to absorb power and convert it into the desired useful form. **3)** To insert a program or data into central memory under operator control.

load resistor: A resistor connected in parallel with a high- impedance load so that the output circuit driving the load can provide at least the minimum current required for proper operation.

local I/O: See *I/O, local.*

location: A storage position in memory; a bit, byte, or word.

logic: The process of solving very simple to very complex problems through the repeated use of Boolean operators, AND, OR, and NOT.

logic diagram: A diagram that uses interconnected logic symbols to represent control logic operations.

logic level: The voltage magnitude associated with signal pulses that represent ones and zeroes in digital systems.

loop: 1) A sequence of instructions executed a defined number of times until finished or tested conditions are met. **2)** Loosely refers to control loop. See *open loop system, closed loop system.*

low = true: A signal type in which the lower of two voltages indicates a logic state of ON (1). See *high = true.*

M

manipulated variable: That parameter or parameters changed by the controller to maintain the controlled variable at the desired value.

manual control station: In control systems, a device or control panel designed to act as a backup to an automatic control system by allowing the operator to manually control a device or control loop.

MCR (master control relay): A hardwired control relay that can be de-energized by any series-connected emergency stop switch for the purpose of removing power from the control system. Also see *MCR instruction.*

MCR instruction: A programmable controller ladder diagram output instruction that functions similar to a master control relay in a hardwired control system and used to activate or de-activate the execution of a group of ladder rungs. Each MCR output rung has an associated END MCR rung to create a "zone" or "fence" around the ladder rungs whose execution is determined by the state of the MCR output.

MCR zone: See *MCR instruction.*

memory map: A diagram showing memory addresses and how memory is allocated for storing various system data and application programs and data.

memory protect: A method by which the contents of all sections or only certain sections of memory are protected from alteration.

mini-programmer: See hand-held programmers.

module: A modular plug-in type printed circuit board designed to serve a particular function.

MOV: See *metal oxide varistor*.

N

negative logic: The use of binary logic in such a way that "0," represents the voltage level normally associated with logic 1 (e.g., 0 = +5V, 1 = 0V). Positive logic is more conventional (i.e., 1 = +5V, 0 = 0V).

noise: Random, unwanted electrical signals, normally caused by radio waves or electrical or magnetic fields generated by one conductor and picked up by another.

noise immunity: The relative ability for a device or system to function in the presence of noise.

noise spike: A noise disturbance of relatively short duration.

nominal voltage: A range of voltages over which the actual voltage may vary and still provide satisfactory operation. The nominal voltage of a system or device is near the voltage level at which the device normally operates and provides a per unit base voltage for system study purposes.

non-retentive output: An output, along with any of its programmed contacts, that is reset to zero when power is cycled off.

non-volatile memory: A type of memory that retains its programmed contents even if power is lost or removed (e.g., EPROM, EEPROM).

normally closed contact: 1) A relay contact-pair that closes when the coil of the relay is not activated and opens when the coil is activated. **2)** A ladder diagram program symbol that allows logic continuity (power flow) if the referenced input is logic 0 when examined and prohibits power flow if the input is logic 1 when examined.

normally open contact: 1) A relay contact-pair that opens when the coil of the relay is not activated and closes when the coil is activated. **2)** A ladder program symbol that allows logic continuity (*power flow*) if the referenced input is logic 1 when examined and prohibits power flow if the input is logic 0 when examined.

numerical I/O devices: Any input device whose input to a programmable controller is a numeric value, and any output device that is controlled by a numeric value sent from the controller (e.g., BCD I/O, analog I/O, pulse inputs and pulse outputs).

numerical I/O modules: A generic term used to classify programmable controller interface modules that provide the means for interfacing devices that generate or accept a parallel or serial bit pattern that represents a numeric value. This class of I/O modules include modules such as analog, BCD, encoder counter, and positioning modules.

off-delay timer: A timer that is activated and starts timing the enable signal goes OFF. After the timed delay expires, the timer coil de-energizes.

off-line: The state of a device, such as a programming unit, that may be operational but not necessarily connected to or in direct communication with the central processing unit.

off-line programming: An ability to create and store a program without being connected to or in direct communication with a central processing unit. Also see *off-line*.

off-line storage: The ability to store data or programs in a secondary device to be later loaded to or from a primary device.

off state leakage: See *current leakage*.

on-delay timer: A timer whose output contacts are energized after the preset time has elapsed.

one-shot output: An output that after being triggered to turn ON, it remains ON for only one program scan and turns OFF.

on-line: The state of a device, such as a programming unit, that is performing its operational duties while connected to and in direct communication with a central processing unit.

on-line editing: To make deliberate changes or alterations to a program that is being executed.

on-line programming: 1) The act of creating or modifying a program that is operational and performing its normal application. **2)** Performing program entry or modification while connected to the CPU; contrasted to off-line programming.

open-loop system: Control system whose output is a function of only the inputs to the system. No feedback is present in the system.

operator: 1) The person who initiates and monitors the operation of a computer, programmable controller, or other such device. **2)** The portion of an instruction that tells the machine what to do.

optical isolation: Electrical separation of two circuits, a primary and a secondary circuit, by an optical coupling device.

output: Information sent from the processor to a connected device via some interface. The information could be in the form of control data that will signal some device, such as a motor, to switch ON or OFF or to vary the speed of a drive. It could also be pure data, such as a string of ASCII characters to a printer or display.

output device: Any connected equipment that will receive information or instructions from the central processing unit, such as control devices (e.g., motors, solenoids, alarms) or peripheral devices (e.g., printers, disk drives, color displays). Each type of output device has a unique interface to the processor.

output image table: A table of bit locations set aside in a PLC memory for controlling the ON/OFF status of connected digital outputs. The number of bits allocated in the table is normally equal to the maximum number of digital outputs. A controller with a maximum of 64 digital outputs would require an output image table of 64 bits or four 16-bit words. During each program scan, the bits in the output image table are set or reset according to the results of solving the program logic (1 = ON, 0 = OFF). At the end of each program scan, the bits of the output image table are used to control the status of the connected output devices during the I/O scan. Also see *input image table* and *I/O scan*.

output module: Any interface module that accepts data sent from the programmable controller.

overload: 1) Output of current, power, or torque in excess of a device's rated output on a specified basis. **2)** In electrical power systems, loading in excess of normal rating of the equipment.

overvoltage: A voltage above the normal rated voltage or the maximum operating voltage of a device or circuit.

overvoltage protection: The effect of a device operative on excessive voltage to cause and maintain the interruption of power in the circuit or reduction of voltage to the governed equipment.

#

parallel circuit: A circuit in which two or more components are connected to the same pair of terminals so that current may flow through all the branches; contrasts with a series connection in which the parts are connected end-to-end so that current flow has only one path.

parallel input module: An input module designed to accept discrete inputs as a word of data.

parallel output module: An output module designed to control discrete outputs as a word.

peripheral equipment: Equipment that may communicate with or enhance a primary piece of equipment, such as a computer or programmable controller, but is not a part of the primary equipment and is not required for operation.

PID: A mode of controller action in which proportional, integral, and derivative actions are combined.

PID module: An intelligent programmable controller I/O module that performs PID functions independent of the central processor.

pilot lamp: A lamp that indicates the condition of an associated circuit.

port: A place of access to a device or network where signals may be input or output (e.g., programming port, communication port, I/O terminal).

positive logic: The use of binary logic in such a way that logic 1 represents a positive logic level (e.g., 1 = +5V, 0 = 0V). This is the conventional use of binary logic.

power flow: The ability of electricity to flow from the first element in a circuit to the last.

power supply: In general, a device that converts AC line voltage to one or more DC voltages.

power supply overloading: A condition caused by drawing more current from a power supply than it is rated for. In programmable controller applications, this condition may be caused by installing a combination of processor and I/O modules in a chassis that exceeds the maximum current that can be supplied.

programmable controller: A solid-state industrial control device, member of the computer family, designed specifically to be programmed to perform relay logic functions, timing, counting, arithmetic, and data manipulation, all for the purpose of implementing control over industrial machine and processes. The programmable controller consists of a central processor, memory system, input/output system, and power supply, all of which are designed to withstand harsh industrial environments.

program scan: A programmable controller processor function for evaluating the control program on a continuous basis, based on the latest status of the inputs and outputs read during the I/O scan.

program scan time: The time required by the processor to complete one execution cycle of the entire PLC program. Also see *I/O scan time.*

Programmable Read Only Memory (PROM): A nonvolatile memory that can be written into only once but can be continually read from.

PROM: See *programmable read only memory*.

proportional control action: Corrective action that is proportional to the error, (e.g., the change of the manipulated variable is equal to the gain of the proportional controller multiplied by the error).

R

rated voltage: The nominal operating voltage at which a device or system will operate safely and with integrity.

real time: 1) The actual time during which a physical process transpires. **2)** The performance of a computation during the actual time that the related physical process transpires so that results of computation can be used in guiding the physical process.

real-time clock: A clock that indicates the passage of actual time, in contrast to a non-real-time set up by a computer program.

redundant controllers: A programmable controller configuration in which two central processors are connected to have control over the same machine or process I/O. One processor is designated as the primary, the other as secondary, each have identical programs and access to the other's operational status. The primary unit maintains control, unless a malfunction is detected, in which case automatic switchover to the secondary unit takes place.

register: A memory word or location used for temporary storage of data used in mathematical, logical, data transfer, or other operations.

relay: A mechanical or solid-state device that switches electrical circuits. A electromechanical relay completes or interrupts a circuit by physically moving electrical contacts into contact with each other.

relay type instructions: The most fundamental of ladder diagram programming instructions that provide the programmable controller with the ability to implement hardwired relay-equivalent functions, but with greater flexibility. Basic relay instructions include *Examine ON*, *Examine OFF*, *Energize Output*, *Latch Output*, and *Unlatch Output*.

relay replacers: Typically, the very low-end PLCs, with an input/output capacity of less than 64 I/O.

remote I/O: See *I/O, remote*.

report generation: The printing or displaying of application data by means of a data terminal. Report can be initiated manually or under program control.

retentive: The ability to retain last state when power fails or is removed.

retentive output: An output that retains its last status if power fails or is removed.

retentive timer: A timer instruction that retains its accumulated value even if logic continuity is lost or power is lost or removed.

rung: See *ladder rung*.

S

sampling rate: The rate at which measurement of physical quantities is made. In a given sampling period, a physical quantity may be sampled one thousand times.

scan: 1) A programmable controller term relating to the processor function of reading the input devices, executing the control program, and controlling the output devices. 2) A process of sequentially monitoring or reading signals generated by sensors.

scan time: The time required by the programmable controller processor to update all local and remote I/O and to execute the control program.

search mode: A programmable controller utility program that allows the user to search for and quickly display any address used in the program.

self-diagnostic: A hardware or software diagnostic check that a system uses to monitor its own internal operations.

sequencer: A controller that executes a set of programmed instructions through a fixed sequence of events without advancing to the next step until each preceding step is completed.

series circuit: A circuit in which the components or contact symbols are connected end-to-end, and all must be closed to permit current flow.

setpoint: The desired value of a controlled variable in a process control loop.

shield: Any barrier to the passage of an interface causing electrostatic or electromagnetic fields. An electrostatic shield is formed by a conductive layer surrounding a cable core.

shielding : The practice of confining the electrical field around a conductor to the primary insulation of the cable by putting a conducting layer over and under the cable insulation.

single scan: A supervisory-type command initiated by the user while the controller is in the Stop mode. This command causes the control program to be executed for one scan, including I/O update. This troubleshooting function allows step-by-step inspection of occurrences while the machine is stopped.

solenoid: A transducer that converts current into linear motion; it consists of one or more electromagnets that move a metal plunger. The plunger is sometimes returned to its original position after excursion with a spring or permanent magnet.

start-up: 1) The time between equipment installation and the full operation of the system. **2)** The act of bringing a system to the fully operational state.

status: 1) The current mode or operating state of a machine or device. **2)** The binary state (1 or 0) of a device or signal.

status indicator: An LED indicator that signals the operating state of a device or the on/off state of a signal. In the case of binary signals, the light illuminated generally indicates the signal is ON or (1).

stepper motor: An electric motor whose windings are arranged in such a way that the armature can be made to step in discrete rotational increments (typically 1/200 of a revolution) when a digital pulse is applied to an accompanying driving circuit

surge: A transient wave of voltage, current, or power in an electrical circuit. Note: A transient has a high rate of change of current or voltage in a circuit.

switching: Placing a device in either the on or off state.

T

terminal: 1) Any fitting attached to a device or circuit for the convenience of making electrical connections. **2)** An input/output device used to input data and receive data from the system of which it is a part.

thermocouple input module: A special analog input module, designed to accept direct input from thermocouple sensor devices.

time base: A unit of time generated by the system clock and used by software timer instructions. Normal time bases are 0.01, 0.1, and 1.0 second.

timer: 1) An electromechanical relay type device that can be set to time for a certain duration and to open or close a set of contacts, thereby activating or deactivating an electrical circuit after the timed duration. **2)** A programmable controller program instruction that eliminates the need for hardware timers. The software timer can be given a preset value and will begin timing whenever the enabling circuit is activated. Also see *off-delay timer*, *on-delay timer*.

timer accumulated value: The current value stored in the accumulator word of a programmable controller timer instruction.

timer-counter access module (TCAM): Typically a calculator-like device designed to allow monitoring and altering of timer and counter values in a programmable controller program.

timer preset value: A programmed value that determines the number of time-base intervals to be counted in a software timer and, subsequently, the programmed time duration.

toggle: 1) A two-position switch or circuit that on each transition takes on the opposite state (i.e., a flip-flop or bistable action).

trailing edge: The falling edge of a signal (i.e., the OFF-to-ON transition).

troubleshoot: To search for the cause of a malfunction or erroneous behavior to correct the situation.

TTL input module: A discrete input module designed to accept input signals from a TTL (*transistor-transistor logic*) output stage.

TTL output module: A discrete output module designed to drive a TTL (*transistor-transistor logic*) input stage.

twisted pair: A cable composed of two small insulated conductors, twisted together without a common covering. The two conductors are usually substantially insulated so that the combination is a special case of a cord.

U

unlatch output: A ladder diagram instruction programmed in conjunction with a latch output instruction. The latch output, when energized, resets the latch output of the same reference address.

uptime: The time during which a system is either producing work or is available for productive work; contrasted with downtime.

V

variable: A factor that can be altered, measured, or controlled; quantity that can change in value.

variable data: Numerical information that changes during operation. Examples include timers, counters, analog signals, and results of arithmetic operations.

varistor: A resistor whose resistance varies proportionally with the voltage applied to it.

volatile memory: Memory that is subject to loss of programmed contents if power is lost or removed, given that no battery support is available or the battery fails.

INDEX

B

C

G

F

H

I

J

O

S

T

U

V

W

Z

* Page 169-170